Trac~~e~~

Jason Dean spent much of his professional life as a graphic designer before deciding what he really wanted to do was write the kind of international thrillers he's always loved reading. The James Bishop series was the result. He is now working on the next book in the Korso series. Jason lives in the Far East with his wife and their dog.

TRACER

JASON DEAN

CANELO

First published in the United Kingdom in 2021 by

Canelo
31 Helen Road
Oxford OX2 0DF
United Kingdom

Copyright © Jason Dean, 2021

A CIP catalogue record for this book is available from the British Library.

Print ISBN 978 1 80032 407 7
Ebook ISBN 978 1 80032 406 0

Look for more great books at www.canelo.co

Printed and bound in Great Britain by Clays Ltd, Elcograf S.p.A.

1

For Stuart & Jaqi

One

The dead man pulled the keys from the ignition. Grabbing the burner phone from the glove compartment, he opened the door and got out of the Toyota.

As Korso took the thin, black leather attaché case from the trunk, he gave a brief shiver. It was cold in Sofia in February. Seemed every time he came to Bulgaria the weather was the same. He gave a mental shrug and brushed the thought aside. He wasn't there for the climate. Patting his pockets again to make sure he was completely unarmed, Korso locked the vehicle and turned up his overcoat collar as he gave his surroundings another once-over.

Nothing had changed. Everything within sight was a variable shade of grey. The clouds in the sky. The derelict warehouses and slowly rotting factories on either side of the street. The cracked asphalt under his feet. His breath. Litter and huge puddles of black water everywhere. The smell of ancient oil, rust and pollution permeated everything. Not another living soul in sight. No vehicles, other than his silver rental. The faint whine of a jet in the distance. From a factory roof a hundred yards away, a murder of crows glared down at this new interloper and squawked, daring him to come any closer.

It had clearly been some years since this industrial park, located on the outskirts of the capital, had been a thriving

I

concern. Now it was just neglected and forgotten, which naturally made it a perfect spot for certain parties to meet.

Avoiding the numerous potholes, Korso crossed the uneven street and began walking across the empty wasteland that separated two more dilapidated warehouses, heading in a northwesterly direction. He knew where he was going and how long it would take.

Less than three minutes later, he reached the industrial building he wanted. Fifty feet away, a short, stocky man in a badly fitting suit with the requisite shaved head was standing outside the main entrance. When he saw Korso approach, he casually pulled a piece from the holster under his jacket and spoke into an earpiece.

Korso didn't need to lip read to know what he was saying. Although he could have.

He kept walking, not slowing his pace, his free arm far enough away from his body to show he was no immediate threat. The building was another abandoned factory, with a huge open space and a dozen offices on the ground floor and more offices upstairs. There were no windows at street level. The few on the second floor were all missing windowpanes.

When Korso was ten feet from the entrance, the guard motioned with the gun. '*Stoy*.'

Korso stopped.

'*Ruki*.'

He carefully placed the attaché case on the ground and raised his hands. Another shaved head, this one with a carefully sculpted goatee, appeared from inside the building, clutching an SMG, a Belgian P90. The guard came over and gave Korso a thorough body search, inspecting his keys, his smartphone and his burner phone carefully before finally returning them to his coat pocket.

He glanced down at the briefcase with the combination locks on either side of the handle.

'You open this,' he said.

'Ask your boss first.'

The guard looked at him for a couple of beats, then shrugged and said, 'You come.' He turned and began walking back inside.

Korso picked up the attaché case and followed, knowing that the other one was right behind him, ready to shoot at a moment's notice. Korso didn't let it bother him.

Inside, the building was as cold, dark and depressing as the outside. There were huge holes in the roof, and rubble and rusted machinery everywhere. At the far end, Korso could see metal stairs leading to the second-floor mezzanine. A hundred feet away, standing next to a large steel table in the middle of the factory floor, were three more men. There was a third guard with a rapidly receding hairline, his long grey hair tied back in a ponytail. Next to him was a thin bespectacled guy in an expensive suit whom Korso had never seen before. And finally, there was an overweight, middle-aged man in a tracksuit with deep-set black eyes and salt and pepper hair cropped close to his skull. Tattoos covered his hands.

His name was Boris Gancharov. Korso knew he was involved in a whole horde of illicit enterprises both in Bulgaria and back home in Russia. He also knew Gancharov had ordered more than his fair share of killings over the years. Probably performed a fair few of them himself.

Gancharov checked his watch and smiled. 'One fifty-nine. I like this.' His deep voice echoed around the empty interior. 'I place great importance on punctuality.'

3

'I'd heard that about you,' Korso said, and came to a stop ten feet from the table. He watched the guard he'd followed move away to his right and then turn to watch him. The other one was still lurking somewhere behind him.

'Among other things, I am sure. So, my friend, I assume that handsome briefcase contains the item I commissioned you to recover, or why would we all be here. Am I right?'

'The customer generally is.'

'Ha. Excellent philosophy. Kindly bring it over here.'

The three men made a space and Korso walked over and placed the case on the table surface. He stepped back a pace and said, 'The code is seven three nine four.'

Gancharov lost the smile. 'You will open it for me.'

'Of course.' Korso moved forward, dialled the code into the two locks, and opened the case.

Two

Korso took a few steps back again to allow Gancharov room to view his prize. He watched and waited.

The attaché case interior was packed with grey, semi-rigid Ethafoam cubes. Resting securely within the carefully sculpted space in the centre was a small semi-automatic pistol. It was a 7.65 millimetre Walther PP with an intricately designed golden barrel and trigger. The italicised letters 'AH' on the off-white ivory grips were inlaid with gold. It also had something of an enviable history. To a certain type of collector, at least.

It had sure taken Korso a lot of time and effort to trace the damn thing. And even more to recover it.

Gancharov's smile was back as he looked down at the gun. 'Yes. Yes. This is it. See, Ivor?' He pointed. 'That tiny scratch on the lower part of the grip there? I still remember every detail like it was yesterday.'

The bespectacled man leaned in and spoke softly to Gancharov. Korso managed to catch a few Russian words in there, and acted as though he understood none of them.

'*Znaiyu, znaiyu,*' Gancharov said irritably, not taking his eyes from the gun. 'You don't have to remind me again, Ivor. *Zamolchi.*'

He reached down with his right hand and very carefully removed the antique weapon and brought it closer to his face. '*Krasivaya.*' He turned to Korso. 'Beautiful, is it not?'

'A touch gaudy for me,' Korso said. 'But I admit there is something about it.'

Gancharov let out a long breath. 'Yes, you recognise it too. A kind of mystique. Like an aura almost, no doubt due to the gun's history and long line of ownership.'

'The original owner's probably got something to do with it too.'

'Very true. And all that history only adds to its value,' he said, turning to the man in spectacles, caressing the gun like a lover. 'Carl Walther presented this specially made piece to the Führer on his fiftieth birthday on April 20, 1939, who then shipped it to his exclusive Munich apartment, where it remained in a desk drawer for the next six years.'

Ivor nodded. 'I have heard about this golden gun, sir. They say he blew his own brains out with it in that bunker of his.'

Gancharov gave a loud snort. 'Don't be an ass, Ivor. That's the kind of romantic horseshit I expect from Hollywood, not my accountant. Besides, his bunker was six hundred kilometres away in Berlin. As far as anyone knows he never set eyes on this gun again. No, the allies reached Berlin just before the end of the war, and when the Americans crashed Hitler's empty apartment, an enterprising GI found the piece in his office drawer and took it for himself. I would have done the exactly the same.'

He popped the magazine, confirming it was empty, and carefully replaced it. 'For some unknown reason, when this GI returns home he gives it to a friend of his, a church pastor in Georgia, who shows it off to his flock at every opportunity. No surprise then when one of these

God-fearing fools decides to take it for himself and sell it on for a profit. That is in 1947. It is next spotted by a detective at a gun show in the Fifties and because he cannot afford to buy it, he photographs it for posterity. Then in 1966, it appears on the cover of a men's magazine, along with an article that claims it is up for sale by a Cleveland gun dealer.' He turned back to Korso. 'You already know all of this.'

'I couldn't do my job if I didn't.'

'So maybe you will bring us up to date.'

Korso shrugged. 'The Cleveland gun dealer sells it to a Canadian collector of Nazi memorabilia as the centrepiece of the museum he's built on his farmland, but the tourists fail to come. It's next seen again in the late Eighties, where it's sold at auction for over a hundred thousand dollars, then the highest amount paid for a piece of military memorabilia. It gets sold to a millionaire in Australia, who sells it on to a dealer in Georgia again, and then on to another buyer in LA, an art collector named Jonathan Veehers.'

'Who eventually sold it to me,' Gancharov said. 'For a lot of money, I might add. Although not nearly as much as Veehers hoped for. But then I am a persuasive fellow, and I truly enjoy bargaining. Especially when I have the upper hand.'

Korso recognised the not so hidden intent behind that remark, and immediately saw where this was going. He chose not to rise to the bait. Not yet.

Gancharov went on. 'And then two years ago that beautiful whore of mine, Tanya, decides to run away from me and takes the piece with her, along with a sizeable chunk of cash from my safe. I almost admire her for that.' He shook his head and sighed. 'Almost. And then she

7

somehow disappears off the face of the earth. No sign of the bitch, or the gun, anywhere in all of those two years. And believe me, I looked.' He smiled at Korso. 'Yet you clearly managed to track her down when I and all my resources could not.'

'All part of my job.'

'Yes, your job. How did you phrase it to me originally? "Covert salvage operative"? I like that. It has a good ring to it. So tell me, where is she?'

'My not answering that is part of the deal I made with her. The main part, actually.'

'I could make you answer. My men could.'

'Unlikely. It wouldn't make any difference anyway.'

The Russian furrowed his brow. 'Because she is not there anymore.'

'Long gone. And she's got a talent for vanishing.' *Among other things*. Korso recalled once again the soft breath in his ear, the cool touch of long nails against his shoulder, the smooth curve of a naked hip pressed against his thigh. That particular night had been an enjoyable, if brief, interlude in an otherwise tortuous journey. 'Like you said, she's an admirable woman. Resourceful, too. Let's leave it at that. I got you what you wanted.'

'True. But paying out eight hundred thousand dollars for something that was already mine did not make me happy. Plus there is still your fee on top, of course.'

'You knew it might cost from the outset. It could have been a lot more.'

'And you could have just taken it from her and spared me the additional expense.'

'Tanya's not that stupid. She'd prepared a lot of safe-guards between it and me, and it was obvious the only way to get it back was to pay her price.'

8

'Obvious to you, maybe. The fact is, despite being this so-called finder of lost or stolen property, you could not recover my piece without a large sum of my own money.'

Korso shrugged. 'That's the way it goes sometimes.'

'Perhaps. And so now you no doubt wish to be paid your percentage of this item's market value. How much was that again? Thirty-three per cent?'

'That's right. Which is still less than the standard fifty per cent for salvage recovery. And payment on delivery, as originally agreed.'

'So tell me, how do we value an antique with no defined market price?'

'Well, you paid Jonathan Veehers two point seven million dollars for that gun fifteen years ago.'

'How could you know that?'

'I asked him. And that was a fraction of the gun's true value back then, let alone now. You must have been at your most persuasive that day. But I'm not greedy. I'll just use the amount you wired to Tanya as my yardstick, so we'll value it at the same bargain-counter eight hundred thousand dollars. US dollars, that is.'

'Very reasonable of you. And that brings your commission to…?'

'Two hundred and sixty-four thousand,' Ivor said.

'Precisely,' Korso said.

'Still a great deal of money,' Gancharov said, wiping the back of his free hand across his forehead. 'Far too much, I think.'

Spotting movement to his right, Korso saw the guard with the goatee casually pull out his P90 and point it in his general direction. Facing forward, Korso saw that the goon at the table already had his piece out, some Russian SMG, and was aiming it directly at him. And he knew the

9

hidden gunman behind him was just waiting for a chance to shoot him in the back.

Gancharov smirked. 'I think maybe now is the perfect time for us to renegotiate our contract.'

Three

Korso let out a long breath. 'I think maybe you're right.'

'I knew you would see sense. Remember, the customer is always right.'

'Not always. What's the time?'

'The time?' Gancharov glanced lazily at his gold Rolex. 'Two fifteen. Why?'

'And you took the gun from the briefcase at around five after, or thereabouts?'

Gancharov stared at him for a moment, then dropped the Walther on the table. All three men were glaring at the briefcase as though it had grown tentacles. 'What is it, a bomb? What?'

'Nothing so melodramatic,' Korso said. 'Just a little insurance policy I took out to ensure we all play fair. Tell me, do your palms feel clammy at all yet?'

Gancharov turned to him and gulped. He looked down at his open hands, rubbed them together. He looked a lot paler than before. 'The gun. You put something on the gun.'

'Just a thin coating of a toxin that evaporates after about six hours, once exposed to oxygen,' Korso said. 'It's had about three hours already. This particular poison starts taking effect as soon as it comes into contact with your skin, and it works fairly fast. I noticed you wiping your forehead just now, so your body temperature's already starting to rise. You picked up the gun around ten, eleven minutes ago, right?'

'I shoot him, sir.' The gunman at the table was still pointing his SMG at Korso.

'You do and I'll have your entire family mutilated,' Gancharov snapped, without turning. 'Holster your piece and shut up. All of you. That is an order.' The gunmen quickly did as they were told. 'How long?'

'Hard to tell with any great accuracy. The medical texts say forty minutes, minimum. You're a big man, though, so possibly a full hour. I understand it's very painful at the end.'

'You're making a very big mistake, Korso. You don't want to kill me.'

'You're absolutely right, Mr Gancharov. That's the last thing I want.'

The Russian paused at that and visibly relaxed just a little. He took a moment to resume his poise in front of his men, leaning back against the table. 'Meaning?'

'Meaning I'm a specialist who caters to a niche market, and people like that rely on a word-of-mouth reputation. However, I wouldn't stay in business very long if word got around that I kill off my clientele when things don't go my way. That's not exactly sound business sense. Nevertheless, you'd be amazed at how many clients suddenly decide they don't want to part with their cash once their property's back in their hands. And not being paid for my services is not good business either. As a result, I learned some time ago never to come to a handover without taking certain precautions first.'

'So you coat the items with poison.'

Korso smiled for the first time. 'Almost never. My safe-guards differ with each job, but for this particular situation that method seemed the perfect choice.'

'You think like a Russian.'

'Maybe I am.'

'You are also a dead man.'

'Correct.'

'What does that mean?'

'It means I'm a ghost, Mr Gancharov. A shadow. Gives me a certain freedom of movement, which is essential in my line of work. Especially as not all of my clients are as upstanding as you.'

'So Korso is not your real name.'

'Did you ever think it was?' Korso shrugged. 'It's a brand, that's all. And as good a name as any.'

'And the antidote?'

'Close by. I'm going to reach into my pocket for my cell phones, all right? I've already been searched for weapons.'

'Very well. Take out your phones. And I repeat, if any one of you shoots this man, you will die a second after, understood?'

Korso heard three replies of *Da, Ser* as he reached into his overcoat pocket and slowly pulled out two phones, the burner and a generic Android. He displayed them to Gancharov.

'Yes, I see them.' Gancharov wiped his forehead again with the back of his hand. 'So now call your accomplice and tell him to deliver the antidote.'

'I prefer to work alone,' Korso said, and pressed the speed dial button on the burner.

Two seconds later, all heads moved at the faint, tinny, recognisable sound of the Nokia ringtone coming from somewhere nearby. Korso waited until it completed its initial chime then pressed the red button before anyone could get a lock on its location.

'That annoying sound you heard comes from a twin of this one,' Korso said, 'strategically hidden in a neighbouring building with the volume on maximum setting. I placed it there twenty-four hours ago in a thin waterproof package, along with a vial of the antidote and two disposable syringes.'

Korso quickly went into the burner phone's settings and deleted the memory. 'Just in case one of you was thinking of shooting me and taking this phone, I've wiped the SIM so the number for the other one is now known by me alone. Also, that phone and the vials, while easy to get to, are not in plain sight so don't bother searching. It'll take you a lot longer than thirty minutes. Or twenty-five now.'

'Please get on with it then,' Gancharov said.

'It's very simple. Your accountant there wires my fee to the account number I gave you at our first meeting. I'll be checking on my other phone, and as soon as the money's deposited, I leave. Once I reach my vehicle, and assuming you haven't been foolish enough to send one of your men to follow me, I call the number again and let it ring out. Just have your men follow the sound and they'll find the antidote.'

Gancharov turned to Ivor. 'Do as he says. Do it now.'

Ivor quickly pulled a small tablet from a large wallet on the table and began pressing and swiping the screen. Korso used the time to access one of the many anonymous accounts he held around the globe. This one belonged to a very private bank in Lichtenstein. Within seconds of the money being deposited it would be automatically split into seven random amounts and wired to seven other anonymous accounts in different countries, each one belonging to a different offshore shell corporation, each one untraceable. He had learnt long ago never to put all his eggs into one basket.

Once he reached the bank's simple home page, he keyed in his long account number and ever-changing password and pressed enter. Within seconds he was taken to his account page.

'I will not forget this.'

Korso looked up and saw Gancharov glaring death at him. Which was to be expected, he supposed. Every man had his pride. Still, it was irritating.

'I hope you won't,' Korso said. 'But before you start making plans to send a hit team after me, try to look at this in the long term. I provide a fairly unique service for people in your position who can't go through normal channels, and my success rate is very high. Who's to say you won't have a similar problem in the future sometime, when you have need of my talents again? Nobody knows what's around the corner, so why reduce your options unnecessarily? And if you do ever use my services, maybe there'll be an additional element of trust between us and we can forego all the timewasting we're going through now. That sound at all reasonable to you?'

He didn't wait for a response, didn't really expect one, so he stared at the screen again. Waiting.

Twenty seconds later, Ivor said, 'The transaction is going through now.'

Korso nodded and kept watching the screen. Suddenly, there was a faint *ping* and the figure $264,000 appeared in the credit column.

'Excellent,' he said. 'Our business is now completed.' He logged out and pocketed the smartphone, but kept the burner visible in his other hand.

'Your vehicle,' Gancharov said. 'How far away?'

'Three minutes' walk. Please don't follow me.'

'Nobody will follow you. I am many things, but stupid is not one of them or I would be long dead by now.' He grimaced momentarily, then said, 'Also, there is truth in what you said before. You and I are much alike, I think. I am simply a businessman looking after my own financial interests, so why would I expect you to be any different? And I respect the man who goes that extra mile to get the result he wants. As you say, maybe we will do business again.' He wiped his forehead once more, looked at his damp palm. 'One thing.'

'What?'

'Do not forget that call. I am starting to feel very... uncomfortable.'

'I'll walk fast.'

Four

Two months later, Korso was leaning back in his ergonomic chair as he absently brushed a hand through his short hair. His eyes were narrowed as he studied his laptop screen.

He was in his home office in Bermuda. A converted bedroom, really. The house itself was a modern, one-storey, two-bedroom town home in Warwick, about twenty minutes' drive from the capital, Hamilton. Like everything else in the British overseas territory, it was expensive. The rent was a shade under $7000 per month. But Korso had done a great deal of research during the house-hunting stage, and this was the only piece of real estate that ticked every box on his very demanding list. Which made it a bargain.

The original lease had been signed using one of the three identities in his possession. Each alias was entirely 'genuine', complete with all the requisite identification. Each one had cost Korso a small fortune, although he would have willingly paid double the amount. In a world where access to almost all human knowledge was but a finger swipe away, true anonymity was something that could no longer be measured in dollars or pounds. It was far more valuable than that.

To prove the point, Korso hadn't used his own birth name in over two decades. He never would again.

Occasionally he even had trouble remembering it himself, which pleased him greatly.

Like almost everything in his life, his current home was a temporary one. Korso made it a rule to change his base every two years, or sooner if his internal radar warned him it was time to move on. Previously, he'd resided in Geneva, Switzerland, prior to that, Kowloon, Hong Kong. Before that, he'd spent twenty-eight months in the coastal town of Sorrento, in southwest Italy.

Sorrento counted as his longest period of residence in any one place. Korso had rented an old cottage on the outskirts of town, away from the tourists, and had stayed there for far longer than was wise. He even knew that at the time. It was one of the only times in his life he had acted against his better instincts. But he hadn't regretted it. There was almost nothing about the town he didn't like, and he'd even learned a passable amount of Italian while he was there. Enough so that, with his naturally olive-skinned complexion, he was mistaken for a local on more than one occasion.

So after twenty months in Geneva, Korso had decided he wanted to experience some sun again, and a mental coin toss had given him Bermuda as his current country of residence.

It wasn't Sorrento, but he liked it. The subtropical climate was pleasant, if unspectacular. The pink sand beaches were beautiful, and people minded their own business, and didn't bother him unless he wanted them to. For Korso, who generally preferred his own company to anyone else's, that last quality was the most important of all.

Currently, Korso was doing what he usually did between salvage assignments: attempting to track down an extremely rare first edition that may or may not even exist. Since he cherished the written word himself, this doubled as both work and a pastime.

He had a perennial roster of very wealthy clients who also shared the same obsession. On those infrequent occasions that he found a book on his list and was able to verify its authenticity, he knew at least one of them would pay whatever outrageous price the seller demanded for its sale. *If* he or she decided to sell, that is.

But it was the quest itself that gave Korso purpose, rather than the outcome.

The image on his laptop screen was a detail from page seventy-nine of a folio his contact claimed was an original first edition of the first volume of *Don Quixote de la Mancha*, printed by Francisco de Robles in late 1604, and published in early 1605. That edition was full of typographical errors due to the rush job imposed by the original publishing contract. Naturally, the text was in Spanish. Since Korso was fluent in the language, he was able to easily spot the three errors on the page.

So far, it looked like a winner.

He leaned forward again. His desk was covered with open textbooks, legal pads, sticky notes, photocopies and sheets filled with handwritten annotations. Korso moved one of the legal pads aside and picked up a black notebook underneath, opened it to the bookmarked page and reread the impressions he'd jotted down almost seven years ago.

That was the problem with these super-rare books. They showed up so infrequently that it was difficult to get concrete information on their exact contents. Amassing any kind of hard data on the volume in question was often just as gruelling as locating the actual book itself. Added to which, the last time a *Don Quixote* first edition was ever seen in public was in 1989, when a copy fetched a ludicrously low $1.5 million at auction. The book's present-day value was incalculable, since nobody knew how many copies were still in existence.

But seven years ago Korso had bribed a museum curator in Barcelona, where they very briefly had a copy on loan for private academic viewing, to allow him to view the volume himself one night. It had cost him a great deal of money at the time, but it was a necessary expense. With the curator standing over his shoulder and carefully turning the fragile pages himself, Korso had speed read the text over a couple of hours and taken notes of any typo and anomaly he came across for his own personal use.

Now that foresightedness was paying off.

His notes confirmed the exact same three errors on page seventy-nine as those onscreen. First, *venederos* was misspelt as *venedaros*. Second and third, on the penultimate line, the word *¿Quién* was missing not only the accent over the *e*, but the question mark as well. Since these and numerous other mistakes had been corrected for the second edition, published later that same year, they seemed to confirm he was indeed looking at a page from the first edition.

Which, if true, made the book almost priceless.

Korso leaned back in his chair, allowing himself only a small smile of satisfaction. Best to remain pragmatic at this early stage. It was far too easy to let yourself get carried away with these small victories. And besides, there was no need to rush to judgement. These projects always moved at a slow pace, with plenty of back and forth between the concerned parties.

Turning to his laptop, he closed the photo app, opened his browser and keyed in the address to his highly secure email site.

Email was the only way anyone could get in contact with him. At least initially. Phone contact was out, for obvious reasons. He had a good supply of disposable cell phones he used for mundane activities, such as restaurant or theatre bookings, that kind of thing, but never for anything important. And he only used a phone once, then destroyed the SIM card and dumped the phone in the trash.

All his incoming emails were redirected around the globe through a number of anonymous forwarding services until they got to his inbox, the data passing through numerous servers in Scandinavia, Europe and the Far East along the way, and were only accessible via a specially encrypted 128-bit key that he changed every week. The procedure for sent messages was a little more convoluted since the recipient couldn't use his unique encryption key. But the result was the same.

Nobody could trace his IP.

Nobody could track him.

Nobody ever had. In his line of work, with the kind of people he dealt with, there was no such thing as being too paranoid.

After keying in a twenty-one-digit password to access his account, Korso saw two new messages waiting for him. The first was two days old, the other from the day before. He opened the first one and raised an eyebrow when he read the opening line: *'You have been recently recommended by a Mr G who collects antique WWII-era weapons...'*

Interesting. So it seemed Gancharov had been genuine about bearing him no malice for the poisoning incident.

The man apparently possessed more strength of character than Korso had given him credit for. Korso liked it when people surprised him. It happened so rarely.

The rest of the email was brief and vague, like always. The anonymous sender needed a lost something or other recovered and wanted to meet. Probably stolen rather than lost. That was usually how it panned out.

The second email was from one of his wealthier clients, Xian Li, asking him to 'keep an eye out' for a first printing of Chaucer's *Canterbury Tales*. Korso had to smile at the turn of phrase. As though the 1477 folio, of which only a dozen copies were known to exist, might suddenly crop up in a yard sale. He'd do as asked, of course. No need to let Li know that two other clients had already made the same request.

He quickly composed a reply to Mattheus, his German contact, about the *Don Quixote* situation. He wrote that the signs were promising regarding the book's authenticity, but he still wanted Mattheus to get the owner to photograph another page for him, page 113 to be exact, to cast any further doubts aside. Korso knew that it was one of the very few pages from that edition with no typographical errors at all. If the owner's page was perfect too, then perhaps they'd be able to move on to the next stage.

As he sent the message on its long, convoluted journey, his stomach made a faint rumbling sound. He checked the time in the top right corner of the screen and was surprised to see it was 17:04. Time really did fly when you were enjoying yourself. He thought briefly about making himself something, but on a whim tossed his mental coin. It came up tails – he'd eat out instead.

Korso got up from the chair and was stretching his arms wide when he heard the chime of the front doorbell.

Which hardly ever happened.

Wearing a deep frown, he walked into the front room and glanced through the window. Outside, there was a FedEx van parked on the otherwise empty street. He'd used the local office before, of course, but he'd not once received anything from them. Mainly because nobody outside of Bermuda knew he lived there.

This was anything but good. For a brief moment Korso considered refusing the delivery, or not answering altogether. Signing for anything would only confirm to the sender that the package had been delivered successfully. But he still had to know. No doubt the sender had counted on that too.

Accepting the inevitable, Korso crossed to the front door and opened it. He vaguely recognised the courier as a genuine islander, sure that he'd seen his face around Hamilton several times before. He was holding a thin cardboard envelope with the purple and orange FedEx logo running up the left side.

The man gave him a huge smile, a Bermudian trademark. 'Mister Graves?'

'That's right.'

Ricardo Graves was the name Korso had signed on the lease, the same one as on the Portuguese passport he was currently using. His other two passports were housed in two extremely private safe deposit boxes. One in London, the other in Helsinki.

'Sign here, please, sir.' The courier held out his electronic signature capture pad. Korso made an indecipherable scribble on the screen with his index finger.

'That's just fine. You have a wonderful day, sir.'

'Thanks.' Korso took the envelope and watched the man stroll back to his van. He got in and slowly drove off to his next delivery, like he had all the time in the world.

Korso closed the door and looked down at the hand-written address sticker on the envelope. He groaned inwardly. It was enough that somebody had sent something to Ricardo Graves in Bermuda. But in brackets after the Graves name were two more words, each as bad as the other.

AKA Jara.

It was the name of a dead man.

Five

There was no letter. No note. Just six colour photos. Each one five inches by seven. Properly developed photos at that, not cheap laser copies. They all showed Korso at various locations.

The top one depicted what looked to be the busy Rue de Berne in downtown Geneva. So most likely taken three or four years ago, back when he lived on the city's outskirts. The photographer had clearly been on the other side of the street, possibly behind a store window, using a telephoto lens. It was a sunny day. There was a blur on the left as a vehicle sped out of shot.

Korso was in profile; just one man among the sea of commuters. He carried nothing. He wore a dark suit, but no tie. Where had he been going that day? His brown hair was a little longer than now. His expression was serious, his facial characteristics as unremarkable as ever. Neither handsome nor homely, just average-looking. Exactly as he'd planned nine years ago, when he'd had them altered.

The next one was a close-up of Korso sitting at an outside cafe, reading a newspaper. He could see it was the international edition of the *New York Times*, but couldn't make out the headline or front-page photo. Which meant Switzerland again. That was the only place he'd ever bought it with any kind of regularity. Usually once or twice a week.

The third shot was of him leaving Bermuda's L. F. Wade Airport, just sixteen kilometres northeast of his current location, apparently looking for a cab home. His hair was cut to its current short length, and he wore tan chinos with a navy shirt and black windbreaker.

Korso stared out the window at the rear garden and thought back. He'd made over a dozen flights in the past year alone, but he'd only worn that Harrington jacket once. *When was it? Last year? The year before? No. Got it.* Six, maybe seven months before, he'd worn it on a brief trip to Boston for a visit to one of his safety deposit boxes.

He scanned the rest of the photos. Two more from Geneva, one of him looking at his watch, another as he bought some fresh fruit from a street market stall. And one more of him in Bermuda. A zoomed-in shot of him lying on a towel on an almost empty beach, reading a paperback in the sun. The paperback cover was in deep shadow and blurred, so no clues there. From the trees in the background it looked to be Long Bay Beach, just a few hundred yards away from where he was sitting. He went there often to read, sometimes to jog.

Korso placed the photos in two rows before him. A couple of points immediately sprang to mind. Three, actually.

The first was obvious. Unless there were shots from other countries yet to be delivered to him, which seemed unlikely, it was clear that somebody must have first spotted and identified Korso in Geneva and kept track of him from that point onward.

Secondly, his Graves identity, which he had also been using in Switzerland, was now essentially worthless. Well, not worthless exactly, as there were always parties interested in buying a clean identity complete with equally genuine biometric passport, but it was no good to him anymore. There was also always the chance that his other two aliases might be compromised. He hoped that wasn't the case, but he couldn't discount the possibility. Not until he knew more.

And thirdly, the photos themselves weren't the message. The method of delivery was. It would have been a lot easier, not to mention safer for the sender, to simply send him an email with the photos attached. Whoever it was, they had to know his email address. It was no secret, after all. Instead, they wanted him to know that they knew exactly where he lived, under which name, and what his name used to be. So they sent it all via FedEx, directly to his front door. To show that they were serious.

All of which meant one thing. There would be a follow-up communication very soon. Most likely to explain what it was that they wanted from him. Maybe that part would be by email. He'd have to check regularly from now on.

All in all, it was worse than he'd thought. Using the Jara name suggested that the people behind this knew him, or knew about him, during a period of his life he'd hoped to erase entirely. But what was done was done. All he could do now was wait for their next move, and deal with each problem as it came.

Korso went back to his office and spent a minute clearing up his desk. He routinely scanned all his notes and photocopies as he went along, and they were already safely stored as attachments to a blank email sitting in his drafts folder. With the exception of the black notebook, he now fed his papers into the shredder. The textbooks he placed on the bookshelf, along with all the other paperbacks.

He saw it was still light outside and checked his watch: 5.27 p.m. Two hours till sunset. His current life might be coming to an end, but he was still hungry. And because the very last thing he wanted to do right now was go out, he decided to do exactly that.

Grabbing his billfold and helmet from the living room, Korso locked up and left by the rear door. In the car port by the side of the house was the mauve 50cc Suzuki motor scooter he'd bought second-hand from the realtor who'd leased him the house. Since the island was only twenty-one miles long, the government limited automobile use to nationals only. For everyone else, it was a choice of bicycle, motor scooter, electric mini-car, or walking.

It took him fifteen minutes to reach Hamilton. He found a parking spot for the Suzuki close to Cafe Tamara, a recently opened Indian shisha place that he frequented now and then. It was the island's only competitor to a long-established Egyptian-themed hookah cafe and nightclub located two streets away. He'd have gone more often since the food and service were both well above average, and he also possessed a natural affinity for the underdog, but it was embedded in Korso's DNA never to develop any kind of regular routine.

Entering the cafe, he saw half a dozen groups spaced around the place, eating or smoking. Two slim Indian waitresses in traditional garb and heavy make-up were at the bar area scanning the booths, waiting to be of assistance. They were sisters. The younger one with the ponytail smiled when she saw Korso enter, and came over to him.

'Hello, Mr Ric,' she said. 'We haven't seen you in a while.'

Korso shrugged. 'Work.'

'Tell me about it. So have you finally come to ask me out? We can go clubbing later. In the morning, I'll make you my special Indian breakfast. You'll be mine forever.'

'I can't take that risk, Jasmine,' he said, forcing a smile. This had been an ongoing thing between them, and just one more reason to visit. She was very pretty, but he never knew if she was serious or not. 'Can I get a booth against the wall? And no pipe, just dinner.'

She joined her palms and gave a sardonic low bow. 'We can fulfil any desire you wish, Mr Ric. Follow me, please.' Turning, she led him to one of the multi-cushioned booths near the rear, and he took a seat. He ordered iced tea, chicken madras and some side dishes from the menu, and Jasmine flirted some more and then went away.

Leaning back in the settee, Korso spent a few minutes visualising the photos again in his mind. Wondering if he had missed anything. Some clue. Anything at all. But there was nothing more than what he'd already seen. Like he'd surmised, the photos were only part of the message. He needed more to work from.

Jasmine brought his drink and appetisers. He sipped some tea and watched as two more couples and another group of tourists entered the venue. Each were led to their booths by one of the girls. The place seemed a little busier than usual for a weeknight.

As Korso ate, he half considered making an attempt on FedEx's database for the sender's information as he had a hacker on partial retainer for special jobs like that. *M. D. Dog* was the guy's – or girl's – handle. But for security reasons, Korso didn't like using Dog too often. Also, Dog's services were expensive, and Korso felt sure the sender would have given a false ID anyway.

He watched as another customer entered the place. A Caucasian woman with short dark hair and an athletic build. Attractive. About five-eight, five-nine. She wore a tank top and combats. She was alone. Jasmine went over to her, but the other woman was looking around the cafe and when she saw Korso, said something to Jasmine and then began walking to his table, looking in all directions as she moved.

That was quick, he thought. He'd expected to have to wait a lot longer.

When she reached him, Korso could see a faint scar running down from her left temple to under her left ear.

'Good evening,' she said. Her voice was husky. Her eyes were pale and large. 'Do you mind if I join you?'

'And if I do mind?' Korso said, trying to place her accent.

'Then I will persuade you.' She sat down in the seat opposite. 'But I think you will want to know me. I believe we have very similar interests.'

Eastern European, he decided. 'Such as amateur photography, you mean?'

She gave a meaningless smile. 'What is the food like here?'

'Recommended. What do I call you?'

'My name is Natasha.'

'Well, Natasha, I'm very good at placing faces, and I've never seen yours before. I would have remembered.'

'I'll take your word for that.'

'So if I don't know you, that means you're allied with someone I do know.'

'That's essentially correct.'

'And so now that you've reconned the premises and detected no threats, you can call your partner and tell him, or her, that it's safe to enter. Or is partner the wrong term?'

'Close enough.' She made a vague gesture.

Pulling a thin phone from her back pocket, she dialled a number and put it to her ear. 'We are in a booth against the wall, to the left as you enter.' She hung up and looked at Korso. 'Is your heart starting to beat faster now? I bet it is, just a little.'

'Sorry to disappoint you.' It was the truth. Korso had the calmness of spirit of a marksman. A virtue learned long ago under extreme pressure, and never forgotten.

The door opened, and a man in a Hawaiian shirt and tan chinos entered. He wore a baseball cap, sunglasses and several days' worth of stubble. Looking around, he smiled when he saw the two of them at the table.

Korso recognised him immediately. He should have known.

Sardoca.

The one man he should have taken care of nine years ago. An error, it seemed, that he was going to pay for.

Six

'Such a long time, Jara,' Sardoca said, taking the seat next to Natasha. He took off the cap and sunglasses, revealing close-cropped black hair that was a little thinner on top than Korso remembered. But the hooded, dark brown eyes were still the same. Unreadable. 'You don't know how glad I am to see you again. In person, I mean.'

'I wish I could say the same,' Korso replied.

Sardoca grinned. 'Do you really?'

'No. Also, nobody calls me Jara anymore.'

'Of course they don't. Because Jara died nine years ago. So what shall we call you instead? Is it Korso now? Or Senor Graves? Or just plain Ricardo? So many choices.'

'Pick one. I don't care.' At least Sardoca hadn't mentioned the names on his other two passports. That was something.

'Korso, then.' He sniffed. 'That food smells good. Natasha, please?'

She looked around and quickly caught the attention of Jasmine's sister, Avni, who came to the table with two more menus.

'Order us something interesting, Natasha,' Sardoca said. He was still looking at Korso. 'Also, a pipe or two. I like a good smoke with a meal. You agree?'

'It depends on the company,' Korso said.

'Now, comrade, let us be civil.'

They waited in silence while Natasha placed their orders. She also asked for two pipes, along with some ambrosia and blue mist shishas.

Once Avni had left with their orders, Sardoca said, 'You received the photos.'

'You know I did.'

'And you know what they signify. Or you think you do.'

'I know my time here's come to an end. Beyond that, I'm still collating.' He turned to Natasha, watching as she lazily rubbed her left earlobe, then turned back to Sardoca. 'Out of interest, who identified me?'

'An old associate of mine in Geneva. I have many. Let's just say I had my doubts about the timing of your apparent death all those years ago. That warehouse explosion with the burnt body inside was all a little too coincidental for me. Everyone who mattered believed it was you in there, but I had my doubts, and so I decided to keep my eye out for any possible sign of your reappearance.' He paused a beat. 'The actual details I'll keep to myself, I think, but it looks like I was right to remain vigilant, doesn't it? Incidentally, who was the corpse they identified?'

'Some homeless guy I stole from the morgue a month earlier.'

'And then kept on ice until the right moment.' Sardoca grinned again. 'This man needs to be watched very carefully, Natasha. He is always thinking ahead. Just like me.'

He studied Korso's face carefully. 'Very nice job, by the way. If I passed you on the street and had my mind on something else… who can say? But once you do know, it is like those magic-eye posters. Everything becomes obvious. I hope the surgery was painful.'

Avni came back then with their dishes, and they waited in silence as she placed them on the table. Meanwhile, one of her brothers came over with two shisha pipes, each one containing three hoses, along with the necessary accoutrements. He placed several mouthpieces in wrappers on the table, then deftly sprinkled the flavoured tobacco over the clay bowls and used large tweezers to place the little coal bricks on top. He lit them with a small blowtorch until they were red hot. Once he'd got each of the six hoses going to his satisfaction, he wished them all a happy meal and went back to the kitchen with his sister.

They ate.

After a while, Korso said, 'You're still with him.'

Sardoca put down his fork, sipped his beer. 'Of course. Did you ever doubt it?'

'I never really thought about it, to be honest.'

'Perhaps you should have. Mr Nikolic is a definite factor in our new relationship. For instance, how do you think he would react if he somehow discovered you were still alive after all, with all those secrets of his still running around in that brain of yours?'

'Not well.'

'Knowing him as I do, I can safely predict he would feel very angry at having been publicly tricked by somebody he believed he could trust. Murderous, even. You remember how he would get when faced with personal disloyalty of any kind.'

'Yes.'

'Of course you do. The more intense the feelings in any relationship, the more intense the hatred once things go wrong. Sometimes I felt he treated you like the son he never had, which is just one of the reasons I hated you.

34

So imagine his rage now if he were to find out you faked your own death to get away from him.'

'You've got it all twisted, Sardoca. I was just an employee, like you. Nothing more. I wasn't even with him for that long. Just a couple of years.'

'And those two years were just long enough to make the right impression.'

'If you say so.'

But Korso wondered. He'd never spent much time analysing his brief relationship with Nikolic, so he couldn't completely discount Sardoca's perspective on things. Maybe the man was actually onto something there.

Natasha had finished her food and was taking a long drag from the ambrosia pipe. She tilted her head back and breathed a long plume of smoke that coiled up to the ceiling.

'Good?' Korso said.

'Very,' she said. 'Try some.'

'I already have.' He turned back to Sardoca. 'Is Natasha your muscle? She seems competent.'

'Natasha is my right hand, and experienced in most situations. I advise you not to test her. Or me, for that matter.'

'Noted.'

Korso returned to his meal. He didn't like dining with Sardoca, but he hated wasting good food more. Besides, this would probably be the final time he ate here. Once he'd finished the last of the rice, he sipped his iced tea as he watched Sardoca.

'So you want me to recover something for you.'

Sardoca furrowed his brow. 'What makes you say that?'

'It's obvious. For almost four years you've known I didn't die in that warehouse fire, yet you've done nothing

35

with that information until now. I'm sure you know how I currently make my living. Which suggests you've been keeping me on ice until the right moment came along.'

'There, Natasha,' Sardoca said happily. 'You see? I told you he was fast.'

'Yes, you told me,' she said, blowing two perfect smoke rings into the air.

'And what else have you deduced, Korso?'

'That you were most likely tasked with tracing this whatever-it-is in the first place, probably by Nikolic, and have gotten precisely nowhere. Since Nikolic was never a patient man, and with time now ticking away, you felt compelled to knock on my door.'

Sardoca shared a glance with Natasha and reached for the other pipe. He unwrapped a mouthpiece, placed it on one of the hoses, and began to suck the aromatic vapour into his lungs. He blew out a huge cloud of smoke and watched it rise up to the ceiling fans.

'Let's assume you are right,' Sardoca said. 'For the most part.'

'Then the next obvious question would be what exactly is it you want found?'

'A missing shipment of caviar.'

Korso snorted. 'You're not serious.'

'Why not? Have you any idea how much six crates are worth?'

'Peanuts,' Korso said. 'Nothing. Zero. Considering Nikolic's net worth was close to a billion dollars when I was with him, and I can only assume his fortune has grown exponentially over the years. What kind of caviar are we talking about?'

'Obviously not the fresh kind, but still top of the line. Tell him, Natasha.'

'It is White Pearl Albino Sturgeon caviar,' she said, cleaning her mouthpiece with a napkin. 'Very rare, very exclusive. Pasteurised, so good for another six months or more. All in one-kilogram tins, each tin worth approximately three thousand US dollars wholesale. Two hundred and forty tins per crate. Six crates in total.'

Korso made a quick calculation. 'Which makes four million three hundred and twenty thousand dollars. Like I said, pocket change to a man like Nikolic. It can't be just that.' He raised a hand. 'But let's put all that aside for the moment. You seem pretty certain I'll recover this shipment for you.'

'Well, you've built up a sizeable reputation over the years for doing just that.'

'That's not what I meant.'

'I know.' Sardoca smiled. 'Shall we talk about the photos? They were just a small sample, of course. I have many more of you in Switzerland and a few more of you here, all safely stored in the clouds and just a simple mouse click away from being released publicly if I wish to do so. If Mr Nikolic saw them, which I can pretty much guarantee he would, he might not believe at first, but it would not take long for him to see the true face beneath your new one. He would stop at nothing until you were brought to him, and you know the kind of resources at his disposal. And how painful it would be for you in the end.'

Korso knew. It was why he'd arranged his own death in the first place. Nikolic was the most ruthless crime lord in Eastern Europe, with fingers in every pie and connections in every corner of the globe, even though most of the world didn't even know he existed. He'd never been arrested for a crime, and there were no photos of him in existence anywhere, which was almost unheard of in this day and age. But loyalty came above all else to him, and he would do anything to get his hands on Korso if he knew he was still alive. Anything. Fake passports and plastic surgery wouldn't be much help against that kind of pressure.

'That's interesting,' Korso said.

'What is?' Sardoca said, frowning.

'You mentioned the resources at Nikolic's disposal, and I agree. They're practically limitless. But it does raise the question of why he isn't utilising them to find this alleged caviar shipment instead of his lieutenant. You *are* his lieutenant, aren't you?'

'One of them. As you well know.'

'There you go. It doesn't fit. Clearly, if Nikolic considers this missing shipment important enough that he assigns its recovery to one of his few trusted employees, then it obviously contains something else besides fish eggs.' He splayed his hand. 'So what is it?'

Natasha and Sardoca glanced at each other. After a couple of seconds, she shrugged one shoulder and he gave a single nod of agreement in return.

'One of the tins in that shipment,' she said, 'is not like the others.'

'I'm shocked. So what does it contain instead?'

Sardoca gave a sigh, and said, 'Something called the Tiger's Tears.'

Seven

'Very enigmatic,' Korso said. 'And what is this Tiger's Tears, exactly?'

'That's not anything you need to know,' Sardoca said. 'It's enough that the tin contains something valuable belonging to Mr Nikolic, and that he wants it, and the rest of the shipment, found and returned to him as soon as possible.'

Korso studied the man's face, then smiled. 'So you don't know what it is, either.'

Natasha coughed, and quickly covered her mouth. Sardoca ignored her. 'I told you not to test me, Korso. I hold all the aces here. Don't ever forget it.'

'I'll try to remember. So, assuming I even agree to this assignment, what time frame are you talking about here?'

Sardoca looked at his watch. 'The deadline's roughly ninety-six hours from now. That's Thursday at six o'clock, Bermuda time.'

'Four days?' Korso said. 'Now I know you're joking. Have you any idea how long it takes me to track down some of the—'

'Don't waste time arguing with me,' Sardoca interrupted. 'That's the deadline Mr Nikolic has set. Ninety-six hours from now. No negotiation.'

Korso sighed, knowing it was pointless. 'And when did he actually set you off on this goose chase?'

'Ten days ago.'

'So he actually gave you two weeks, most of which you've used up already. Brilliant. And did you make any progress in that time?'

Sardoca just shook his head.

'It just gets better and better, doesn't it?' Korso sighed again. 'So now I know I'll be starting basically from scratch, maybe we should discuss my cut.'

'What are you talking about?'

'You know how I work, Sardoca. Whatever I find, I get thirty-three per cent of the salvaged item's market value. And thirty-three per cent of four million three hundred and twenty thousand dollars is one million four hundred and twenty-five thousand dollars. But since this is kind of a special case, I don't mind rounding it down to an even million. That's less than twenty-five per cent.'

Sardoca was already shaking his head. 'No, no, no, *compadre*. Other than expenses, this is one job you will do gratis. I don't need to remind you of the alternative.'

'No, you don't.' Korso indicated his empty plate. 'Are you paying for this meal?'

'Sure. I can do that much.'

Korso nodded, drank the last of his iced tea and stood up. 'Goodbye.'

He slid out and was about to walk when Sardoca grabbed his wrist. Korso stopped and looked down at it. 'Where are you going?' Sardoca said.

'Home to pack. Then the airport. Then elsewhere. I'll take my chances.'

'You're bluffing.'

'Try me.'

'You will have no chance at all, Korso. Not with Mr Nikolic after your blood.'

'Maybe. But I imagine he'll be after yours too if you don't recover this shipment he wants so badly.' He waited. 'Am I wrong?'

Sardoca stared at him for several beats, then released his wrist. 'Sit down.'

Korso sat back down. More seconds passed. 'Well?'

'All right. You will get your money. Payment on delivery, of course.'

'Naturally. Which still leaves the matter of the photos.'

'What about them?'

'Assuming I'm successful, and that's a very big assumption at this stage, what's to stop you from using your hold over me again? Let's face it, there's no love lost between us, and in a digital world it's not like I can demand the negatives back. What guarantee have I got that you won't get into another fix sometime in the future and decide to blackmail me into solving your problems again? And then again after that?'

'I appreciate your concerns, but you'll just have to take my word that I'll delete them permanently. I know when to keep a bargain. Besides, I assume you will have further surgery done on your face once this is over, making them essentially useless anyway. Correct?'

Korso looked at him. He'd had to bring up the subject, because anyone in his position would be expected to. But he already knew there was only one way to guarantee Sardoca would never try this again. And Sardoca was far from stupid. He had to know that as well.

'I guess I'll have to believe you for now,' Korso said.

'Excellent.' Sardoca gave a smug grin. 'So we are all friends again.'

'Don't push it.'

Sardoca took another vape, letting out another thick plume of smoke. 'One thing I have always been curious about.'

Korso said nothing.

'I know Jara was never your real name, and Korso certainly isn't, either. Nor Graves. So what is? The one you were born with, I mean. I've always wondered.'

Korso blinked at him. 'Maybe I'll tell you sometime.'

'Really? When?'

Before he could answer, Natasha said, 'At the point of dying?'

Korso turned to her. One side of her mouth was turned up.

'Yes, I have seen that movie, too,' she said. 'Sergio Leone. One of the better westerns.'

Korso gave an appreciative nod, turned back to Sardoca. 'I like her.'

'Good, because she's also going to be with you every step of the way.'

–

Korso entered his house for what would be the last time and switched on the lights. 'Drugs,' he said.

'What?' Natasha said, closing the front door behind her.

She had followed Korso back to Warwick on her own rented scooter. Once Sardoca knew Korso was on board, he'd given Natasha some last-minute instructions, then left them to catch his flight to wherever. Korso hadn't been sorry to see him go.

'This Tiger's Tears,' he said, dropping his keys on the living room table, 'is a prototype of some new synthetic designer drug Nikolic has been developing overseas. Seriously addictive, too, would be my guess. Am I close?'

'What makes you think I would know?'

'Call it a hunch.'

'I hope you have better ones,' she said, looking around the simply furnished room. 'I am puzzled, though.'

'About what?'

'At the restaurant, I expected you to be more… hostile about my coming along.'

'Well, I could see Sardoca's mind was already made up, and I felt I'd already pushed him as far as I could. Besides, if I were him I wouldn't trust me, either.'

'You're honest, at least.'

'Most of the time. So I assume he arranged for you to contact him at pre-arranged times, with particular code phrases to alert him if something's wrong, such as my holding a gun to your head, for example? Or if I attempt to make a run for it?'

'Something like that. Why, are you planning to do something stupid? Because you should realise that you're not un-expendable, and I won't hesitate to kill you if I must.'

'That's useful to know.' Korso smiled. He much preferred it when everything was laid out in the open like this. 'But you won't have to. I'll see it through, like I said. Also, I have to admit I'm kind of curious. Not that Sardoca has to know that. Let him sweat.'

She arched an eyebrow. 'You two have a strange relationship.'

'He hates me. I couldn't care less about him. It seems perfectly straightforward to me. Now I take it you can give me a complete rundown on everything that's happened up until this moment?'

'There's little point in my being here otherwise.'

'Good. Let's get started, and try to leave nothing out. The more information I have, the better our chances for success.' He walked out of the room.

'Where are you going?' she said, following him.

'I've a few loose ends to tie up before we leave here. I can do two things at once, sometimes more. You talk, I'll listen.' He sat at his office desk, opened his laptop, motioned toward the only other chair in the room. 'When did this shipment of yours go missing?'

Natasha took a seat, one leg folded under her. 'March 2. Just over six weeks ago.'

'And the point of origin?'

'The Ukraine. The aircraft was a British Aerospace ATP, or Advanced Turbo-Prop, leased by one of Mr Nikolic's representatives over there. He also used two pilots that we've used before. The plane was a modified version of the ATP, with reduced cargo space to allow for twice the normal fuel capacity, enabling the whole journey to be done in two legs. On March 1, it flew from Poltava Airport direct to Eugene F. Correia Airport in Guyana, remaining there for three hours for refuelling while further cargo was also loaded for the final leg to Toronto, Canada. It never reached its destination.'

Korso paused from deleting files. 'Wait a second. What extra cargo?'

'Mr Nikolic had also purchased a crate of Geisha coffee from the region and wanted it delivered at the same time.'

'Geisha coffee. Don't tell me. From Hacienda La Esmeralda, in Panama.'

'Yes. You know of it?'

He nodded. 'In purely financial terms, it's right up there with Albino Sturgeon caviar. So your boss is based

44

in Toronto now. That's smart of him. But then he always was.'

'You approve?'

'I merely note the fact. For someone in his position, Canada carries all the benefits of an American base of operations, but without the associated disadvantages of actually being in the USA. For example, it's very easy to get lost in all that space if one wishes. That's not so easy to do anymore in the States.'

'So I take it you're not American, then.'

'What makes you think I could be?'

'You sometimes roll your *Rs*.'

'So do Spaniards. So do Canadians.' He smiled. 'So do you.'

She smiled back. 'Point taken. Shall we continue? We have much to cover.'

Korso went back to his laptop. 'I'm all ears.'

Eight

Natasha was able to bring Korso completely up to date in less than an hour. And all from memory too, which he found impressive.

The essential facts were these:

Two months previous, Nikolic had purchased a large caviar shipment from a black-market supplier in Iran. This supplier was willing to transport the cargo to a contact in the Ukraine, but no further. Nikolic was agreeable to the terms, since he had something else stored in a safe place in Russia that he needed to bring over with the shipment, and this would give him the perfect chance to do so without raising suspicion. But since this mysterious asset was something only a select few knew existed, he needed someone trustworthy to hide it and to ensure the plane took off on schedule.

That person was Natasha.

She oversaw the loading of the initial five crates at Poltava Airport in the Ukraine. She was also the one who was personally handed the asset by one of Nikolic's Russian contacts, a man named Yuri, who showed up at the airport one hour before the plane was due to take off. He handed her the item, about which he knew nothing, then left. All without saying a word.

46

'So I was right,' Korso said. 'You do know what it is.'

Natasha shook her head. 'No. All I was given was a plain, stainless-steel tin with no markings. The dimensions were similar to the caviar tins, only slightly smaller so it would fit inside one easily. It weighed roughly the same, about one kilogram, and was welded shut. The contents didn't rattle or make any noise when I shook it. I saw no other clues. But I do know it's coated with a special film containing a faint radioactive residue detectable by any Geiger counter, so I can locate it quickly once we find the shipment.'

'And you have one of those.'

'In my flight bag. You can buy them from Amazon.'

'So tell me, why were you chosen for that particular job, and not Sardoca?'

Natasha frowned. 'Sardoca has many responsibilities within Mr Nikolic's organisation, and couldn't be spared at that time.'

'And Nikolic trusted you to do it instead?'

'I don't believe he trusts anybody. But Sardoca has worked for him for many years and *he* trusts me, so maybe that swayed Mr Nikolic's decision. Of course, that's only guesswork on my part. Why, is it relevant?'

'I don't know yet. It's an anomaly, and they're generally worth following up. Here's another one. Why didn't you travel with the cargo all the way to the end?'

She rubbed at her earlobe again. 'If you know Mr Nikolic, then you know he likes to compartmentalise assignments so that the left hand rarely knows what the right is doing. Often he uses people who never know they actually work for him, and most of those are not even aware that he exists. In my case, once I'd supervised the loading and secreted the asset in one of the crates, my role was over. Another man was to guard the cargo en route – Anton Borozan. He also body searched me before I left the plane, to make sure I took nothing with me. As I said, Mr Nikolic trusts nobody. As soon as the aircraft took off, I flew in the opposite direction, as I had urgent business in Cambodia.'

'And who is this Anton Borozan?'

'One of Sardoca's men. I recognised him from a previous job. Capable with a gun, but not much imagination. The perfect foot soldier. So as I was saying, the BA ATP took off from Poltava Airport in the morning of March 1, and reached Eugene F. Correia Airport in Guyana seventeen hours later without incident. Once it was on the ground, Borozan and both pilots remained on board while the plane was refuelled for the final leg, and the final crate was loaded into the cargo hold with the others. Again, all without incident.'

'Allegedly.' Korso had opened his browser and found a political world map on one of the geology sites. He zoomed in on South America to remind himself of the precise geography. And there was Guyana, sitting atop Brazil on the northeast coast, sandwiched between Venezuela and Suriname. Above it, the numerous islands that made up the Caribbean.

'What time did it take off from Guyana?'

'Thirteen minutes past midnight on March 2. Their final radio transmission was logged by Correia air traffic control at 00:37. Just a routine request from the co-pilot for any weather updates. It was clear that night. Not even cloud cover. Then they simply disappeared off the radar at 00:42. That was the last anyone heard from them.'

Korso zoomed in further. He figured twenty-five minutes' flying time would have easily taken them over the Caribbean Sea. Theoretically, at least. 'Since it's only been six weeks, I assume the official investigation is still ongoing?'

'Yes. The Guyana Civil Aviation Authority is working alongside their Ukrainian counterparts, the State Aviation Administration. So far they haven't been successful. There are no clues. No debris. We have a source in the SAA investigative unit who says unlawful interference by a third party can't be ruled out, but the current line of thinking is the plane was lost at sea due to either pilot error or sudden mechanical failure.'

'Do you believe that?'

Natasha smiled. 'Mr Nikolic doesn't believe it, and that's all that matters. He thinks it all far too convenient to be an accident.'

'In this case, I agree with him. What about the emergency locator transmitter? If I remember correctly, most aircraft are fitted with at least one ELT. Often more. Don't tell me this plane was one of the exceptions.'

'It wasn't. There were two automatic fixed ELTs permanently mounted aft, programmed to give off continuous distress signals on 406 megahertz the moment the aircraft became immersed in water or impacted against something solid. But there have been no SOS signals on that frequency, or any of the alternative frequencies. We have a man listening at all times, as do the SAA, but it seems the ELTs either malfunctioned or were tampered with before the plane left the airport.'

'The latter seems more plausible, don't you think?'

'Well, I discovered on reading up on previous air disasters that there are reported difficulties with ELT signals in deep water, but I admit it seems unlikely in this case.' She frowned as Korso continued deleting files from his laptop. 'Why bother with all that? Just revert to factory settings or destroy the hard drive and you'll get the same result.'

'I like to be thorough, especially where my own security is concerned.' In a casual voice, he said, 'Out of interest, does Sardoca use one of these or does he prefer to do everything on his smartphone?'

'He mostly does his business on a laptop,' she said, pulling a packet of gum from one of her pockets. 'He says it's more secure. Why do you ask?'

'I'm the curious type. And it's always good to know your enemy's habits.' He leaned back in his chair and frowned at the ceiling, thinking. He vaguely heard Natasha unwrap a stick of gum and put it in her mouth. Minutes passed as he mentally ticked off the numerous possibilities that occurred to him, one by one. There were a lot of them.

'Have some gum,' Natasha said. He turned to her and took the proffered spearmint stick. 'Share your thoughts, please.'

Korso unwrapped the stick, stuck it in his mouth, started chewing. 'It wasn't pilot error or mechanical malfunction. The plane was hijacked, for want of a better word.' He looked at her. 'But you already know that.'

Natasha gave a single nod in reply.

'After that last transmission,' he continued, 'the pilots, who had to be in on it too, most likely dropped their altitude to beat the radar, and then either doubled back or flew on to a pre-arranged site. Lot of islands in that part of the world.'

'Yes, that makes sense. Although it's possible only one of the pilots was involved in the plan, and he forced the other to go along at gunpoint.'

'Granted. But what's definite is that this was an inside job. It had to be. At the very least, somebody from within your organisation leaked the information about that shipment to an outside party. And don't write off this Borozan either. It's possible he could have been in on it too.'

Natasha made a face. 'I agree with the first part, but not Borozan. He was never much of a thinker.'

'I don't see what difference that makes. At this stage, everyone's a suspect. Which leads us to the next obvious question.'

'Who was behind it?'

Korso shook his head. 'You're jumping the gun. The big question is, did they know about that special tin of Nikolic's? If this was just some opportunist heisters looking for quick money by stealing a shipment of black-market caviar, then that's one thing. But if they knew this asset was on board as well, that opens up a whole host of further possibilities. And none of them good.' He scratched his chin. 'Can I assume this mysterious asset is extremely valuable, and can be sold on the open market or auctioned off to the highest bidder?'

She paused. 'From what Sardoca has intimated to me, very much so.'

'Good. Because that suggests the thieves aren't aware of its existence, that it's just the caviar they're interested in.'

'Really? How can you know that?'

'I can't, not for certain. But I do know Nikolic has an information network that would be the envy of most countries if they knew about it. He's got eyes and ears everywhere on this planet, and if there was even the slightest rumour that his prize was up for sale, he'd be aware of it within seconds.'

Natasha was already nodding.

'So that narrows things down a little. But we still can't rule out the possibility of this asset being the primary target. For all we know, they could be waiting for things to die down before off-loading both it and the caviar. What about this man who gave you the tin at Poltava Airport, this Yuri? Has he been questioned by your people?'

'Sardoca wanted to, but Mr Nikolic said he'd take care of that end. That was a week ago, so I can only assume he's been cleared of suspicion, or we would have been told.'

Korso sighed. 'I really enjoy working in the dark like this. It makes my job so much easier.'

'That's the way things are with Mr Nikolic. You know this.'

'All too well.' He shook his head, brushing his irritation aside as though turning a page. With every job, essential information was invariably denied him. Often for no reason. It was always the same. He simply worked with what he had, and did things the hard way. 'Let's go back to the two pilots. What are their names?'

'Alex Azevedo and Dominic Palma. I can email you their dossiers if you wish.'

'Good,' he said. Natasha pulled out her phone and began tapping. 'Who compiled these dossiers?'

'A large private investigation firm in New York which Mr Nikolic owns a part of. Although they're unaware of this, of course.'

'Of course.'

'We use them often for background information, personal histories and such. Mr Nikolic likes to be thorough in all things. Like you. There, it should be in your inbox now.'

Korso entered his email site and checked. Attached were two PDF files. He opened the one marked Palma and was greeted with a professionally compiled history of the man from the age of eighteen upward. Jobs, employers, finances, family, friends, lovers, close family members, relationships, and more. Everything of note was in there, and all in chronological order. A forty-five-year-old man's life compressed into half a dozen pages of small bullet points. It was impressive. He went through it all quickly, but nothing jumped out at him. Not that he expected anything to. It was never that easy.

He opened Azevedo's file next. This pilot was younger by eight years, so fewer pages. Again, nothing unusual. Various jobs with different airlines. Married young. No kids. Currently divorced. Several overseas girlfriends to break the monotony. A spell in the local jail at age twenty-two on a drunk and disorderly, but nothing came of it. More interesting was the man's finances, which always seemed to be in the red. Korso was scanning the final page, the one containing details about various family members, when a name made him pause. It was like a feather landing on the back of his neck. Barely a tickle. But there.

Natasha sensed the change in him. She came over and looked at the screen. 'Something?'

'His younger sister, Amelia Azevedo, was a real maneater before she finally got married ten years ago.'

'It would seem so. Eighteen boyfriends in the space of three years, according to this. Which one interests you?'

'Don Kujan. At the bottom of the list there.'

'I see it. Do you know him?'

Korso shook his head. 'But that name… Kujan. It's an odd name. For some reason, I get the feeling it's connected to a robbery. Maybe. But where? When?' He closed his eyes and concentrated, chewing his gum and tapping his fingers lightly against his forehead. A minute passed. He opened his eyes, went to Google, and typed some words into the search box. He pressed return and got a page of results immediately. He clicked on the second one and was taken to an archived story from the *South China Morning Post* website.

'Something,' he said.

Natasha leaned in to look. '*Six arrested after thieves steal $2 million US in cash from KLM cargo plane on tarmac in Brazil*,' she said. 'Quite the headline.'

Korso said nothing, just scrolled slowly down, speed-reading the fifteen-year-old story as he went. The article told of how a group of thieves entered Viracopos International Airport's freight terminal late one Sunday night, using a pick-up on which they'd placed stickers identical to the runway security company's logo. The KLM plane had been making a brief stop at Viracopos with Amsterdam as its final destination. The heist was completed in a matter of minutes. The thieves threatened the security agents with guns, but no one was hurt. The police had quickly arrested six suspects, but all had been released through lack of evidence. Surprisingly, three of those suspects were actually named in the story.

And one of them was a Don Kujan.

'You either have a very good memory,' Natasha said, her face close to his as she stared at the laptop screen, 'or you must read a great deal.'

'Guilty on both counts,' Korso said, suddenly aware of her closeness and the faint scent of sandalwood. He shut it off like a faucet. 'That doesn't mean it's the same man, but that surname is pretty unusual. And as vague as it is, it's the only connection we have.'

'So what are you suggesting?'

Korso shrugged. 'It's all theory at this stage, but it's possible that Azevedo met this Kujan while he was going out with his sister, right? And since one's a pilot and the other's familiar with airports, it's also possible that they talked shop a little, maybe over a beer or two. So what if Kujan said a little more than he should have, such as intimating how he was possibly involved in a certain high-profile robbery at a Brazilian freight airport a couple of years before? Azevedo could have filed that information away for future use. And then when he heard about this valuable caviar shipment he was due to transport, maybe that name came back to him and he remembered this guy who knew a thing or two about taking planes for profit. If I were in Azevedo's shoes, and I had larceny in mind, I might give him a call.'

'To help organise the robbery.'

'That's what I mean. Azevedo always seems short of money, but he's a pilot, not a planner. And if Kujan claimed to have previous experience in this kind of thing, why not?'

Natasha made a face. 'It sounds thin.'

'It sounds skeletal,' Korso said, 'but I've worked with less. Look, when you've exhausted all other possibilities, as you claim to have done, that's when you have to take chances. And in case you've forgotten, we're on a deadline here.'

'I'm unlikely to forget that.'

'So there you go. What other leads have you got?'

'None,' she said.

'Exactly. When your options are reduced to zero, every choice you make from then on is the right one.'

'So our next step is to find this Kujan's last known address.'

'It would be a starting point, at least. Maybe that private investigation firm of yours could help with that. Give them a call.'

While Natasha went to the kitchen to make her calls, Korso packed. It didn't take long. He already had an emergency bag prepared for such contingencies. It contained US$15,000 in cash, a handful of pre-paid burner phones, disposable razor, toothbrush, and some spare clothes. To these he added the Graves passport, two of his notebooks, a flash drive, a gun that wasn't really a gun, a set of precision wrenches, a couple of fibre-optic scopes he always took with him on assignments and a black windbreaker he'd barely worn.

As for the laptop, he'd already restored it to its factory settings. He'd take it along, but there was now nothing on there to lead back to him if he discarded it. The realtor could resell the motor scooter again if she wanted. And he'd read all the books on his shelves. Maybe the next tenant would find them useful.

When Natasha found him in his bedroom, he was ready. All he needed was a destination.

'Tijuana, Mexico,' she said, looking down at her phone. 'Downtown.'

'Go on.'

'Specifically, Zona Norte in the Hong Kong section.'

'The red light district,' Korso said.

She raised her eyes to meet his. 'Apparently, Kujan's last known address is an apartment on one of the back streets in that area. The agency was able to give me the specific address, but I'm not sure it will do much good.

This information is three years old. He may have moved on since then.'

'I'd be surprised if he hasn't. But it's a start. The rest is simple legwork. Can that agency email you headshots of the two pilots? And Kujan too, if possible.'

'The pilots, yes. The other, I'll ask.'

Korso nodded his approval. One of the benefits of Natasha accompanying him was the huge network of information to which she had access. Alone, he could probably accomplish the same, but it would take a lot longer. And the Dog's services didn't come cheap. This way was better all round.

'Anything else?' she asked.

'What kind of expense budget have you got?'

'As far as transport's concerned, almost unlimited. For anything else, if it's necessary to the job, I can use my own judgement.'

'Good,' he said, zipping up his bag. 'In that case, we'll charter a private jet to Mexico, and keep it on standby for the next four days. There are a few business charter firms near the airport, but the one I've used before should suit our needs. They're expensive, but discreet.'

'One always goes hand in hand with the other.'

'It does seem to. Let me use your phone.'

She passed it to him.

'I hope you've got a good credit limit on your card,' he said, keying in a number. 'You'll need it.'

Nine

83 hours, 45 minutes and counting…

'We will be landing in thirty minutes.'

He came awake immediately at the sound of Natasha's voice. She was sitting opposite him in a matching leather seat, sipping mineral water. There were six more identical seats in the small, luxurious cabin. There was also a large settee and galley up front, and a decent-sized bathroom set aft. The sound insulation was excellent. All he heard was the muffled hum of the Cessna's twin turbofan engines and the faint clinking of ice cubes in Natasha's glass. Back in Bermuda, they had chartered the Cessna Citation for four days, along with the two pilots currently working the cockpit. The price was $4000 per flying hour. The rate was substantially less when the plane was idle, but still exorbitant. To her credit, Natasha had handed her Platinum Visa card to the charter firm's night manager without batting an eyelid.

'What time is it?' he said.

She looked at her phone on the table between them. 'Two-fifteen, Pacific Standard Time.'

He made some quick mental calculations. After all the paperwork had been completed and the plane fuelled up, they'd finally lifted off from Bermuda at a quarter to midnight. The flight time for the 3000-mile journey was six and a half hours, five of which he'd slept through. The four-hour time difference meant it was still early morning on Mexico's west coast. Korso thought that might actually work in their favour. Often he got the best results during the hours of darkness.

'I don't think Mr Nikolic will be happy when he sees my expenses,' Natasha said, rubbing her earlobe as she stared out the window at the blackness beyond.

'Men like Nikolic are never happy,' Korso said. He was studying her profile carefully. 'Are they?'

She turned to him, her brows together. 'You're asking me?'

'You've spent a lot of time with him. You must have seen first hand how he is.'

'That's a strange thing to say. Not once have I ever given any indication that I spent time with Mr Nikolic.'

'You didn't have to.' He rubbed his own earlobe between thumb and index finger. 'He used to do this a lot when he was thinking. Probably still does. I've noticed you doing it three times now. I guess when you're in close proximity to someone powerful, it's natural to start appropriating some of their mannerisms.'

She sneered at him. 'And you think that's what I'm doing? Mimicking my employer's habits? I have always done this.'

'If you say so.'

He suspected there was more to it than that, but now wasn't the time. Stifling a yawn, he undid his belt and got up and walked back to the bathroom. When he returned a few minutes later, he grabbed a small bottle of coke from the fridge in the galley area, and took it back to his seat. He took a long swig and immediately felt more awake.

Frowning at the drapes separating the cockpit from the cabin, he said, 'How much cash are you carrying?'

'Enough.'

'Let me have a thousand.'

'For what reason?'

'Why do you always answer a question with a question? Expenses.'

She looked at him for a moment, then reached over to the adjoining seat and grabbed her flight bag. After rummaging inside for a few seconds, she pulled out a manila envelope and carefully extracted some notes from within. She passed them to him. 'Should I bother asking for a receipt?'

'Not this time,' Korso said as he counted the twenty fifty-dollar bills. 'This is strictly off the books.'

He got up and made his way to the front of the plane again. Sliding the drapes across, he peered into the small cockpit. The only illumination came from the three large LCD touchscreens on the instrument panel, each one displaying various facets of the flight management system. To his left, the captain kept both hands on the stick while he spoke quietly into his headset mic. The co-pilot was busy eating an apple.

The captain sensed Korso standing behind him, and turned in his seat. So did the co-pilot. They looked to be around the same age as him, mid-to-late thirties.

'Anything wrong, sir?' the captain asked, one hand over the mic. 'We're just about to start our descent.'

'For you,' Korso said, and handed ten of the bills to him. He gave the co-pilot the other half of the money. '*Per diems*. I never got your names.'

Both men were smiling now, their professional demeanours momentarily forgotten. The captain thumbed the notes. 'Thank you, sir. I'm James. This is Paulo.'

'Okay, James, Paulo. After we land, I want you to get yourselves a couple of hotel rooms near the airport. Some female company too, if you want. But no alcohol, for obvious reasons. There's no telling when we might need you next, but there probably won't be much notice. So the closer you are, the better. I assume that's acceptable?'

'No problem at all, sir,' the co-pilot said. 'Clients aren't usually this, uh, generous.'

'Just do as I say, and you can expect the same again at the end of the four days. Fair enough?'

'More than fair, sir.' James raised a hand to his earpiece, and said, 'Okay, if you could both fasten your seatbelts back there, please. We're about to begin our descent.'

–

'I don't see why you had to waste a thousand dollars,' Natasha said, staring down at her phone as she checked their progress on Google Maps. 'Their living expenses already come out of my original deposit. Which was considerable, by the way.'

'Additional incentive never hurts,' Korso said, watching the neon signs flash by on his side of the taxi. 'Especially on those we may have to rely on should we need a quick getaway. It's always best to prepare for the worst.'

They'd landed at the General Aviation terminal building at Tijuana International Airport at 02:46, and finally passed through customs forty minutes later. Not having any luggage helped. They'd left their bags on the jet, after securing much of their cash in a small safe located under the galley. All part of the service. Then a taxi from the airport to Zona Norte in the Hong Kong section of the city.

Korso had been to Tijuana before, but a long time ago. He'd been a different man then. And an entirely different kind of hunter. He could see the main thoroughfares had recently smartened themselves up for the tourists, but the back streets still seemed as seedy as ever.

'*¿Adónde voy?*' the taxi driver asked again, watching them in his rear-view.

'Where *are* we going?' Korso asked Natasha.

'*Flores Magon.* The next junction on the right.' She looked out the windshield. 'Past those traffic lights up ahead. He can drop us off there. We can walk the rest.'

Korso translated her instructions to the driver, and he grunted back.

Past the lights, he made the right turn and stopped. Natasha paid the fare and they both got out. As the driver moved off to look for his next customer, Korso checked their surroundings while Natasha did the same. Three-thirty in the morning, and the place was still buzzing with life. Discordant music blared out at maximum volume from the numerous bars, cafes, clubs, restaurants and massage joints lining the street. Traffic was steady on both sides, with cars moving along the street at a snail's pace. Some had double-parked, and scantily clad women leaned in to talk to the drivers. Numerous patrons walked the pavements unsteadily, looking for their next jolt of excitement.

At this time of night, everyone was searching for trouble of some kind or another. Most would get it.

He turned to Natasha. She motioned east, so they began strolling in that direction.

'How far?' Korso said, ignoring the catcalls from an open doorway they passed.

'Two blocks. We want an apartment building next to a bar called The Purple Mermaid.'

She was still scanning the area in all directions, as though looking for something specific. Korso was about to ask her what, when she stopped mid stride. She was looking at a dimly lit side alley across the street, set between a shuttered store and a shabby townhouse. Korso looked over and saw human-shaped shadows moving over there. Local dealers, no doubt. It was the same in every city. Everybody had to make a living.

Natasha said, 'Wait here, please.'

'Why?'

'I have business. If I leave you for a minute, you won't run?'

'Not now you've got me so curious.'

She paused a moment, studying him. Then she turned and crossed the street, walking with purpose. She entered the side alley and then a couple of drunks passed in front and Korso lost her. All he saw were shadows. He wondered what kind of dope she was after, and how its effects might affect her usefulness in the hours ahead. Or maybe he was misjudging her. After all, she didn't seem the type.

A hand caressed his spine. He turned quickly to see a dark-haired, full-bodied girl smiling up at him. She wore high heels, skin-tight leggings and a tank top that emphasised her many curves. Under all the make-up, she could have been anything from sixteen to thirty-five.

'¿Quieres salir conmigo?' she asked, in a fake girlish voice.

Korso wondered how many other men tonight she'd asked that same question to. '*Mi esposa me mataría,*' he said. '*No estoy bromeando.*'

'*No tiene que saber,*' she said, and mimed zipping her mouth shut. But the reference to his jealous wife killing him had clearly put her off. She started to turn away.

'*Espera.*' Korso pulled a twenty from his pocket. The girl stopped and looked at it hungrily. He asked her if she knew a Don Kujan who lived around here.

'*¿Kujan?*' She thought a moment, then shook her head. '*No lo conozco, perdón.*'

'*No hay problema,*' he said, and gave her the twenty anyway.

'*¡Gracias!*' she said, and he watched as she trotted off to find her next victim.

He turned back and saw Natasha already returning from across the street. True to her word, she'd been gone no longer than a minute.

'More expenses?' she said.

'I asked if she knew our guy. No luck. Did you get what you wanted?'

'Yes.'

Korso decided not to press her for more. Her business was her business, his was his.

They soon reached the address they wanted. The Purple Mermaid was simply a bar containing a few dedicated drinkers and not much else. Not even neon. Next to it was a drab three-storey stucco building with graffiti all over the front shutters. There was a door next to them. Korso tried the handle and was surprised to find it unlocked. He pulled it open and saw a flight of stairs ahead, illuminated by a dim light on the next landing.

Inside, affixed to a shelf on the right-hand wall, were two columns of mailboxes.

He entered for a closer look. The twelve boxes were numbered 1A to 3D. There were no names on any of them. Not even crossed-out ones.

'A place for transients,' Natasha said at his side.

'Looks that way. But we'll check anyway. What apartment is it?'

'2B.'

They climbed the stairs to the second floor. At the top was a long corridor leading to the rear of the building. The light was a little better up here. A small alcove to the right contained another stairwell leading down again, presumably to the ground-floor apartments. Korso led the way down the corridor. The first door he passed had 1A painted on it. From inside, he heard a TV and canned laughter. He carried on to the second apartment. This one had no identification at all, but it had to be the one they wanted.

Natasha placed her head against the wood. 'I hear nothing.'

Korso rapped his knuckles loudly on the door three times. They waited. No response. He knocked again. Still nothing. He glanced at the lock. A deadbolt.

'We've come this far,' Natasha said. 'We have to go in.'

'Agreed.'

'I can kick in the door, but it may take a few attempts. It will also be very noisy.'

'Let's try the subtle approach.'

Reaching into his trouser pocket, he pulled out two of the essential items he'd brought along for the trip. A small lockpick gun and a thin, double-ended tension wrench. He rarely went on an assignment without them.

Crouching down, he worked the thin wrench into the lock's keyhole, then inserted the needle of the 'gun' just above it. He kept pressing the gun's trigger, while simultaneously applying torque pressure to the wrench with his thumb. After a few attempts, he felt the pins jump into the hole casing. There was a faint click, and he pushed the door open an inch.

'I want one of these gadgets,' Natasha whispered.

'Try eBay.' Pocketing his tools, he pushed the door open wide.

Ten

The room was dark. The only sounds were the muffled, bass-heavy beats coming from the street outside. Korso detected a faint musty smell in the air, mixed in with that of old food left out in the open. There was a window straight ahead. The drapes were drawn, but enough external light came through for him to make out a few objects dotted around the room.

He turned and spotted a light switch near the door. He pressed it, with no result.

'A door on the right here,' Natasha said. She opened it, and felt around for a few moments. 'Bathroom,' she said, then a light came on from within, the light spill helping to illuminate the rest of the apartment.

It was one step up from a studio flat, consisting of a living room, a small bedroom and bathroom. The furnishings were sparse. The living room contained a couple of easy chairs, a low table and a large, ancient cathode-ray tube TV. Next to the TV was a small lamp. Korso went over and pressed the switch, immediately bathing the apartment with light.

'That's better,' he said.

Another light came on in the bedroom, where Natasha was. 'One double bed,' she called out. 'Empty and unslept

67

in. The sheets look unruffled. There are some men's clothes in the cupboard. But only men's clothes.'

Korso also checked the small windowless kitchenette, a set of bead curtains serving to partition it off from the living area. There were some plates in the sink. Unwashed, which partially explained the old-food smell. And something else underneath that. A very faint odour of decay.

Back in the living room, Korso noticed an old retro wooden work desk behind the TV. The flimsy kind with one drawer on each side. Probably came with the apartment. There was a heavily creased flyer on top, the wrestling event being publicised already two months old. He checked the left drawer. Empty, except for a few broken pencils and pens. But the right drawer contained some old paperwork, stapled together and folded into quarters. He pulled the sheets out and unfolded them.

Photocopies of a standard short-term tenancy agreement. All in Spanish, but no less tedious to read through. Korso quickly skipped to the last page for the signatures. The tenant's signature was just a scrawl, but underneath he'd written his full name in caps. And there it was. The name they wanted. *DON HECTOR KUJAN*. The handwritten date underneath was from four years before.

'I've got something,' he said.

Natasha came over, leaning in to see where he was pointing. 'So he still lives here.'

'Not necessarily. This could have been something he just left behind. Any number of tenants could have stayed here since then.'

'In which case, we're no better off than before.'

Korso shrugged. 'Under normal circumstances I'd simply wait for whoever it is to return. *Some*body lives here now. But that takes time. And patience.'

'And we have neither.' She gave a sigh. 'I am hot, annoyed and thirsty. I very much hope our mysterious tenant left us something cold to drink.'

She walked over and slipped through the bead curtains to the kitchenette. He heard her pull open the refrigerator door.

Natasha gave a low whistle. 'Come here,' she said.

Korso rushed over and saw the open refrigerator door, and now understood where that faint odour of decay had come from.

The fridge was only small, so the corpse had been folded to fit inside.

The inner trays had been removed to maximise storage capacity. The naked man was in a tight foetal position, both knees pressed up against the stomach, arms hanging down. Cut marks peppered his upper arms and parts of his upper torso, and there were probably more cuts he couldn't see without removing the body. The face was pale and bloated, and there was a large black area around the right temple. A towel was also stuffed into the mouth. The head lay horizontally in an unnatural position, facing out, the dead eyes staring directly at them. None of the cuts looked fatal, so Korso thought the man's neck had been broken prior to insertion, and was most likely the cause of death. At the lowest points, the feet and anus, there were dark purple skin discolourations where the heavy red blood cells had finally come to rest. A large puddle of blood had coagulated at the bottom of the fridge.

Korso reached in and touched the man's left wrist, moved it back and forth. The arm felt like a rag doll's.

'Rigor mortis has been and gone,' he said. 'Meaning he's been in here for at least forty-eight hours. Maybe a lot longer.'

Natasha knelt down, studying the interior. She pointed to the temperature dial, which was at 5, its highest setting. 'This explains why the stench is not ten times worse.'

'Something to be thankful for. So is it Kujan?'

She pulled her phone from her pocket and navigated to her emails. She tapped the screen a few times until a colour headshot of Kujan filled the screen. It looked like the agency had managed to find her a passport photo. The man's dark, receding hair was combed back. His skin was a little darker than average for a Latino. The eyes were deep-set, the nose thin and angled slightly to the right, and the cheekbones were pronounced.

Natasha tilted her head sideways at the corpse. 'It's hard to tell.'

Korso reached in, gently pulled the towel from the man's mouth, then closed it again. 'What about now?'

'Possibly. The hair's receded a little more since the photo… yes, maybe. The nose pulls to the right like the picture. I think it is him.'

Korso noticed four bottles of Sol beer lining the inner door tray. He grabbed two and pulled them out.

'It's him,' he said, handing her a bottle as he closed the fridge door. The air immediately smelled better. 'Too much of a coincidence otherwise.'

Natasha wiped the top of the bottle with her shirt, then used her teeth to pop off the cap, while Korso used the corner of the sink. They each took a long slug.

'That tastes pretty good,' Korso said, and got a thin smile from Natasha in return. 'I see this as both good and bad, but veering toward the positive.'

Natasha made a face. 'After ten days of no progress we finally get somewhere, only to come to a dead end when we've barely started. I fail to see the positive aspect.'

'Welcome to my world.' Korso raised his bottle. 'In my business, nothing ever comes easy, and if it does it's usually a false trail. So now we simply search this place from top to bottom, and see what turns up. Something usually does.'

'Very well.' She finished her beer, put the empty bottle down on the table. 'I'll check the bedroom again.'

Korso watched her go, then went back to the kitchen. He studied the linoleum floor carefully, but saw no obvious signs of blood. Breathing through his mouth, he opened the fridge door again for another look at the body. Those cuts didn't look like torture cuts. More the kind you got in a fight or scuffle. And then there was the fact he was naked. Why remove his clothes, unless you were going to torture him for information? It didn't make sense.

Unless the killer had surprised Kujan in the bathroom, where he was already unclothed. Then it would make perfect sense.

Korso shut the fridge door and walked back to the bathroom, the one place they'd not really looked. He stood in the doorway, staring in. It was a small, windowless space, maybe six feet by four, consisting of shower, toilet, sink, with a rickety bamboo laundry basket in the corner. Affixed to the wall above the sink were the remains of a large shaving mirror. Whole shards were missing, and in the centre there was a large crack, as though something or someone had been slammed against it.

That would explain the dark area on Kujan's temple.

He studied the tiled floor, but saw no signs of blood. Getting down on his knees for a better look, he caught a faint whiff of ammonia. Somebody had cleaned up in here recently. He checked the floor of the room inch by inch, and finally saw what looked like dried blood in one of the corners. Not much, but there.

Getting to his feet, Korso looked around again and realised what was missing from this picture.

He went over and removed the laundry basket lid and the vague ammonia smell immediately became more pronounced. And there were the bathroom towels. The ones Kujan had used to shower and the killer must have later used to clean the place up. He reached in and carefully pulled out three thick towels, each one stained with large patches of dried blood. He dropped them on the floor and looked in the basket again. The broken shards of mirror were at the bottom. The jigsaw pattern fell into place.

He stood there a few moments, visualising the most likely scenario.

After a while, he called out, 'Anything?'

'I think so,' she called back. A few seconds later she joined him in the bathroom, holding a vinyl wallet. She noticed the bloody towels, the broken mirror.

'Looks like this is the room he was killed in,' Korso said. 'I think the killer surprised Kujan in here, either in the shower or as he was drying himself off. There was a close-quarters scuffle. Maybe the killer had a gun and dropped it in the fight. But Kujan had his head smashed against that mirror at some point, then maybe they used the mirror shards as knives, until the killer ended it by breaking his neck.' He indicated the floor. 'He cleaned up in here, then stuck the body in the fridge, setting the temperature to maximum. Assuming Kujan's rent is paid up, he might remain undiscovered for a few more weeks yet.'

Natasha's brow became furrowed. 'He came here to kill Kujan, not to question him.'

'From the looks of things, he was simply tying up a loose end. I see you found his wallet.'

'In a jacket pocket in the clothes cupboard. The driving licence proves the body is definitely Kujan's, which is helpful. Not much else, except a few thousand pesos and a Visa credit card, which expired four months ago. Also some business cards for auto mechanics, local massage parlours, bars, things like that.'

'Let me see.' She handed him the wallet and he sifted through the business cards. Like she said, not much of interest. No handwritten names on the back of any of them, for example.

'What about the laundry basket?' she said. 'Is there anything else in there?'

'Just the remains of the mirror.'

She stepped over and picked up the basket to see for herself, and as she did so, her foot made contact with something that clattered along the floor.

A cell phone.

Eleven

It looked like a standard Android smartphone, except the front display was smashed. Korso reached down and picked it up. He tried to turn it on. Naturally, there was no power.

'What did I tell you,' he said. 'It must have slid under the basket during the fight. If the killer had seen it, he'd have taken it with him for sure.'

'Let me have it, please.'

Korso handed it over. Natasha tried switching it on and off a few times, then removed the rear case and pulled out the SIM card. Placing the damaged phone in the sink, she turned off her own phone, opened the back and exchanged her SIM card for Kujan's.

'I hope he had no password,' she said.

They both listened to the start-up jingle, then the screen quickly came to life. They waited a few seconds for a password prompt, but none came. All that appeared onscreen was Natasha's standard black background, and the current date and time.

'We seem to be in lu—' she began when suddenly a large white prompt took up the entire screen. But not the password prompt they were expecting.

You have received 9 missed calls.

74

Natasha pressed for more details and they saw all the missed calls had come from the same person: *Yolanda*. The first had been four days before. The most recent was from last night at 23.14.

'A girlfriend, maybe,' Korso said. 'If the relationship was an on-going one, that first missed call suggests Kujan was killed four, maybe five, days ago, and she's been checking back ever since. Try the contacts.'

Natasha swiped to the icons and pressed the one for contacts. A list came up. There were thirty-three in all. All identified either by first name or initials, no surnames. Yolanda was right at the bottom. There were at least ten other female names in the list.

'Go back to the top,' Korso said.

Natasha scrolled up to the first contact. *Al*.

'Could be our pilot, Alex Azevedo,' he said. 'Did your agency supply you with his cell phone number? And if so, is it the same as this one?'

'Yes to the first question. As for the second, it does look familiar. Wait.' She opened the Firefox browser and went straight to her emails. She clicked on the one she wanted and scrolled through some text until she stopped. 'Yes,' she said. 'The same number.'

'Call it.'

She pressed several buttons, then brought the phone to her ear. After a few seconds, she said, 'Disconnected.'

'He's probably dead too. Still, at least my theory wasn't as far-fetched as we thought. That's encouraging.' He leaned back against the bathroom wall, thinking.

'We should speak with this Yolanda,' she said. 'She must know something that will help us.'

'I know. I'm just wondering whether she'll respond better to a man's voice or a woman's.'

'You speak the language fluently,' she said with a shrug.

'Good point.' Korso took the phone from her, scrolled down to Yolanda's number. They both listened to the regular ringing tone, waiting for a connection.

'What will you say?' she asked.

'I'll play it as it comes.'

The ringing tone continued. Then there was a crackling sound as the phone was answered, and a gruff, female voice shouted, '*Don, bebé. ¿Dónde has estado?*'

The voice was slightly distorted from the loud music in the background.

'*Yolanda*,' he said, ignoring her question. '*¿Dónde estás?*'

'*En le bar.*'

'*¿Cual bar?*'

'Lucky Lady. *Dónde más.*'

Where else indeed. Korso ended the call quickly before she could ask anything further.

'She's at the Lucky Lady,' he said, 'wherever that is. From the way she said it, I'm assuming she works there. Let's see.' He opened the browser again, and googled the bar's name and general location.

'There it is,' he said, a few seconds later, 'just seven blocks south of our location.' He turned off the phone, just in case Yolanda tried to call back, and handed it to Natasha.

'We should go,' she said. 'The sooner we leave this apartment, the better.'

–

The Lucky Lady was another late-night drinking establishment, set on a back street containing a dozen similar-looking bars. There was even a working neon sign above

76

the entrance. The music coming from inside sounded exactly the same as on the phone. Inside, the lighting was very subdued, almost non-existent. The room was fairly narrow, but seemed wider thanks to the mirrors on each side. Korso spotted a raised platform at the back where two girls in bikinis danced to music that was loud without being deafening. Several men sat on stools beneath them and threw them money as they watched, jeered and drank. There were booths on the left, with a long bar running down the right side. Half of the booths were empty. A number of men sat drinking at the bar, a few on their own, the rest flirting with, and fondling, the female staff. Presumably the lucky ladies in question.

Korso led Natasha to the long bar. One of the bartenders, a young, long-haired guy with a toothy grin, came over and asked for their order.

Natasha said, 'Two bottles of Sol, *por favor.*'

He went away, and soon came back with two uncapped bottles.

'*Gracias.*' Natasha took one of the bottles, and placed a 500-peso note on the bar. 'Is Yolanda here?'

'*Si,*' the bartender said, pointing at the dancers. 'On the left.'

Korso looked over and saw a full-figured woman with long, frizzy, dark hair, an attractive oval face and a wide mouth that smiled a lot. He asked the bartender to tell Yolanda to come join them when the song finished. And also to keep the change. The bartender smirked, gave him a thumbs-up, and the money disappeared.

They took their drinks over to the booth nearest the door and took seats opposite each other, silently sipping at their beers as they waited for the song to finish.

Eventually, the dancer with the frizzy hair made her way over to their table, wearing a short, silk, black kimono and holding a bottle of coke with a long straw poking out. She looked to be in her mid twenties, and was studying each of them with a questioning half-smile.

Korso asked her to sit, and she gave a small shrug and slid in on his side. On the way over, he and Natasha agreed the wisest strategy would be to play straight with her as much as possible. Working girls could generally tell straight away when they were being lied to.

'*¿Habla usted Inglés?*' he asked.

She nodded again. '*Sí*. I speak English good.'

'*Bueno*. Yolanda, it was me who called you on the phone earlier, not Don.'

Her mouth opened, then closed. 'You are... *amigos* of Don? He is okay?'

'Not really. And no, he isn't.'

Korso briefly switched to Spanish and explained how they'd been looking for Don, hoping he could answer some questions about a missing shipment. And how they'd just come from his apartment where they found him dead, his neck broken. He spared her the gory details, but added that it looked as though he'd been dead a few days.

'*¿Muerta?*' she said quietly, staring at them both. '*Dios mio*. No joke? Don is dead?'

'No joke,' Natasha said. 'Sorry. Once we leave, you should call the police.'

She sucked some of her cola through the straw, and said, '*¿Quién?* Who did this?'

'We don't know,' Natasha said. 'We hope you can help us answer that question. Were you two close?'

'Close?' She frowned.

'*Relación seria*,' Korso said.

'Ah, no, not close. We like to have… fun together. You know… sex? I know Don three, no… four months. Since New Year, we have good sex together one time or two times every week.'

'I understand,' Korso said. That partly explained the lack of grief. 'And when you were together, did you ever see any of his friends?'

She shrugged. 'One time, sure. But these were not friends, I think. More like…' She clicked her fingers until the word came to her. 'More like *colegas*. Yes, that.' She shook her head with a sigh. '*Muerta. Madre de Dios.*'

'Tell us about these colleagues, Yolanda. Whatever you can remember.'

She blinked at him with dry eyes. 'Sure. You have some money for me?'

They had expected this. She was a working bar girl, and deserved to be recompensed for her time. Natasha pulled ten crisp 500-peso notes from her pocket, splayed them out on the table. Korso noticed a solo drinker sitting at the bar, wearing a dark baseball cap, watching them with mild interest.

'Yours, once you've finished,' Natasha said. 'Now, about these colleagues of Don's.'

Staring at the money, she said, 'Okay. One time I see him with these two *gringos* in his apartment. It is my day off. Sometimes they talk about work things in English. I make burritos for them, give them drinks, but sometime I listen also.'

'*Gringos*,' Korso said. 'Americans, you mean?'

'Sure, I think so.'

Natasha leaned forward. 'What did they talk about, Yolanda?'

'Oh, about women, and drinking, and football, and these things they wanted from a plane. Fish things. I do not know what fish things. They are not painting pictures for me, you know?'

Korso and Natasha exchanged a glance without making it obvious. He turned back to Yolanda. 'These fish things. Was it caviar?'

She frowned at him. 'Caviar? Like Mexican caviar? *No entiendo.*'

'No, not Mexican caviar.' He understood the confusion. In Mexico, it was the name of a common dish containing beans, chillies, tomatoes and corn. 'Never mind. These two men, do you remember their names?'

'Sure. One was called Mickey.' She grimaced. 'Too ugly. He smiled at me a lot. Other guy was Joe, I think. No… Joel. *Si*, Joel. He was okay.'

Natasha was already scrolling through Kujan's contacts on her phone. 'No Mickey,' she said, 'but there is a Michael here. Also a Joel.' She looked up at the woman. 'Yolanda, what else did they say about these fish things they wanted to take from the plane?'

'*Nada.* But… Oh, yeah, there was a fourth man.'

'A fourth man?' Korso said. 'You mean at the apartment?'

'No, not there. This man they talked about, but I never saw him. He was like *la jefa*, you know?'

'The boss.'

'Sure, like he made the planning and things. One of the *gringos*, he talked to this *jefe* on the phone, I think. I don't listen to that part.'

'Which *gringo* called him?'

'Uh, the ugly one, I think. Mickey.'

'And did they mention this fourth man's name?'

She just shook her head and took another sip of Coke.

'When was this?' Korso asked.

'*Febrero*. What day, I don't know. But I been screwing Don about a month then.'

'Mid February, maybe?' Korso suggested.

She gave a careless shrug. 'Sure. Okay, I go now? I dance next.'

Korso turned to Natasha, wondering if she had anything else to ask, but she shook her head. She slid the money across to Yolanda.

'Yours,' she said.

With a smile, Yolanda grabbed the notes and put them somewhere inside the kimono.

'One last question before you go,' Korso said. 'Were there any weeks when you and Don didn't see each other? When he was out of town, maybe?'

'Sure. Two days after *Dia de la Bandera*, he goes somewhere. Whole week I call, but he don't answer the phone. He comes back and says he had to go work. I don't know where.' She sighed. 'I thought the same this time when I call, but is not the same. *Mierda*.'

She slid out of the booth and stopped. 'Hey, you call *la policía* about Don, okay? I don't need trouble with those guys.'

'Sure,' Korso said.

'*Gracias*,' Yolanda said, and left them.

'Tough woman,' Natasha said.

'It's a tough world.'

'What is this *Dia de la Bandera*?'

'Flag Day.' Korso took another sip of beer. 'A Mexican national holiday. It's on the same day every year, February 24.'

Natasha gave a slow smile, clearly thinking the same thoughts. Kujan leaves on the 26th to whereabouts unknown, and the cargo plane goes missing less than five days later. The timings worked out. Things were coming together, at least on the surface.

Natasha replaced Kujan's SIM card with her own, pressed a button and put the phone to her ear. A few seconds later, Korso heard her speak with her source at the investigative agency. She recited two phone numbers, and told the person on the other end that she wanted all information related to these numbers as soon as humanly possible.

'It's 04:43 now,' she said, after ending the call. 'He said he'll call back in less than an hour, although he cannot guarantee anything.'

'Nobody can. They have people at that place working all through the night?'

'For certain clients, yes.' She took a sip of her beer. 'So if this girl's telling the truth, she's told us a number of interesting things. This Joel and Mickey, for example. And the fourth man one of them spoke to, who apparently did the planning. And then there's this talk about "fish things".'

Korso nodded. 'That part suggests to me that they were after the caviar shipment alone, with no knowledge of your last-minute addition.'

'To me, also. So the way things look, Kujan, Joel and Mickey were the ones who physically took the plane, with help from the pilot, Azevedo.'

'And possibly even the other pilot, Palma, and Borozan too. We can't discount any of them yet.'

She nodded her head. 'As you say. While the actual details and planning came from this unknown party, who currently remains in the shadows. One or both of the Americans could even have entered the plane's cargo hold with the coffee shipment and waited for their moment. Do you agree?'

'It sounds plausible enough,' Korso said. 'It also seems likely that this mysterious man at the other end of the phone is either the leak in your organisation, or is in direct contact with that leak. Either way, I'd very much like to find him. In the meantime I think we should wait somewhere quieter, maybe where they serve coffee instead of beer.'

'Good idea.'

As Natasha put down her bottle, Korso noticed the man who'd been watching them get up from the bar and turn their way.

'Wait,' he murmured. 'Company's coming. Let's see how this plays out.'

Natasha said nothing, but immediately picked up the beer bottle again, without paying the slightest attention to the man walking their way. At the same time, she slipped her other hand under the table, as though scratching an itch. Korso felt something metallic touch his knee, and casually reached down and took the item she was passing him. He recognised its shape immediately. It was a butterfly knife, or *balisong*, the tang currently sheathed between the twin handles. Now he knew what she'd been doing with those dealers in the alley. When in hostile territory, the best method for picking up a weapon at short notice is to simply take one from the nearest lowlife. Korso had done it himself more than once. He suppressed a smile as he slipped the knife into his shirt cuff. It was always a comfort when working alongside a fellow professional.

The man approaching them was in his early thirties, and stocky, wearing a black jacket over a red t-shirt, and faded black jeans. He adjusted his baseball cap as he pulled out the chair next to Natasha and sat down. He smiled at her, then at Korso. A predator's smile.

'*Buenas noches, amigos.*'

'*Buenas noches,*' Korso said. 'I don't know you, do I?'

Still smiling, the man shook his head. Korso saw his right hand was now inside his jacket. Noticing the two almost empty bottles on the table, he said, 'All that beer. You guys must need the toilet by now, right? It's hard to find in here. I will guide you.'

'We're fine, thank you,' Natasha said.

The man showed them part of the revolver he was holding inside his jacket.

'Please, *amigos*. Don't make me angry.'

Twelve

'What is this?' Korso said, acting the confused foreigner. 'Some kind of stick-up?'

'Just a little private talk,' the man said. 'We will all make our way to the men's room at the back, past the stage. You go first. I will be behind your girl here. If you try anything or try to warn anyone, I shoot her in the back. You understand?'

'I understand,' Korso said. 'Look, just don't hurt her, all right?'

'We'll do whatever you say,' Natasha said, adding a nice quiver to her voice. Playing the little mouse.

'Good,' the man said. 'Very good.'

The man stood, his hand still inside his jacket, and backed up to give them room. The music was still loud, the lights still low. Nobody else was paying them any attention. Korso stood up and waited.

Once Natasha was on her feet, the man said, 'Now walk, *amigos*. And mister, remember what I said.'

'I remember.'

Korso stepped away from the table and turned into the aisle next to the bar. As he walked slowly down the darkened room, passing other customers and bargirls, he took careful note of everything around him. In his peripheral vision, he could see Natasha and the man in the mirrors on his left. To his right, one of the bartenders was making drinks, while the guy who'd served them cleaned the bar top with a cloth. On the small stage at the rear of the room, Yolanda was doing her thing in time with the music, along with another younger girl. They were each smiling at the drunks below, all waving notes around. Past the stage were two doors, the one on the left bearing the universal male and female icons, and a large EXIT sign above. A young Latino man with long hair and beard stubble stood next to this door, watching Korso with great interest, his right hand in his jeans pocket. He looked barely out of his teens.

Korso also noticed a man with a shaved head sitting in one of the booths a few feet up ahead, watching the three of them approach with an intense expression on his face. He wore a leather waistcoat over a white t-shirt, and tattoos covered his arms and shoulders. This guy glanced over at the toothy bartender who'd served them, and in the mirror Korso saw the bartender give an almost imperceptible nod of his head in response.

That told Korso everything he needed to know about the situation.

It was just a common hold-up. Nothing to do with their investigation at all. The bartender had noticed the cash Natasha had flashed around, then called up some cronies to take care of business, no doubt earning himself a nice finder's fee for the tip off. Korso wasn't all that surprised. And at least it simplified things.

Walking slowly, he thought fast.

Rather than allow themselves to get hemmed into a confined space, he decided to act now while they still had room to manoeuvre. And while they still had the element of surprise. The dim lighting would only help matters. Trusting that Natasha had noticed the same signs he had, he moved his left hand behind him, thumb and index finger clenched, his last three fingers splayed wide. He was now two tables away from the man in the booth. He glanced in the mirror to his left and saw Natasha's gaze was lowered. She was watching his hand, waiting for his signal.

He tucked his middle finger away, leaving just two.

Waistcoat shifted his body and began sliding out of the booth. There was a knife holster on his belt. He had one hand on the handle as he made to stand. In the background, as the song on the sound system segued directly into another, Yolanda snatched a bill one of the drunks was waving. Everyone back there shrieked with laughter.

Korso tucked his ring finger away, leaving just his pinkie.

Waistcoat had exited the booth now and stood up straight, waiting. He gave Korso a gap-toothed grin as his right hand gripped the handle of the knife. Meanwhile, Korso shifted his other arm slightly and the *balisong* dropped smoothly into the palm of his hand. He placed his thumb under the catch, ready. Waistcoat was less than five feet away. He was already starting to turn his body in the direction of the toilets. Ready to lead them the rest of the way, while Baseball Cap covered the rear.

Korso tucked away the last finger of his left hand, clenched his fist tight.

Behind him, there was a sudden flurry of movement as Natasha pulled something from her waistband and darted to the left, onto the table in the empty booth. Korso saw a ceiling light briefly flash against another blade. A hunting knife, a big one. There was a shout, followed immediately by the heavy *boom* of a gunshot. Glass shattered all around him.

Even over the music, it was loud. Every head in the room turned in their direction.

But Korso was already running toward Waistcoat, who was still in a state of semi-shock. Flicking his thumb under the catch, Korso twirled his wrist twice in the familiar way and the butterfly knife flipped open and locked.

One of the bargirls screamed when she saw the blade, and then pandemonium erupted throughout the bar as everyone realised what was happening.

Korso was almost on Waistcoat when the man regained his senses and jerked his body backward just as Korso made to thrust the knife at his torso. The blade missed him. Korso kept his forward momentum going, slamming his left shoulder into the man's chest. Both fell to the floor, right next to the booth Waistcoat had just vacated. As he landed, the assailant launched an elbow punch at Korso's temple. It connected hard, slamming Korso's head against the steel leg of the table. Stunned, shaking his head from the impact, Korso saw Waistcoat pull the knife from his holster and he kicked out at him. His heel connected with the man's right arm and the knife dropped to the floor.

As Korso went in for the kill, he spotted movement to his left and ducked back just in time as a crowd of people scrambled past, separating him from Waistcoat.

Chaos and confusion everywhere. A mass of moving feet and legs in front of him as people headed for the front door and safety. Screams and shouts coming from all directions. Loud music still blaring out of the sound system.

Behind him, there was another gunshot, just as loud as before. More screams. A man swore loudly in Spanish.

Once the rush of people had passed, Korso searched for signs of Waistcoat, but he was gone. So was everyone else, it seemed, including the bar staff. No, not everyone. Glancing behind him, he saw Baseball Cap looking around wildly, gun still in hand, searching for a target. Blood was seeping from a deep wound in his shoulder. Natasha must have got a good one in. His eyes suddenly fell on Korso and he turned and began to raise the gun in his direction.

Without a second thought, Korso rushed for the bar, jumped up and dived over the counter. There was another thunderous *boom* and he heard more glass shatter as he landed on the floor on the other side. Small fragments of mirror pattered against his head and hands. Using elbows and knees, and still holding the knife, Korso crawled along the narrow space behind the bar as fast as he could move. Along the way, he saw some bottles of tequila and whiskey that had fallen from the shelves. He grabbed one bottle with his free hand and kept going until he reached the end of the narrow walkway. Rising to a crouch, he peered out and scanned his surroundings. All he saw was a bunch of barstools, an empty dance stage and an ancient pool table. The kid who'd been guarding the exit was gone, along with everyone else.

Over the blaring music, Korso heard shouts from the front. Emerging from the cover of the bar, he stood up and saw Natasha and Baseball Cap engaged in a close-quarters struggle. It looked like he'd lost the gun, at least. Natasha was a blur of movement, swivelling her left foot in a semi-circular motion and delivering an athletic roundhouse kick to the man's head with her right. Her foot struck his jaw, his head rocking with the impact as he fell back against the bar.

She was about to follow up with an upward elbow strike when Korso sensed movement to his right. He ducked down just as a blade swept past his head and struck the bar instead. The hand gripping it belonged to Waistcoat, who must have been hiding behind the stage. Korso dropped the whiskey bottle and lunged at him, thrusting his own knife at the man's midsection, but Waistcoat instinctively jerked his knee upward at the last moment. The hard bone connected with Korso's right wrist, and the *balisong* flew from his grip, landing on the floor.

Waistcoat was still gripping his own knife. He thrust the blade at Korso's face, but Korso ducked his head out of range, throwing a right jab at the man's torso at the same time. Hard knuckles slammed into flesh. His assailant grunted in pain and backed off. Spotting the whiskey bottle he'd dropped on the floor, Korso reached down, grabbed it by the neck and struck the base against the bar. The lower half smashed into pieces, whiskey pouring everywhere, and he now had a weapon. The long, jagged shards of glass looked far deadlier than any knife.

Waistcoat backed off again, staring at the bottle. He no longer looked as confident. Gripping the neck tight, Korso advanced, sticking close to him. The man bumped against one of the barstools fixed to the floor. Unable to progress any further, he said something inaudible and launched himself at Korso, knife hand outstretched before him.

It was the obvious move, and Korso was ready for it. Waistcoat was only two feet from him when Korso swung the bottle in a long backhand strike. The rough glass shards

90

connected with flesh, slicing deep into the man's wrist and lower arm. Blood immediately sprayed from the wounds. Screaming in pain, the man dropped the knife instantly, grabbing at the wound with his other hand, trying to stem the blood loss.

Dropping the weapon, Korso stepped in and grabbed Waistcoat's head with both hands and slammed it hard against the back of the barstool. Once. Twice. Then, applying a ton of pressure and using every ounce of strength in his body, Korso *twisted* the man's head 120 degrees in a single movement. He felt, rather than heard, the snap as the spinal cord was severed. The man's struggles immediately ceased as all life left his body.

Just as Korso was about to turn toward the front of the bar, there was a gunshot from his right and he ducked instinctively. Knowing the bullet had missed, he grabbed Waistcoat's knife from the floor. Holding it by the blade, he swivelled his body to his right and raised his arm, ready to throw it at the shooter.

The third one, the kid, was standing behind the pool table, aiming a small pistol in Korso's direction. He looked scared out of his wits. Korso didn't care. He was already starting to swing his arm forward when the kid suddenly let go of the gun. It dropped onto the pool table, and he raised both arms wide.

There was another gunshot from behind Korso, louder this time. The kid screamed and dropped to the floor on the other side of the pool table. Korso turned, knife at the ready, and saw Natasha walking his way, still aiming Baseball Cap's revolver at the spot where the kid had fallen.

She looked dishevelled but unharmed. Korso turned back and made his way over to the pool table.

The kid was rocking back and forth on the floor, his eyes clenched shut as he clasped his left elbow. Blood seeped from between his fingers. Korso noticed the current song was well into the fade-out, with nothing taking its place.

When Natasha joined Korso a few second later, the room was silent except for the kid's whimpering. Natasha was still aiming her gun at his head.

'The original owner?' Korso asked.

'Dead. Just this one left.' She pulled back the gun's hammer. 'Boy, you should have left while you had the chance.'

'Leave him.' Korso dropped the knife next to the gun on the pool table. It was another revolver, a .22 with a two-inch barrel. Most likely, the kid had never even used it before tonight. 'A bullet's not always the best answer. You never know, maybe he's learned a lesson tonight.'

'He will talk. About us.'

'And say what? That he tried to rob us and we fought back? Let him. We're ghosts.'

Korso went over to the door with the exit sign above it. He opened it and saw a long corridor, even darker than the bar area. At the far end, forty feet away, was a fire exit door. It was wide open, leading to what looked like an alley beyond.

'Make a decision,' he said, turning back to Natasha. 'We need to make tracks. The police could show at any moment.'

She paused for a moment, then said, 'Get up, boy. I won't ask twice.'

The kid looked up at her, then carefully got to his feet. Still holding his bloody arm, he looked at her with wide eyes. '*Por favor…*'

'This is your lucky day,' she said, still pointing the gun. 'Leave. Now.'

The kid stared at her for a moment. Then he turned and ran past Korso, and through the open doorway like the devil was on his heels. Korso watched him sprint down the corridor and run out into the night.

'I hope that was not a mistake,' Natasha said, joining Korso at the door.

'It's done now. Let's go.'

'What about these weapons? Our fingerprints are all over them.'

'Who cares? My prints aren't on any database, and I doubt yours are either. Just leave the gun here.'

With a shrug, Natasha threw the piece under the pool table. Then they followed the kid's example.

Thirteen

When the young, heavily pregnant waitress finally came over to their table, Korso ordered two coffees. She nodded, left him a menu, then waddled back to the kitchen.

Korso had been flagging down a cab three blocks west of the Lucky Lady when two police interceptors screeched into the street they'd just left, sirens wailing, red and white lights flashing. He and Natasha watched them pass like all the other rubberneckers. Once they were gone, he calmly told the cab driver to take them to Aqua Caliente Boulevard in Zonaesta, a few miles south of their location. Well away from the danger zone.

The all-night cafe they found was mostly empty so early on a weekday morning. It was still dark out. The few customers seemed to be either late-night revellers winding down, or early risers filling their stomachs before heading off to work. Mostly the latter. He and Natasha took seats in a window booth as far from the other customers as possible.

As Korso watched the retreating waitress, Natasha said, 'Why did you stop me?'

'Is that what I did?' He turned to her with a frown. 'I thought you were the one with the gun.'

'You know what I mean. Leave no witnesses is a good rule to live by. Maybe the most important rule. Do you not agree?'

'It depends on the situation. Maybe if he was able to identify you...' He shrugged. It was pointless explaining the obvious. The kid was no longer a threat, and you don't kill when you don't have to. It can all too easily become a habit. A bad one all round. Often, the best sword is kept in its sheath.

'You must enjoy living dangerously, Korso,' she said.

He shook his head. 'I generally walk where the ice is thickest. I imagine you're probably the same.'

'You know almost nothing about me. For all you know, I might enjoy the danger. And the killing.'

'The first, possibly. The second, no. Unless I'm completely wrong about your character.'

She smiled with one side of her mouth. 'Who knows anyone, really?'

'You've got me there.'

'I must admit you're more proficient in close-quarters combat than I expected.'

'You mean Sardoca didn't give you any background on me?'

'Some, but little that put you in a good light.'

'That figures. So slipping me the knife back there was a test on your part?'

'Partly. I was interested to see how you'd react in that situation. Also, it was the only other weapon those dealers had on them. I had hoped for a gun, at least, but they turned out to be surprisingly ill equipped.'

The waitress came back to their table then. She set two large cups of coffee down and asked if they wanted breakfast. Korso decided he wanted a Mexican omelette and orange juice, and Natasha ordered the same. The waitress took their menu and waddled away again.

'That one looks about to pop,' Natasha said, adding milk and sugar to her cup. 'She shouldn't be working at her advanced stage.'

'Tell that to her landlord.' Korso took a sip of his black coffee. Rich and strong, just what he needed. 'Are any of them still breathing?'

'The dealers? All three, although two are now probably wishing otherwise. The third was sleeping when I left him. Maybe he still is.'

'You sure didn't waste time, I'll grant you that.'

'I also like to be prepared for the worst.'

'I'll remember that if I ever have to face you down.' He sipped some more coffee. 'Shouldn't your contact have called by now?'

Natasha pulled her phone from her pocket and checked the time. 'Five minutes late. I suppose I had better—'

The phone chose that moment to start vibrating on the table. She checked the caller number, then raised the phone to her ear. 'Tell me,' she said.

She mainly listened, occasionally making a sound to show she was still there. After a few minutes, the waitress returned with their orders and Korso helped her put the dishes on the table. Once she was gone, he added some seasoning to his breakfast, cleaned the fork with a napkin and began to eat. The omelette was excellent, with plenty of cheese and spices.

Natasha finally ended the call. 'Good news and bad news. Which do you want first?'

'What difference does it make?' he said, placing another forkful into his mouth.

'Very well. There's no trace of this Michael at all. The number I provided was disconnected some time ago and there's no record of its owner. My source tried a number of semi-legal approaches to trace it back and still came up with nothing.'

'Probably a pre-paid burner.' Korso sipped his orange juice.

'Most likely. Assuming this man is the same Mickey that Yolanda described to us, of course. We have no way of knowing.'

'Not yet, we don't. I hope that was the bad news.'

Natasha ignored the sarcasm and used her own fork to try some of her omelette. She chewed a little, then nodded with approval. 'Now,' she went on, 'the one named Joel is a different story. Again, the number's no longer in use, but my source was able to track down the owner's identity and provide me some details. His full name is Joel Adamson, and he lives and works in Fort Worth, Texas. In the Northside district.'

'That's more like it,' Korso said. 'So what is he?'

'A man who likes variety, apparently. He's had a number of jobs in recent years, including nightclub bouncer, real-estate salesman, night watchman. Some jobs he left by choice, others he was told to leave, usually because of absenteeism. My source informed me that he also had a financial interest in a growing fast-food franchise five years ago, but then decided to cash in just before the business exploded and became hugely successful.'

'So either an unlucky man or a stupid one.'

'Probably a little of both,' Natasha said, nibbling at her own omelette. 'This is very good, by the way.'

'I'll tell the chef. What else?'

She continued speaking between mouthfuls. 'He's twice divorced, and now lives alone. He and his most recent wife had two children, but she was awarded full custody in the separation and they all now reside in another state. He rarely sees them. He currently works as a security guard for a local auto parts business. Or, rather, he did. Now... who knows?'

Korso wiped his mouth with a napkin. 'And your people got all that in less than an hour? That's fairly impressive.'

'No less than it should be for the money I am paying them.'

'That your employer is paying them.'

'Semantics.'

'Anyway, it looks like we're taking a trip over the border. Let me have your phone.'

She passed it and returned to her food. Korso called the number James had given him. He finally got an answer on the seventh ring. The pilot clearly sounded out of breath. Korso didn't ask what he'd been doing, or with whom, but just instructed him and Paulo to get out to the airport as soon as possible, as they were leaving for Texas within the hour.

'I think I interrupted him from something,' Korso said, after ending the call.

'Do you care?'

'Not really.' He raised his hand to signal for the check. 'Are you all right to enter the United States? What I mean is, is your passport completely legit?'

'As legitimate as yours,' she said, finishing off the last of her food. 'I will have no problems at US Immigration. I never have before.' She smiled. 'Maybe you should worry more about yourself, Korso.'

Fourteen

75 hours, 28 minutes and counting...

Less than five hours later, Korso and Natasha were sitting in a Chevy Impala rental parked outside a dollar store in the Northside area of Fort Worth. Each of them was carefully studying the terrain.

Although it varied from block to block, Korso's impression was that Northside wasn't one of Fort Worth's more affluent neighbourhoods. Which suited their purposes perfectly. He felt the area's residents were far less likely to call 911 for suspicious behaviour. The dollar store was situated on the northeast corner of a crossroads, with an auto-insurance place located on the opposite corner. There was a Texaco station a half-mile west, but everything else was residential. Mainly one-storey houses in varying conditions, set back from the tree-lined streets, usually with two or three cars in the driveway.

He checked the dashboard clock again. The time changed to 12:33.

Sardoca had dropped into his life like an atom bomb last night at 18:00, Bermuda time, along with his laughable ninety-six-hour deadline. Which meant they now had just over seventy-five hours left. Three days and change. Barely any time at all. If they hadn't chartered the plane for the extended period, it would have been an impossible task.

It could still be.

As it was, the flight to Fort Worth International Airport had used up three hours, and then another forty minutes before they passed through immigration. Once they'd navigated that obstacle course, Natasha got them a rental from Hertz, and Korso drove them here in just over thirty minutes.

Time ticking away.

A pick-up pulled in to the parking area, settled into a spot two spaces down from theirs. The driver adjusted his Stetson, got out and locked his vehicle. Korso watched him go into the store, then looked in the rear-view again at Adamson's place behind them.

Seventy-two Willoughby Avenue was a neat, one-storey brick house set on a large plot, with a wide driveway leading to a double garage at the side, also made of brick. The grass in the front yard was faded and hadn't been cut in weeks. There were no vehicles in the driveway. No other obvious signs of habitation. Still, it was one of the more impressive-looking houses in the area. And plenty of tree cover at the front and back.

'What do you think?' Natasha asked, also watching the house from her side mirror.

'Possibly a revolutionary new chemical nerve agent,' he said. 'One that attacks the central nervous system and kills immediately before dissipating, leaving no trace in the victim's body. A perfect weapon for those in the market for that kind of thing.'

Natasha turned to him with heavy-lidded eyes. 'Again with this.'

'Am I hot or cold?'

'How should I know?' She sighed. 'I already told you, I'm not privy to Mr Nikolic's private plans. I think we should use our time better by concentrating on the task at hand.'

'I am,' he said, and opened his door. 'Let's see if Mr Adamson's at home.'

The sun was still out, but the air was fairly cool. Good spring weather. Crossing over to the pavement, they waited for two cars to pass, then confidently walked across the street without hesitation. Looking for all intents and purposes as though they belonged.

Korso let Natasha go up the driveway first. They reached the front door of the house and Natasha rang the bell while Korso casually turned round and assessed the line of sight. They could be seen from the road, but only by anyone passing directly in front of the house. And the large sycamores out front and the smaller maple trees on the side borders also gave them ample cover from any neighbours. Not perfect, but better than nothing at all.

Seconds passed. There was no answer. And no sounds of movement from within.

'We'll try round the back,' Korso said.

They walked down the driveway, slipped past the garage at the end, and entered the backyard. The grass was discoloured and messy back there as well. Two huge oak trees at the end of the garden provided excellent cover from the neighbours at the back. A large wooden picnic table lay on its side, its usefulness apparently a thing of the past.

Natasha led him to a portico rear entrance and stood there, waiting. Korso joined her, looked at the door's lock and was glad to see it was another deadbolt. He got out his lockpick tools and crouched down in front of the door.

He was about to go to work when Natasha placed a hand on his wrist.

'Will you teach me?'

'All right.' He stood up and let her take his position in front of the lock. Handing her the snap gun and tension wrench, he said, 'Now what this gun does is create a short, sharp impact within a pin tumbler lock, allowing it to be opened without a key. You saw me do it before, so first you want to insert the thin wrench into the keyhole, and then the needle of the gun just above it.'

He waited as she performed both actions.

'Like this?'

'Right. Now the way it works is, once the steel rod is in the lock like so, pulling the trigger fires that rod against all of the bottom pins at the same time, bouncing them upward. And this momentarily frees the lock cylinder, allowing it to be turned with the tension wrench. You understand?'

'I think so. And this technique works on all locks?'

He shook his head. 'No, just those with simple pin tumbler mechanisms. All right, so what you need to do is pull the trigger, but don't apply any pressure to the tension wrench until a split second after the needle has snapped against the bottom pins. Because that allows the top pins to shoot straight up into the shell before the plug is turned. It's all about timing. Often it takes over a dozen pulls of the trigger to open a lock, but like everything, practice makes perfect. Just remember to keep the tension light and try not to force it or you might damage the mechanism. Okay, give it a try.'

He watched as she squeezed the trigger, listening with great concentration, and gently turned the tension wrench. No result. Then again. And again, after that. She stayed calm with each failure, never losing patience. She tried again. Failed again. He nodded in silent appreciation. She had the right attitude.

On the thirteenth attempt, she turned the little wrench and heard something. She turned to him and smiled. Pushing the door open, she passed him his tools back and entered the house. Korso followed close behind.

They were in a kitchen. Unlike Kujan's apartment, there were no dirty plates lying around, and the room looked clean and tidy. Adamson clearly took a little more care of his domestic surroundings. Korso listened hard, but heard nothing except their own movements. And no musty smell, either, which meant the place hadn't been uninhabited for very long.

Korso watched as Natasha stepped through the open doorway and disappeared from sight. He continued to inspect the kitchen, looking at the floor for any tell-tale food bowls, and was glad to see none. Half-starved attack dogs he could do without. He also checked the pantry and the utility room, finding nothing of interest in either.

Passing through the same doorway as Natasha, he entered an open space that ran down the centre of the house, with more rooms leading off from it. The two on the left were bedrooms. On the right was a well-fitted bathroom and an empty-looking dining room. At the end, at the front of the house, was a large living area. He saw Natasha down there, moving around. He also noticed an access panel right above his head, flush with the surface of the ceiling, which obviously provided access to the attic.

Korso checked the smaller bedroom quickly, found nothing, and tried the larger one next. The bed sheets were clean. No old clothes on the floor. He opened the built-in wardrobe and saw twenty or thirty shirts and jackets hanging inside. He was about to check the pockets when he heard a female voice coming from another room. One that wasn't Natasha's.

He exited the bedroom, turned left and saw Natasha was still in the living room, alone. She was standing next to a bookcase, frowning at the telephone on the middle shelf as she listened to a recorded message: '…*wrong with you these days, Joel, because I'm sick and tired of constantly chasing you up for my goddamn back alimony. They're your kids too, you know, and while we're on the subject, that's another—*'

'Adamson's ex-wife, no doubt,' Korso said over the tirade. 'When was this call?'

Natasha leaned in closer to check the small display. 'April 8. Last Wednesday. There are three more messages after this.'

'Skip to the next. I can already see where this one's going.'

Natasha pressed the arrow button on the handset. There was a beep, then a man's voice: '*Adamson? It's Ryan. You there, man? If you are, you better pick up. 'Cause this is the second day this month you've taken off without warning me. I covered your ass with Williams twice before now, but I ain't doing it again, and he told me if you ain't in today, not to even bother turning up tomorrow. You hear me, man? He's seriously pissed, so don't say I didn't warn you.*' There was a click as Ryan hung up.

'That was also the same day,' Natasha said, pressing the arrow button again.

The next message was another man's voice: '*Adamson, this is Gary Williams at Lantern Auto. Since you've now failed to turn up to work for two days in a row, or even to contact us by phone, you can consider your employment with us terminated immediately. We'll send your final check in the mail tomorrow,*' *along with the standard letter of termination. Don't bother asking us for a reference.'*

While Natasha pressed for the next message, Korso walked over to the front door where he noticed a small pile of mail on the floor mat, maybe a dozen envelopes of various sizes, along with a number of local flyers. He vaguely heard some kind of sales call on the machine as he found the envelope from Lantern Auto. It was near the bottom of the pile. There were some more official-looking envelopes that seemed like bills, some junk mail, and even one that was addressed to a Victor Jimenez at 72 Goulding Avenue, which was the next street along. He'd seen it on the rental car's GPS. He dropped the mail back on the floor.

'That was the final one,' Natasha said. 'From three days ago. A salesman wanting to know if Adamson would like to change his internet provider.'

Korso nodded. 'So if we assume Adamson was working on the 7th, then he's been missing since Wednesday.'

'Or dead, like Kujan.'

'Nothing would surprise me. You find anything else?'

'Not yet.'

'Let's keep looking.'

Korso walked back to the bedroom, and was about to start checking the clothes in the wardrobe when he looked down and noticed the shoes on the floor. Or more specifically, the carpet underneath. It was made up of six separate tiles, one of which was slightly out of line with the rest. He knelt down, pulled this tile up, and saw a square, hinged, wooden panel in the floor underneath. It was about eight inches by eight, with a simple cylinder lock on the right side. Fifteen seconds later, he had the thing unlocked.

The hiding space was maybe three inches deep. Inside was Adamson's hidden stash of handguns – a Sig Sauer P938 semi-automatic, a Ruger .38 compact pistol, a S&W Model 17 revolver – along with some boxes of ammunition and two belt holsters. It wasn't exactly what he'd been hoping for, but nor was it surprising. This was Texas, after all. He took the compact Ruger, checked the magazine was full, and left the other two. Wherever Adamson was, Korso doubted they'd be of any use to him anymore.

He stood up and carefully went through the man's clothes, checking every shirt pocket, every jacket pocket. After five minutes of searching, all he'd found of value was half of a crumpled boarding pass. It was for a United Airlines flight from Tijuana to Fort Worth on February 16 at 16.55, which chimed with Yolanda's account of the three men meeting at Kujan's apartment. She'd said it was sometime around mid February.

Korso returned to the living room where Natasha was perched on an easy chair, leafing through paperwork. There was another small pile on the coffee table in front of her.

'Any luck?' he asked.

'Very little,' she said, still thumbing through the papers slowly. 'On the top there, on the table, is something that might be relevant. Also, some photos. I'm still checking the rest.'

Korso went over the paperwork on the table. On the top was a sheet of stationery that looked like a bill of some kind. He picked it up. Underneath the sheet was a strip of three passport-sized photos. They showed the face of a dark-haired, Caucasian man in his thirties, with large eyes under pale eyebrows, pronounced cheekbones and a widow's peak. The typed letterhead confirmed it was from the Motel Neuvo Cortez in Tijuana, with an address not far from the red light district. There was no phone number, email address or website listed on the page. Clearly not one of the more upmarket hotels. The bill was for two nights' stay, the 14th and 15th of February.

'Okay,' he said, 'this tallies with a boarding pass I found for a flight back to the States on the 16th, which more or less confirms Yolanda's version of events. Also, Adamson hid a small stash of handguns in his wardrobe, so you won't have to send any of the locals to intensive care this time.'

'I'll look,' she said, dropping the rest of the paperwork on the table. 'Apart from that hotel bill, I've found nothing else of interest to us. And also no cell phone.' She stood up, stretched, then went off to the main bedroom.

Korso was about to join her when he heard a car door slam on the street out front. Then another. He also heard what sounded like chitter-chatter from a walkie-talkie. Pocketing the hotel bill, he went over to the main front window and peered through the thin net curtains.

There was a black and white police cruiser parked on the street directly outside.

Two uniformed policemen stood by the driver's side door, conferring with each other as they looked toward Adamson's place. One of them already had his hand resting on his belt sidearm, as though expecting the worst.

Fifteen

Korso ran to the bedroom and poked his head round the door. Natasha was kneeling in front of the wardrobe, inspecting the Sig Sauer.

'We've got problems,' he said.

'What kind?'

'The worst. Someone called 911, or we tripped a security alarm. Maybe both. We need to move right now.'

She got to her feet and joined him in the hallway. 'How many?'

'Two uniforms.' He closed the bedroom door behind her. 'And they're already approaching the house. Any second now.'

'Can we not exit the way we came in? There are plenty of houses at the rear. We can use them for cov—'

'Not enough time. One will cover the rear while the other tries the front entrance. It's standard procedure. If we run now, they'll spot us and we're done. They may even start shooting right away.'

'Then the choice is simple.' She racked the Sig's slide. 'I'll not be placed under arrest, Korso. Am I making myself clear?'

'As glass. But let's try stealth first.' He closed the other three doors in the hallway, concealing them from view from the outside, then pointed to the access panel in the ceiling. 'Come over here and give me a boost.'

She paused a moment, then tucked the gun into her waistband and joined him. When she was directly underneath the hatch, she spread her legs wide and interlocked her fingers at waist level to make a pair of stirrups.

The front doorbell suddenly rang, the chimes echoing loudly throughout the house. Then came three hard knocks on the door. A stern, muffled voice called out, 'Mr Adamson? This is the police. Open up.'

Korso stepped onto Natasha's hands and let her take his weight as he raised himself to his full height. He pressed one hand to the ceiling to steady himself. There were three more loud knocks as he reached up with his right hand, pushed the wooden panel inward and slid it to the side. He saw nothing but blackness up there. The air smelled stale and dank. He grabbed both sides of the opening and used just his arms to pull himself up until both elbows were able to take his weight, then hauled his body all the way up. Once he was all the way in, he quickly slid his body round and extended his right arm through the opening, motioning for her to take his hand.

Natasha gripped it tightly in hers, and as she jumped up, he clenched his arm muscles and pulled hard. She grabbed hold of the opening with her other hand and clambered up the rest of the way within seconds. Once she was in, he let go of her and she lay down on her stomach on the wooden flooring opposite him.

'We could do with some light,' he said.

She pulled her phone from her back pocket as Korso reached over for the access panel. He was glad to see this side had a recessed handle at each end. Clasping both, he waited for Natasha to activate her phone, then once the light came on he carefully lowered the panel until it fit snugly into the space.

'So now we're trapped,' she whispered, her face a white mask from the harsh light.

'Only if they find us,' he whispered back. 'Play that light around. Let's see what else is up here.'

She got to her knees and rotated herself slowly in a full circle, right arm outstretched, the phone's light strong enough to illuminate even the furthest corners. There wasn't much to see. None of the usual battered boxes or garbage bags full of old possessions. Only the angled wooded rafters inches from their heads and the rolls of insulation stuffed between the naked floor joists. Either fibreglass or rock wool, he couldn't tell which. They were both sitting on a three-foot-wide wooden platform that ran down the length of the attic. Other than that, nothing.

'Obviously not a hoarder,' he said.

'No place to hide at all,' Natasha said. 'Korso, I promise you if one of them decides to check up here, my face will be the last thing he ever sees.'

'There you go, jumping the gun again.' Then he swore softly, under his breath.

'What?'

'I just remembered the rear door. You didn't latch it behind you, I suppose?'

She winced. 'It didn't occur to me. But can the police here enter a private residence without the owner's permission?'

'If they're responding to a 911 call, they can. And if the door's unlocked, they will.'

Korso lay on his stomach and placed an ear against the access panel, listening. But he could hear nothing down there yet.

'We have to assume they'll check the inside of the house,' he whispered. 'When you took the Sig, did you cover up that floor hatch again?'

'Not very well,' she said, laying herself flat. 'If they are even halfway competent, they'll observe something is amiss in there.'

'And once they see the boxes of .38 ammunition and an empty space where two guns should be, they'll know their suspects are now armed and danger—'

He suddenly stopped and raised a finger to his lips, sure that he'd heard voices down below.

Natasha was as motionless as a statue, breathing through her mouth. Watching him. Neither of them made a sound. Korso pressed his left ear hard against the wood, straining to hear anything that would give him some clue as to what was happening.

Then he heard a faint, muffled voice say, '...*got anything?*'

'*Zip*,' came the equally muffled reply. This one was louder, though. Which meant nearer. '*Hold on.*' Silence for a few more moments, then, '*Hey, Tanner, get in here.*'

After a few seconds, the first voice said, '*Well, how about that. Guess whoever called this in wasn't pulling our chains, after all.*'

His partner said, '*Dispatch, this is Adam 31. We got signs of intruders at that Willoughby address, possibly the same two suspects as initially reported. The rear door's open, most likely from forced entry, and there are handguns missing. No sign of the homeowner yet. Still searching the house. Over.*'

'They've found Adamson's stash,' he whispered, and saw Natasha was already gripping the Sig Sauer, still watching him with great intensity.

He ignored her and thought for a moment. The two cops clearly weren't dummies. It hadn't taken them long to find the hidden panel in the wardrobe floor. So how much longer would it take before they noticed the hatch to the attic and decided to check there too?

Not long at all, was his guess.

Not good, but he'd been in worse situations. There had to be a solution to their problem. He thought of the caller the cop mentioned. Apparently, somebody had seen them and done the exact opposite of what Korso had predicted. Which was all wrong, according to what he knew about human behaviour in neighbourhoods like this one. Unless. Unless the unknown caller hadn't seen them at all. At least, not in person.

And that gave him an idea.

Korso reached into his back pocket, and carefully pulled out the burner phone he'd brought along. He activated the screen, lowered the volume and called 911.

'What are you doing?' Natasha breathed.

'Complicating matters.'

After two rings, a female voice came on the line. 'Nine one one, fire and police. This call is being recorded. What's your emergency?'

Korso whispered, 'Police. Can't talk any louder or they'll hear me.'

'Who will hear you?'

'Two guys with handguns. They ran into my backyard, then jumped over my fence and are trying to break into my neighbour's house at seventy-four.' Still keeping to a whisper, he added some intensity. 'I'm outside right now, at the side of my house. I was just dumping some trash. I don't dare move or they'll see me.'

'Please remain calm, sir. Just give me your name and address.'

'My name, right. This is Victor Jimenez. I live at seventy-two Goulding Avenue, in Northside, Fort Worth. I think they came from one of the houses on Willoughby. Just get the police over here, right now... *Oh, Christ, they're looking this way.*'

He ended the call, and turned the phone off. He opened the back and removed the SIM card and snapped it in two.

'Goulding Avenue?' Natasha said under her breath. 'Where is that?'

'It's the street directly behind this one.'

'So what did that accomplish? It will only take the dispatcher seconds to check that address against the police database. Once they see the name you gave is false, they'll treat the call as a hoax.'

'Who says it's false?' he whispered, lowering his ear to the panel again. Waiting.

Seconds passed in silence. They turned into a minute. Finally, a voice right underneath them said, '*Hey, Lew, what about the attic? Worth a look, you think?*'

Korso and Natasha glanced at each other. Nothing needed to be said. They were down to the wire now. He pulled the Ruger from his waistband, and very slowly and silently chambered a round.

'*Yeah,*' came the eventual reply, also right underneath them. Just inches away from their position. '*They'll chew our asses out if we don't check everywhere. Go grab a chair from the kitchen. I'll take a look.*'

Here it came. Presumably, the other one was getting the chair. Korso carefully slid his whole body away from the panel until both arms were at full stretch. He aimed the Ruger at the opening. Natasha did the same opposite him. She raised her phone, arched an eyebrow. He nodded back at her. She turned off the light.

The resulting blackness was total.

'Your play,' Korso whispered. 'I'll back you up.'

'Copy,' she whispered back.

They heard the jarring sound of a chair being dragged along the floor, and getting louder. Then the sound stopped.

'*Okay, give me your flashlight.*'

Seconds to go. Korso had done what he could to avoid this, but it was out of his hands now. They'd have to move fast, in tandem with each other. He knew Natasha would double tap the first cop the moment he showed his face. So as soon as he dropped, Korso would have to scramble forward and lean his top half out of the opening and put two in his partner as well. It was messy, but you couldn't always choose your battlefield.

Korso controlled his breathing, flexing and unflexing his shoulders. He could already feel his pulse slowing. Just as it always did before a combat situation. And his mind also felt clearer than before. Sharper.

He was ready.

Just then he heard the familiar sound of somebody communicating through a walkie-talkie. He couldn't make out the words. It was too muffled. It sounded like a female voice, but he wasn't even sure about that.

Once the message had been relayed, one of the cops said, '*Say again, dispatch.*'

More chitter-chatter. And even more unintelligible than before. Long seconds passed.

'*Copy that, dispatch,*' the cop said, finally. '*Seventy-two Goulding. We're moving now.*'

'*Sounds like our perps, all right. I'll take the back way. You drive round, cover the front. And watch your ass, okay?*'

But Korso noticed that voice was already growing fainter with each word. As though he was running from the hallway.

He remained in position for a while longer. Counting the seconds. Always better to be safe than sorry. He judged a minute had passed without a single sound coming from below when Natasha said, 'They are gone.'

Korso thought so too. Placing the Ruger back in his waistband, he slid his body forward carefully until he felt the access panel, then clasped each of the recessed handles on either end. He gently pulled it up. Light flooded the attic again. And still no sounds from below. He looked down and one of the kitchen chairs was directly underneath him. Gripping the opening with both hands, Korso hung down until his feet touched the chair, then he let go and stepped down onto the tiled floor.

He saw nothing. Heard nothing. Except for the two of them, the house was empty once more.

'Okay,' he said. 'We're clear.'

Natasha's face appeared at the opening. She dropped lithely down to the chair, reached up to slide the panel back into position, then joined him on the floor.

'It won't take them long to conclude the call was not genuine.'

'I know it,' he said, jogging into the living room. He peered through the net curtains again, but this time the street outside was clear. No black and white. And just as importantly, no interested locals. At least, none in sight.

'Looks clear,' he said. 'We'll leave by the front. It'll look more natural that way.'

Pulling up her shirt and slipping the Sig into the belt holster she'd taken from the bedroom, Natasha stepped over to the front entrance and pulled the door open. She waited for Korso to join her, then took his hand in hers. He blinked at her in surprise.

'This will also look more natural,' she said. 'What can this loving couple have possibly done wrong? Those policemen must have been looking for somebody else.'

They exited the house together, walking down the driveway hand in hand. Korso forced himself to keep his walk casual and unhurried. She looked over at him and smiled before facing front again. He couldn't help noticing she had a very attractive smile.

'Now I'm telling you about something amusing that happened to me yesterday,' she said. 'And whatever it is I'm saying you find funny, so you laugh lightly.'

Korso laughed on cue, and said, 'Or you could actually tell me something amusing. Wouldn't that be more natural?'

'Not for me.'

This time his chuckle was genuine.

Crossing the street, Korso handed the keys to Natasha, and she used the remote to unlock the Chevy. They got in. Natasha started the engine and turned to him.

'Where to?' she asked.

'Anywhere but here.'

Sixteen

Natasha kept them under the speed limit as they left Northside behind. Korso continued checking the mirrors to make sure nobody was following, or taking undue interest in them. It seemed clear.

Once they'd passed through a few similar-looking neighbourhoods, Korso saw a road sign for Arlington Heights. Left at the main crossroads, one mile up ahead. He told her to take the turn when it came.

'Why there?'

'Why not? We need to be somewhere until we figure out our next destination.' From his jacket pocket he pulled the bill from the Motel Neuvo Cortez while musing on the best way to get the information he wanted. 'You should smile more often, by the way. Makes you look less lethal.'

She frowned. 'Was that a compliment?'

'I'm not sure.'

'And just what is there to smile about anyway?'

'How about the world and everything in it, for a start?'

She nodded at that. 'Ah, now I begin to understand. Life is the biggest joke of all, and we're all insignificant specks whose little power games are beneath contempt to those who remain above it all. Like yourself. Is that what you mean?'

'Well, I wouldn't have put it in those exact words...'

'No doubt.' The crossroads she'd been waiting for came. She indicated left and took the turn. 'And what makes you so high and mighty when compared to the rest of us?'

'Nothing. I'm down there in the mud with everybody else. I've just got a little more perspective than most, that's all.'

'How fortunate for you. And does this perspective help you sleep at night?'

'I wouldn't know,' he said. 'I've never had trouble sleeping. Not even when I was with Nikolic. How about you?'

'My sleeping habits are none of your business.'

A faint smile flickered across his mouth. 'Naturally. But I've found perspective breeds clarity, which is essential in my line of work. It always helps to see the bigger picture.'

Korso lowered the side window, threw out the burner phone he'd used at the house, then raised the window again. He reached into the back seat for his bag, unzipped it and pulled out his thin laptop. 'Let me borrow your phone again, Natasha.'

'As long as you don't throw it out the window.'

She removed her cell from her pocket and passed it to him. He busied himself configuring his MacBook's wifi to her mobile data connection. 'Did you notice anything strange about what just happened back at the house? Stranger than usual, I mean.'

'Yes,' she said. 'We were there less than fifteen minutes before the police showed. That was very odd. And I don't believe any of Adamson's neighbours called them.'

'Me, neither. In fact, I'm sure they didn't. Not in that neighbourhood.'

She glanced at him for a moment before turning back to the road. 'You said we could have tripped a security alarm when we broke in.'

'I said that then, but I'm not so sure now. I think we tripped a sensor of some kind, but a home security system with a linked-in police response seems unlikely. For one thing, Adamson doesn't strike me as a man who'd want police showing up at his door for any reason. And for another, there's nothing in that house worth stealing, except for maybe a couple of handguns. And their worth is negligible.'

Having successfully set up the gateway connection, Korso opened up his browser and went straight to the Google home page. He began searching for what he wanted.

'But somebody must have called 911,' she said. 'Maybe via a hidden motion-detection camera we missed?'

He nodded. 'That's what I think. And these days they make spycams so small they're practically invisible unless you know precisely what you're looking for. Which we didn't.'

Natasha was silent for a few moments. 'So we trip the sensor when we break in, which activates the camera while also sending an alarm to whoever installed it.'

'Right. Probably via a simple cell-phone app. My guess is there's a password-protected web page where this person can access a live video feed whenever the alarm goes off. And possibly from more than one camera, too. So this person sees us enter the kitchen and immediately calls 911, pretending to be a concerned neighbour, like I did, and tells them they've just seen two armed intruders break into Adamson's house. The police show up and arrest us. Problem solved.'

'So who installed the alarm?' she said.

'You know who. Unless there are other interested parties unknown to us, it can only really be one person.'

'Kujan's murderer.'

'Correct. And if you know the who, you also know the why. If he's tying up loose ends, it means he's thorough. And a thorough person would want to make sure his back's covered at all times. He'd assume Nikolic wouldn't lie down over the missing shipment, and would send people in to investigate. Hence, the hidden alarm system.'

'Maybe he set one up in Kujan's apartment as well,' Natasha said. 'That could explain the ambush by those three thugs.'

Korso shook his head. 'It's possible, but that whole situation felt too haphazard and random. And I don't believe the killer would have stayed in that apartment any longer than necessary to set up a tripwire, not with a fresh corpse in the fridge. And if he had, alerting the Mexican police would have been a far surer method of getting us out of the way than using those three morons.'

'Yes, that makes sense. So you believe this Adamson is dead too?'

'I suspect he is. But I'm keeping an open mind.'

She continued driving in silence, lost in her own thoughts. Korso looked up from what he was doing and saw they were on a main street, possibly in Arlington Heights. Various stores passed by on each side. Some shuttered, but most open for business. He saw a familiar green and red sign up ahead. 'Stop at the 7-Eleven over there. I could do with a sandwich, and maybe some coffee.'

She signalled right, then pulled in to the small parking lot and found a space. She looked over at Korso. 'You can access the internet just as well on my phone. Why bother with the laptop?'

'I was also checking my emails, and I never do that on a phone.'

'What are you searching for anyway?'

'I'll tell you when you come back with my sandwich.' He smiled. 'And coffee.'

'Yes, *master*.' She sighed and got out, taking the keys with her.

He watched her go into the convenience store, then reached back and grabbed another burner phone from his bag. He activated the screen and keyed in the number he'd found for the hotel.

After three rings, a bored female voice said, '*Motel Neuvo Cortez.*'

Korso identified himself as Detective Jimenez from the *Comandancia de Policia Villa Fontana*, and said he wanted to speak with the manager immediately.

'*Un momento*,' she said. There was a sharp clang as she put the phone down.

Less than a minute later, a male voice said, '*¿Cómo puedo ayudarlo, Detective?*'

Korso said he could help by answering a few questions.

Natasha returned five minutes later, carrying a paper bag bearing the 7-Eleven logo. She got in the driver's seat and set the bag on the central partition. Reaching in, she handed Korso a styrofoam cup, and pulled out one for herself.

'Thanks,' he said.

'There's also a chicken sandwich and a BLT in there. The BLT is mine.' She removed the plastic cover from her cup, the coffee aroma immediately filling the car interior. 'So now you can tell me what you found.'

Korso took a sip from his cup. 'Well, I had a rewarding conversation with Senor Orantes, the manager of the Motel Neuvo Cortez, in Tijuana. And after consulting his records, he confirmed that Joel Adamson did stay at his establishment on the nights of 14th and 15th of February.'

'Which we already knew.'

'But once I pressed him, he also informed me that an American named Michael Papsidera also stayed there on those same two nights. He told me they had rooms on the same floor, and that they each checked out within minutes of each other.'

'Michael Papsidera,' she said. 'Mickey.'

'More than likely. Senor Orantes didn't see him and Adamson together, but he did remember this Papsidera as a short, bullish man with a heavy brow. Not a conventionally handsome man, in other words.'

'Or plain ugly, according to the dancer,' Natasha said, nodding slowly. 'So now we have a name. Or do we have more than that?'

'We also have an address. Or at least the one they took from his driver's licence: twenty-seven Cornell Avenue, Amarillo, Texas.'

'Texas. Good.' Natasha took her sandwich from the bag, opened the triangular packaging. 'Very good. How far is that from here?'

'About three hundred and forty miles northwest of our current location. I just checked. It's about a five-hour journey by car. Faster by jet, obviously.'

'Hmm. Flying would save two, maybe three, hours. But then we lose the firearms we just obtained.'

'There is that,' he said. 'There's no telling what we might come up against, though. And as much as we need to save time, I vote we drive.'

'I was not aware this was a democracy,' she said, inserting the keys in the ignition. 'Fortunately enough, I agree with you. We drive.'

Seventeen

'I could have killed you anytime in the last three hours,' Korso said.

He was behind the wheel, and had been for those three hours, having switched with Natasha in Wichita Falls. They'd passed the Amarillo city limits sign on US-287 a few miles back, and traffic was beginning to thicken slightly as they entered the city proper. The sky was overcast, with dusk closing in.

Natasha had her elbow against the door, hand supporting her chin as she watched the scenery go by. If you could call it that. She turned her head slightly to look at him.

'Is that so?' she said.

He nodded. 'One in the back of the skull while you were looking out that window, then a shallow grave behind any one of the derelict-looking farmhouses we passed along the way. No effort at all. And nobody would ever find you.'

'I feel very lucky to be alive. What stopped you?'

'For one thing, I'm not a psychopath. For another, I really don't want a man like Nikolic hunting me down for the rest of my natural life. And finally, I told you before that this case had piqued my interest. I take it you now believe me.'

She yawned. 'Please remind me why we're having this conversation.'

'I'm making a point that you don't seem too bothered about my being armed now.'

'Why should I be?'

'"I won't hesitate to kill you if I have to". I believe those were your exact words to me, back in Bermuda. And a threat like that really hinges on only one of us carrying a weapon. Namely, you. Or is it that I'm sensing an element of trust entering into our relationship?'

'Maybe that's it.' She started to rub her earlobe, then stopped herself. 'After all, you could have simply walked away at the 7-Eleven, but you stayed. I learned long ago that trust is never to be taken for granted, that it must be earned over time. So it is with us.'

'And is that how it is with you and Sardoca?'

She turned back to the window. 'That's a different kind of relationship altogether.'

'Or between you and Nikolic?'

She gave a deep sigh. 'There *is* no me and Nik… Mr Nikolic. I told you before he rarely deals directly with underlings such as myself.'

'Oh, that's right, you did. I forgot.'

Korso smiled to himself. He'd catch her out sooner or later. He already had one or two theories rattling around his head. Very interesting ones, too.

'While we're on the subject of Sardoca,' he said, 'aren't you supposed to keep him updated at regular intervals, and assure him I'm toeing the line?'

'If you must know, I called him in the 7-Eleven while I was waiting for the coffee. And also at various other times when you were out of earshot. Would you like to know what he said to me?'

'My interest doesn't run that far. I stopped caring what Sardoca thought or said a long time ago.'

She turned her face to him again. 'You mean back when you worked together?'

'We never did. I worked alone, even back then. However, I am interested in how he found and recruited you. It shows a level of insight I never imagined he possessed.'

'I must be hearing things. That actually did sound like a compliment.'

'Anything's possible. So what branch of the military were you before? Army? Navy? Special forces?'

She tilted her head. 'One or the other. There's little difference between any of them. I was trained to kill at an early age. I found I was good at it. My country made use of my abilities to their best advantage, until I eventually became surplus to requirements and moved on. What more needs to be said?'

'And which country is your country?'

'You mean you don't know? I thought you knew everything.'

'Well, I know your accent is East European, but that covers a fairly wide area. If I had to guess, I'd say either Romanian or Bulgarian.' He paused a moment. 'Probably the former.'

She did that half-smile again. 'And you'd be correct. What gave me away?'

'Those large almond-shaped eyes, for a start. They're a common trait amongst your people. But mostly, I've noticed you pronounce your Ds and Ts by touching your teeth with your tongue, instead of the roof of your mouth.'

'I see. And is that a tell?'

'To me, it is.'

'Interesting. So languages are a hobby of yours?'

'More like a general interest. It also gives me a slight edge in my line of work, where I often have to deal with a wide variety of nationalities. So back to my original question. Did Sardoca recruit you, or did you approach him?'

'Maybe it was a little of both,' she said in a bored tone. 'What difference does it make?'

It might make all the difference, he thought. But he gave a shrug and said nothing.

They passed a large showroom-cum-warehouse selling building materials on their right. The building covered almost two blocks. More depots and businesses for machine parts passed by on the left. Also a few auto dealerships, mostly used vehicles. Very quickly, general stores and diners started appearing with more frequency. Traffic grew steadily heavier.

Natasha grabbed her phone from the dash and activated her GPS app. After a few moments spent enlarging and minimising the screen, she said, 'We're close now. Just over four kilometres to Papsidera's place.'

'Miles, not kilometres. America still uses the imperial system.'

'Good for America. However, my GPS app is attuned to the metric system like the rest of the civilised world. Just keep on this road and turn left when I tell you.'

'Yes, sir,' he said.

They found the address they wanted less than ten minutes later. Located downtown, 27 Cornell Avenue wasn't what either of them had expected.

It was a narrow, single-storey, stucco building with Westside Electronic Repairs in large block letters above a set of closed shutters. There was a steel mail slot just to the right of them. A large vacant lot that was doubling as a makeshift parking area was its neighbour on the left, while the building on the other side was home to Alamo Jack's, a tattoo parlour. It was still open, from the looks of it. At least, the lights were on inside.

'I'll circle the block,' Korso said.

After the body-art place, there was a vape store called CryoVape, also still open. A large supermarket took up the rest of the block. Korso turned left at the intersection and spotted an access road at the rear of that store, presumably for deliveries and such. He carried on at a slow crawl, passing two discount stores and a few vacant-looking office buildings before ending up where he started.

'No other access from the front except through those shutters,' Natasha said, checking Google Maps on her phone. 'But the satellite view shows that the road we pass at the next turn leads to the rear entrances of all three businesses, not just the food market. And there are also further spaces for parking. Maybe Papsidera actually lives there.'

'There's probably an apartment at the back. Let's ask.' Korso pulled in outside Alamo Jack's. He killed the engine and turned to Natasha. 'That is to say, you ask.'

'Why me?'

'Basic psychology. People are generally more open with women than men. Especially attractive ones. Just try not to kill anyone while you're in there.'

'I'll restrain myself… somehow,' she said with a straight face, and got out of the car.

Korso watched her pull open the front door and enter the shop. Natasha might well be very attractive, but he'd been on this earth far too long to let looks affect his judgement. He was far more concerned with the current task facing them, as well as figuring out ways to deal with Sardoca's inevitable double-cross once, or *if*, they were successful in recovering the shipment. Whatever Sardoca's other shortcomings, he was no fool. He had to know that using Korso was a one-time-only deal.

Sardoca was like a kid who'd trapped a scorpion in a glass jar, laughing to himself as it tried to escape its fate. He knew if he ever set the scorpion free, it would come back and sting him. So, better to simply kill it once he'd had his fun.

Or even better, get someone else to do it.

Like his boss, Nikolic. A long, drawn-out, painful death for Korso would definitely appeal to the sadist in Sardoca. But if he didn't want to go quite that far, Natasha could just as easily be assigned the task. Maybe she already had been. She certainly had the resolve to do whatever she felt was necessary. Korso had no idea what Sardoca's instructions to her were, but he very much doubted they were beneficial to him.

So, plenty to think about, and plan against. But he was good at planning ahead. He always had been. That's why he was still walking around, when so many of his contemporaries had fallen to dust by the wayside. Sardoca being one of the few exceptions. But maybe not for too much longer.

It was five minutes later when Natasha exited the shop. She walked round to the Chevy's passenger side and got back in.

'Anything useful?' Korso asked.

'Not much,' she said, scratching her neck. 'The owner – who's called Jackie, by the way – was busy tattooing a man's shoulder, so there were many pauses in the conversation. But she told me that next door has been shuttered for a week now, and that she has seen no sign of Papsidera in that time.'

'Does she usually see him around?'

'Once or twice a week, she said. They're civil, without being friends. Apparently, the owner of the vape store is on much closer terms with him, and might know more. She also confirmed that the building has a small apartment at the back, which is where Papsidera lives.'

'Or lived. Did she say anything else?'

'Only that my love life would be much improved if I let her design a dream catcher tattoo for my back. I thanked her, but declined.'

'Maybe it would.'

'Would what?'

'Improve your love life.'

She said nothing.

'So not a tattoo person then.'

'I have no opinion on them, one way or the other. You?'

'I prefer anonymity. The last thing I need on my body is something people will remember.'

He was studying the small row of shops with narrowed eyes, absently tapping the wheel with his fingers.

'Why are we waiting?' she asked. 'You have your lock-pick tools. Let's go.'

'These are business premises,' he said, 'and business premises generally have security alarms. Papsidera's sure to have one at the front entrance, and possibly another at the back. And the lock itself is likely to be more complex than a simple pin tumbler mechanism, thereby making my snapgun useless. I'm thinking another approach might be in order.'

She frowned. 'What approach do you have in mind?'

'The official kind.'

Eighteen

69 hours, 34 minutes and counting...

Korso opened the door to CryoVape and allowed Natasha to enter first. He followed her inside and stood there, looking around the small store with a bored, disdainful expression on his face.

The interior layout was fairly similar to that of a standard drugstore, but with added vibrancy. Three large glass display cases along the left contained a variety of multi-coloured pipes, e-cigarettes, e-cigars, carrying cases, starter kits and other paraphernalia. The shelves lining the walls on each side were crammed with e-liquids of every flavour and colour. The room smelled vaguely of incense, although Korso saw nothing burning. Facing the entrance was a long sales counter, behind which a young, long-haired Asian man sat, doing something on a laptop. There were no other customers.

The man looked up at them both, and smiled. 'Help you, guys?'

Natasha walked over to him while Korso stayed near the door. They had planned it that way, as though he was covering the entrance. He'd also instructed Natasha to make sure her belt holster with the Sig was visible.

'Homeland Security,' she said in an officious tone. She pulled a wallet from her back pocket and flashed it at him briefly before putting it back again. All he'd seen was her international driving licence, but it looked official and that was what counted.

'Hey, I'm clean.' He raised both hands, still smiling. 'Honest.'

Natasha just glared at him. He soon stopped smiling, and lowered his hands.

'Your name is Isaac Varma, correct?'

'That's right. What's the problem?'

'Let us ask the questions. You know Michael Papsidera, the owner of the repair shop two doors down?'

'Mickey? Sure, I know him a little.'

'From what we've been told,' Korso said, inspecting the glass display, 'you know him more than just a little.'

'What do you mean? Told by who?'

'Funny how they never know what we mean,' Korso said.

'Isn't it,' Natasha said. 'You see, Mr Varma, we've had Papsidera's premises under surveillance for quite a while, yet he's failed to show up for over a week and that worries us. We'd very much like to know his current whereabouts. Maybe you can help us with that.'

'How would I know where he is? It ain't like we're best buddies or anything. All we do is look out for each other every now and then.'

'You hear that, Sakowicz?' Korso said, still not looking up. 'They're not pals after all. Looks like our intel is all wrong.'

'And you have absolutely no idea where he's gone,' Natasha said. 'Is that what you're telling us?'

'Not a clue. Look, why would I lie? I don't understand any of this. What's Mickey done, anyway?'

Korso gave a world-weary sigh. 'You're wasting your time, Sakowicz. He's not going to play ball. Let's just take him downtown with us. If we can't get a line on Papsidera's whereabouts, at least we can produce one of his known associates for Tanner to talk to. That'll keep him off our back for a few days, at least.'

'Hey, wait a minute,' Varma said, clearly alarmed now. 'I'm no associate of anyone's. I've done nothing wrong. You can't just take me in without a good reason.'

'You'd be amazed at what Homeland Security can and can't do, Mr Varma,' Natasha said. 'Especially when it involves suspected domestic terrorists. But to be honest, I could do without the additional paperwork that bringing you in would cause. You said you and Papsidera help each other out. Does that mean you have keys to each other's premises?'

'That's right.' Varma nodded his head eagerly. 'Whenever I have to leave town on business, Mickey lets himself in and feeds my parrot, makes sure everything's okay. I live out the back, see. And if he's away for long periods, I do the same for him, making sure his security alarm's still active, and that there's no burst water pipes or anything like that. Except he never gave me any warning he was leaving this time.'

Natasha turned back to Korso. 'What do you think? Maybe we'll find something at his place. Some clue he left behind. And if a good citizen lets us in with a key, it's not like we've broken any rules.'

'Up to you.' Korso gave an elaborate shrug. 'You know what I'd do.'

Natasha turned back to Varma. 'Where are these keys?'

'I'll go get them,' he said, and disappeared through one of two doors behind the counter.

Natasha turned back to Korso and smiled. He didn't return it. It was best not to break character in these situations.

Varma returned thirty seconds later, out of breath, holding a set of keys. 'You want the front or rear entrance? I've got keys to both.'

'Rear entrance,' Natasha said.

'Okay, follow me.'

He opened the other door, and they followed him through a long and cramped storeroom and then a long corridor until they reached the rear of the store. There was a toilet back there, and a fire exit with a keypad next to it. Varma tapped some numbers into the keypad and pushed the door open. They stepped outside into the rear alley and followed Varma as he turned left. He led them past Alamo Jack's, stopping outside Papsidera's premises.

The rear of the building contained a plain steel door, with a keyhole and no handle, and a barred window on either side. Behind them two parking spaces, both empty. Varma stood by the door, nervously searching for the right key.

'I know it's one of these fat ones,' Varma said, and inserted one of the larger keys into the door. He turned it counter-clockwise. There was a sharp *clak* and he pushed the door open. Stepping inside, he pressed some buttons on a keypad affixed to the wall. 'There. System's disarmed.'

'Good,' Natasha said. 'We'll take it from here. We appreciate your cooperation.'

Varma came back outside, looking a little less nervous than before. 'No problem. Look, do you want me to—'

'We'll return the keys once we're done,' Korso said. 'Say an hour from now.'

'Right. Sure. I'll be in the store if you need me.' Varma paused, as though unsure what to do next, before turning and walking back to his own shop.

Korso and Natasha watched him go, and exchanged a brief glance. Then they entered the building.

Nineteen

69 hours, 19 minutes and counting...

The two barred windows didn't let in much light, so it was fairly dim inside. Korso saw Natasha look around for a moment, before flicking a switch on the wall behind her. The lights came on. He shut the rear door behind him.

They were in a living area. There was an L-shaped settee on the left, a large flatscreen TV in one corner, a small table and two chairs set against the right-hand wall, while a bookcase full of technical manuals, magazines and DVDs took up most of the wall opposite. Straight ahead was a small, partitioned-off kitchen area with a door at the end, which presumably led to the shop out front. To the left was an open doorway to another smaller room, and Korso could see part of a double bed inside.

'This time it's your turn to check the kitchen,' Natasha said.

'I doubt our killer's that obvious,' Korso said as he made his way to the kitchen area. He noticed several unwashed plates in the sink, but at least he didn't smell anything out of the ordinary this time. He reached down and pulled open the refrigerator door, and quickly clamped his hand against his nose and mouth at the stench from within.

'*Whoa*,' he said.

'What is it?' Natasha said, rushing over.

He quickly slammed the fridge door shut with his foot and breathed deeply through his mouth, trying to get rid of the noxious smell.

'Not another body?' Natasha asked, reaching for the fridge door.

'Don't open that.'

She paused. 'Why not?'

'Rotten milk. Weeks' old rotten milk. A carton must have burst or something. It smells like a zoo in there.'

She pulled her hand away. 'I'll take your word for it.'

Korso moved out of the kitchen area and took a brief glance in the bedroom, then headed for the door at the end. He opened it and found himself in a windowless room that was doubling as a stockroom. All four walls were covered with shelves and pigeonholes, which were filled with tools, wires, electrical components, DVD players, stereos, flatscreen TVs, PCs, hard drives, and numerous other electronic items waiting to be worked on. Or more likely, being salvaged for parts. None of them looked new. He even spotted several cell phones in one pigeonhole.

Set against the left-hand wall was a steel filing cabinet, a simple work desk and chair. On the desk was a landline phone, a broadband router and a PC that looked ten years out of date. He picked up the phone handset to check if the line had been disconnected, but he heard the usual dial tone.

Natasha opened the next door and entered the front of the shop. Korso followed. Because the shutters were down, it was almost pitch black in there. After a few seconds fumbling around, he found the wall switch and turned the lights on.

There wasn't much to see, but then it was more a repair shop than anything. There was a large counter with a cash till and a more modern PC. Behind it were more shelves with more tablets, hard drives, stereos and the like. The customer area in front contained a coffee machine, a glass table and some chairs, and a large flatscreen TV attached to the wall. He noticed another alarm system above the front door, and a surveillance camera in one corner of the ceiling. It was above the coffee machine, with a good view of the entire room.

Natasha was searching behind the counter. 'There's a working hard drive back here, Korso. Probably connected to that security camera.' She pulled out a black oblong box and set it on the counter. 'The light was flashing orange until I unplugged it.'

'Good,' he said. 'We'll erase the footage before we go, or take it with us if we can't.'

She pointed a finger at the CCTV above the coffee machine. 'That camera up there is obvious. But if there are others hidden in any of these rooms, then the police could already have been alerted by our watcher. They may already be on their way.'

'Well, we'll know for sure within the next twenty minutes.' Of course, it was also possible there weren't any other cameras. After all, Kujan's place didn't have any. But Korso wasn't about to let his guard down on that hope. 'Whatever happens, we can't rush things. If we don't find anything useful here, we're back to square one again.'

Natasha came around from behind the counter. 'So what are we actually looking for this time?'

'Your guess is as good as mine. Basically, anything that might point us to either this mysterious watcher, or the missing shipment itself. I did notice a few cell phones in the stockroom back there. Maybe you could charge them up, and if they still work take a look at their contact lists. Yolanda told us it was Mickey who called our killer, and if that phone still exists there's a faint chance his phone number's still on it.'

'A very faint chance, I would say.'

'I agree. But Papsidera could have kept a hold of that phone for his own reasons. Sometimes miracles happen.'

'If you say so.'

'And look out for any keys. You never know what they might open. Most stores have a small safe somewhere on the premises, so look out for one of those too. Remember to check the floors.'

'I'll see about the cell phones first,' Natasha said.

Korso watched her leave the room, then turned to the mailbox left of the front display window. The slot was set into the wall, with a steel cage on this side to catch the mail. There was already a pile of envelopes and catalogues inside. He reached in and pulled them out, then walked back and set them on the counter top.

He went behind the counter and inspected the shelves against the wall, looking for more cell phones. But he didn't find any. And no paperwork, either. There was a long shelf under the counter, with a plug extension and a number of till receipts scattered around. Nothing else of note.

Instead, he focused his attention on the mail. He put to one side the trade catalogues, free newspapers and obvious junk mail. That left thirteen envelopes of varying sizes. About half were addressed to Michael Papsidera, the other half to Westside Electronic Repairs.

He started with the personal mail. He opened the envelopes one by one, and scanned the contents of each carefully. He found bank statements, three late payment reminders for his various credit cards, an invoice from his tax accountant, a car insurance reminder, and a short, personal letter from a sister in Nevada who wanted him to come visit.

Korso placed them all with the other junk and started in on the business mail. This was more of the same, though. A mortgage-payment reminder, business-insurance statements, business credit card statements and the like. He found nothing of any interest until he opened the very last envelope. Inside was a letter from a local business that at first glance appeared to be more junk mail. Just a standard mailing circular.

But after reading the letter, Korso realised it was anything but junk.

Twenty

Korso found Natasha in Papsidera's bedroom, rummaging through his clothes cupboard. When she saw him, she stopped what she was doing and said, 'I found chargers for each phone, but they're all missing SIM cards and therefore useless.' She studied his face. 'You found something.'

'Take a look.' He handed her the single sheet of paper.

She sat on the bed and read it. 'A letter from an Ezee Self Storage, asking if Papsidera would like to extend his recent unit rental from six months to a full year?'

'At a thirty per cent discount,' Korso said. 'That's a pretty good deal.'

Natasha ignored him as she continued reading. 'It says here Papsidera paid for his initial six months' rental on the 21st February. That also fits in with our timeline.'

'Not too long after that meeting in Tijuana, and a full week before your plane went missing. Sounds like they were getting themselves ready.'

Natasha frowned at the sheet. 'But no details about the storage unit itself, except a number: twenty-seven. It does not say if the unit is large or small.'

'Large enough to hold six large crates, you mean.' He took the letter back. 'I'll check their website on his computer. There might be a site layout or something. But this makes it all the more important to look out for any keys he might have lying around. Any one of them might open this unit.'

'Unless he kept it with his car keys. In which case, we're out of luck.'

'Let's keep an eye out anyway.'

He left her and returned to the stockroom. He turned on the router and the PC hard drive. While they booted up, he went over to the steel filing cabinet. It consisted of four large drawers, each one with its own individual lock. He tried the top drawer. It was unlocked. Pulling it open, he saw about twenty hanging yellow file folders inside. Flipping through quickly, he saw they were all empty. He slid them back and checked the bottom of the drawer. No keys. Nothing.

The next drawer contained half a dozen unused legal pads and some basic stationery items, like pens, pencils and erasers, but nothing else. The bottom two drawers contained only old computer magazines and well-thumbed trade catalogues.

No keys in any of them.

Next, he checked the tiled floor, looking for any sign of a hidden floor safe. But none of the ceramic tiles looked discoloured, or out of place. All were firmly glued to the floor, and had been for years. He checked again behind the counter out front, but there were no signs of any safe there either.

He returned to the stockroom and saw the PC was now up and running, the screen displaying the standard Windows desktop, along with a pop-up asking for a password. Naturally. But he knew from long experience that people often wrote down important passwords and kept them nearby. Korso opened the filing cabinet again, searching for a sticky note or a piece of paper taped to the inside of the drawers, but there was nothing in any of them. He checked the rear of the hard drive itself, and found nothing there either. He picked up the keyboard and turned it upside down.

There was a yellow sticky note taped underneath. *WestsideER86R* was written in faded blue ink.

Korso sat on the chair, typed in the letters and numbers exactly, hit Enter. The pop-up disappeared. He smiled faintly to himself as he checked the icons running along the bottom of the screen. It seemed Papsidera's browser of choice was Google Chrome, so he opened it up, then keyed in the website address listed on the invoice. A few seconds later, he was greeted with the homepage for Ezee Self Storage, located off Canyon Drive, Amarillo.

At the top of the page were the opening times. Monday to Saturday, 8 a.m. to 7.30 p.m., with gate access from 6 a.m. to midnight, seven days a week. Most of the page was taken up by a slideshow showing exterior shots of their storage units, all with uniform sand-coloured steel shutters. Some were garage-sized, some no bigger than closets. All were located out in the open, but fenced off from the general public. Outside the chain-link fence, there was a small, ranch-style clapboard office building and a dozen parking spaces. The text boasted of Ezee's huge variety of unit sizes, as well as its secured electronic gate access, twenty-four-hour digital surveillance and convenient drive-up access.

Korso dragged the cursor down the side menu and stopped when he reached a button titled *PLAN*. He clicked on the button and a page opened showing a basic layout of the site.

Exactly what he'd been hoping for. Even better, every unit was numbered.

The entire site was essentially a square, with storage units surrounding and enclosing the perimeter. Within that square were ten more long, rectangular buildings, arranged in two columns of five. According to the key at the bottom of the page, the top six buildings and those surrounding the perimeter contained the largest storage units. Units 25 to 32 were located in the second building down on the right.

Things were looking up. All they needed now was an access code for the entrance and a key to the unit itself. And a few other essential items, of course. But they could be found almost anywhere. He leaned back and ran his palm up and down his neck. It also hadn't escaped his attention that they'd been here for over twenty minutes now. If the local police had been alerted to their illegal entry, they would surely have shown up by now.

So they had a little time to play with.

Korso clicked on the menu button in the top-right corner of the browser and opened the Bookmarks menu. He was looking for email sites, and quickly found the one for Gmail. He clicked on it, hoping Papsidera wasn't too security conscious when it came to his own computer. And sure enough, his personal email account immediately began loading, meaning his passwords had been saved on the browser for quicker access.

Once the page finished loading, Korso ran his eye down the sender names and stopped when he saw one from a Linda at ezeeselfstorage.com, sent on February 21, the same day Papsidera had opened his account. The subject line read, *Welcome to Ezee Self Storage*. It was just a standard welcome message, with additional contact numbers if Papsidera had any further queries. It also confirmed his storage unit number, and reminded him to keep his key in a safe place as they would have to charge him $75.95 for a replacement. Korso was hoping this Linda might have included the code for the front gate, but no such luck. That would have been far too easy.

He checked the time in the corner of the screen: 19:04. The office would still be open. In which case, it might be an idea to check up on a few things before they closed up. He picked up the phone handset and keyed in the number on the top of the page. After four rings, a cheerful male voice said, 'Ezee Self Storage, Russ speaking. What can I do you for?'

'I saw your website, Russ,' Korso said, 'and it looks like just what I need. I've just got a few questions I hope you can answer.'

'I'll do my very best. Hit me, partner.'

Korso asked his questions, and Russ answered them in great detail. Korso thanked him for his time, told him he'd call back real soon and hung up. He put the handset back and was just turning off the PC when Natasha came in. She was holding a tatty manila envelope, folded over at the top.

'There's no safe anywhere in the apartment,' she said, 'but I did find this in the bedroom cupboard, tucked inside a computer magazine.'

She shook the envelope and there was the unmistakable sound of jangling keys. She came over and emptied the contents onto the desk. Korso saw three loose keys and five more attached to a keychain, with a plastic key fob bearing the words WESTSIDE REPAIRS in block capitals on the front. One of those on the chain was a Ford transponder key. Most likely a spare.

'This one will interest you,' Natasha said, picking up one of the loose keys and handing it to him.

It was a standard Yale with an octagonal bow. The number 27 had been written in black marker on the bow.

'A break, at last,' Korso said. 'Nice work, Natasha.'

'What about you? Did you find anything else that can help us?'

'Well, that's a matter of opinion.' He quickly updated her on what he'd found out about the storage site.

'I was also looking for anything that could be a code,' she said, 'but I found no other paperwork. Papsidera must have kept that kind of personal data on his cell phone.'

'Probably. But I've been thinking it over, and I may have a way around that hurdle. Along with one or two others.'

'What others?'

'Security cameras, for a start. Every self-storage business has plenty of CCTV surveillance, and this one's no different. You can bet they'll have every square inch of their premises covered at all times. That's one hurdle.'

Natasha frowned. 'What does that matter? We have the key that opens the storage shutters. As far as anyone knows, we are genuine customers accessing our unit.'

'You're assuming that's the only lock we have to worry about. If I was Papsidera and I knew that unit was soon going to house a small fortune in stolen caviar, I'd want my own padlock on there as an extra precaution. And a good one, too. And if that's the case, we'll need to open the padlock by force, which takes time. Meanwhile every move we make is being captured in high-definition by the security cameras. That's not good. Then, of course, there's the code for the gate. Which we don't have.'

Natasha turned to face him. 'But you have a solution.'

'I *might*.'

'And what does that mean?'

'It means you'll have to dip into your expense account again.'

Twenty-One

68 hours, 43 minutes and counting…

This time Korso rode shotgun while Natasha drove. She was steering them southwest, using her phone's GPS app to guide them toward a branch of Home Depot, off South Georgia Street, where he planned to stock up on certain supplies. They'd left Papsidera's building ten minutes before, returning the keys to a relieved Varma before they left. Night was falling fast, but they still had plenty of time. According to their website, Home Depot stayed open until late, even on weekdays.

That was one of the things Korso liked about the States. No matter what the time, there was always somewhere still open where you could get what you needed.

He checked the dashboard clock again. It hadn't changed. Still 19:17. When they were back in Papsidera's stockroom, Korso had used one of his burner phones to call a number from memory. After leaving a brief voice-mail, giving his name and the number of the phone, he'd hung up. That was always the first step. Now he was waiting for the call back.

'When was the last time you called that number?' Natasha said, stopping at a set of red lights.

'Four months ago.'

'Maybe it's no longer in use.'

Korso had no answer to that. Whether she was right or wrong, nothing he said would make any difference. He continued to wait. The lights turned green. Natasha stepped on the gas and they started moving again.

At 19:18 his phone began chirping. From an unidentified number, of course. He answered it on the second ring.

'Hello, Dog,' he said.

'Hey, K,' M. D. Dog said in a young, cheerful, feminine tone. Four months before, Dog had been a gruff male. Before that, a whiny child of indeterminate gender. The modulator he/she was using apparently had a wide and varied choice. 'Been a while since I last heard your voice.'

'I don't think I've ever heard yours. Your true one, that is.'

'You never know, this could be the real me you're hearing now.'

'Is it?'

'Not even close. Sorry.'

'Just as long as you don't use that kid's voice again. That was disturbing.'

Dog chuckled. It came out as more of a cute giggle thanks to the modulator. 'You've always been one of my favourite clients, Korso. I hope you know that. So, have you got something interesting and profitable for me? I can tell you're currently somewhere in Amarillo, Texas. Seriously, what kind of salvage can you be searching for down there?'

Korso froze, the back of his neck tingling like he'd been hit with static electricity. He'd never told Dog his vocation, or anything about himself for that matter. That was the whole basis of their professional relationship. Other than their respective cover names, neither one of them knew anything about the other.

'Salvage,' he repeated. 'What made you use that word in particular, Dog?'

There was that giggle again. 'Come on, Korso. What do you take me for? You know the kind of information sources at my disposal, or you wouldn't use me. How long did you think it would take for me to figure out what you do for a living? Your name comes up more than a few times in some very exclusive message boards on the deep dark web, I can tell you that. And it's not like your email address is a secret. So relax. You're among friends here.'

Korso doubted that. But he breathed a little easier, knowing Dog was right. He knew his rep had steadily grown over the past few years, and part of that must have been due to feedback on those clandestine message boards he occasionally used. Nobody lived completely off the grid these days, no matter how much they might try. Except possibly Nikolic. So it was inevitable that someone of Dog's talents would have picked up a few nuggets of information about Korso along the way.

'Point taken,' he said. 'But don't get too curious about me, Dog. And that's not a threat. It's for your own good.'

'I hear you. Don't worry, deep down I'm a very sensible person. So how can I be of service today?'

Korso put the phone on speaker so Natasha could hear. 'I need to get in somewhere,' he said, 'and I want you to help clear the way.'

'I'm listening.'

He saw Natasha raise both eyebrows at the sound of Dog's chosen voice.

'It's a self-storage facility, not far from my current location.' He gave Dog the name and the address, and said,

'What I want is twofold. First, I need the access code to get through the entrance gate during closing hours. Then, once we're in, I may need you to cut off the power to that particular property for an hour or so.'

'*We*, as in plural? I thought you preferred to work solo.'

'This is a new me.'

'And you also said *may*. Do you want the power shut off or not?'

'Possibly. It depends on the circumstances. That's all I can tell you without having eyes on site.'

'Which is no answer at all.' Dog gave a dramatic sigh. 'Okay, give me a minute while I check which utility companies service that part of Texas.'

Korso listened to the sound of fingers tapping on silicone. He heard faint humming as well. He couldn't identify the tune. He looked up and saw they were approaching a huge store with the Home Depot logo prominent above the main entrance. Natasha followed a station wagon into the large parking lot and then began looking for a space near the entrance. She found one easily and parked up, then killed the engine.

'Okay,' Dog said, finally, 'it looks like it'll either be Oncor or AEP North. I won't know which until I get into their mainframes and check their customer records for myself. Then it's just a case of temporarily misplacing Ezee's last couple of payments and amending the records so their service is programmed for automatic cut-off at a specified time, then restoring it an hour or two later. Getting into Ezee's own database shouldn't be too hard. So let's assume I can do this for you. What time scale are we talking about here?'

'Any time within the next several hours would be good.'

Silence on the line. Then, 'Very funny. But seriously.'

'I am serious, Dog. What's the problem?'

Dog gave another feminine sigh. 'The problem is this isn't just a few clicks of a button, Korso. I have to gain access to at least one, possibly two, major utility company mainframes, each one with firewalls up the wazoo and God knows what else. And that's not mentioning my hacking into this Ezee place and searching for that very specific access code. Also, while you may be my favourite client, that doesn't mean you're the only one. I've got plenty of others in a queue, all with jobs just as urg—'

'Except your other clients don't pay you a twice-yearly retainer to ensure they jump to the head of that queue. Do they?'

Another long silence. 'Okay, you got me there. But this will still cost.'

'I figured it would. How much?'

'Ten thousand. In US dollars, as per usual. And the sooner it gets deposited into my account, the sooner I get started.'

'Let me put you on hold while I confer.'

'On hold? Hey, wait a second, Korso. Who's paying for this call, anyway?'

'I am, in the long run.'

'Oh… yeah, you got a point there. But make it quick.'

Korso pressed the mute button and turned to Natasha. 'You heard her. Or him. What's your answer?'

She snorted. 'Korso, she sounds like a cheerleader. It is disconcerting.'

'I think that's the whole point. Believe me, it could be worse.'

'Is this all really necessary? If there's no padlock on the shutter, we'll have no need to cut the power at all. And

153

surely we can bypass the entry code easily by waiting for another customer to come along. We pull up behind them like regular customers, then once they key in their code we simply follow them in through the gate.'

'That's great for someone with unlimited time on their hands. But what if nobody chooses to visit their storage unit tonight? What do we do then, wait until tomorrow night to make another try? No, I prefer to reduce variables whenever possible, Natasha. Besides, what's the point of having an expense account if you don't use it?'

She paused a moment, then nodded once. 'Very well.' She pulled her cell phone from the dashboard mount.

'Good. So how long will it take for you to transfer the money to Dog's account?'

'Almost immediately. All I need is the IBAN, or the name of the bank, and the account number.'

'Fine. Tell me when you're ready.'

He waited while she began pressing buttons. Less than a minute later, she looked up at him. 'Ten thousand US dollars, yes? Okay, give me the bank and the number.'

Korso gave her the name of Dog's bank in the Caymans and carefully recited the thirteen-digit combination of numbers, letters and symbols that identified the account. It was one of many he'd long ago committed to memory for just such occasions. Natasha repeated it back to him, and he nodded in confirmation. She pressed more buttons, then said, 'Done.'

He unmuted his own phone, and said, 'The money should be in there.'

'Just checking now.' Then a few moments later, 'Ooh, there it is. Look at those nice fat zeroes. As always, a pleasure doing business with you, Korso. I'll get started on this right away, so all being well I'll text you the access code on this number as soon as I'm ready with everything. Word of warning, though, it won't be for at least another three hours, and that's me being optimistic. Then once you get the code, simply text me back the exact time you want me to shut the power off. If I have a problem with that for whatever reason, I'll let you know ASAP. Copacetic?'

'Fine,' Korso said, and ended the call.

'I hope this person can do everything he or she claims,' Natasha said.

'Dog's never let me down before,' he said, unclasping his seatbelt. 'All right, let's go shopping.'

–

At 22:23, Korso was down to the last few mouthfuls of buttermilk pancakes when his phone chirped and vibrated on the diner's table.

After picking up the supplies at Home Depot, they had driven to a nearby Denny's for dinner. Knowing they might have two or three hours to kill before Dog came through, they'd taken their time ordering while making the most of the bottomless coffee refills.

Korso put down his fork and picked up the phone. He checked the text. 'Four seven four zero three five five,' he said.

'Good.' Natasha looked around for their waitress, then raised her hand in the air and called for the check.

When the waitress came over, Korso watched with mild amusement as Natasha engaged her in conversation while covertly passing her a large denomination note. He remembered the tip Natasha had left for that pregnant waitress in Tijuana. That one had been twice as much as the cost of the meal itself.

As they were walking back to their car, Korso said, 'You seem to have an affinity for waitresses.'

'You can probably guess the reason.'

'Your mother was one? Or still is?'

'Was. She died. Many years ago, so commiserations aren't necessary. But it means I empathise with those like Ann-Marie back there, and understand their day-to-day existence.'

He nodded his head. 'I can appreciate that.'

'Can you, Korso?'

'Sure. I've always felt a kinship with the underdog.'

'So maybe you and I are not so different after all.'

'I never said we were.'

They reached the Chevy. Korso unlocked the doors and got in the driver's side, while Natasha got in the back. Through the windshield, he routinely scanned the mostly empty lot once again for cameras, but saw none. Not that it mattered, really. They weren't planning to commit any felonies here. He took off his jacket, and turned to Natasha in the back.

She was reaching into one of the large orange Home Depot shopping bags they'd stuck in the footwells behind the seats. She pulled out the larger of the two coveralls and handed them to him. Both were navy-blue, which was essentially the same as black at night. She also passed him one of the black cotton baseball caps. No logos on the front, either, which was a bonus.

Natasha began pulling the coveralls over her own clothes. 'This seems like overkill.'

'You won't say that if those security cameras are still on,' Korso said, slipping his foot into the left trouser leg of his own garment. 'Should it be necessary, Dog will do his part, or her part, but there's always the possibility Ezee installed a back-up generator for their CCTV cameras. And if that's the case, any footage of us will now show nothing more than two generic, unrecognisable shapes in coveralls and caps.'

Natasha was rummaging around inside the other bag. 'Most of the equipment in here is obvious. But why do you need duct tape?'

'It's an all-purpose item, useful for all kinds of things. But especially useful for covering up our vehicle's licence plates. I'll take care of that once we're closer to Ezee. I don't want to risk the police pulling us over.' He raised the main zip up to his chest. The garment felt a little tight around the shoulders, but it would do.

'Sardoca was right about you,' she said. 'Always thinking ahead.'

'It's the secret to a long life.' He offered her his hand. 'Knife?'

She pulled out the Dewalt three-inch stainless-steel serrated folding knife, and placed it in his palm. 'Should I even ask what this is for?'

'Emergencies.' He dropped the knife into his chest pocket, zipped it closed. 'Events don't always go to plan.'

Natasha finished zipping herself up, then leaned forward, her head close to his. 'Speaking of plans, you seem to have forgotten something. Two things, in fact.'

He turned to her. 'I never said I was infallible. What have I missed?'

'Assuming we find the crates in that storage unit, how do you intend to transport them out? On your back? At the very least, we'll need a small truck.'

Korso shook his head. 'Assuming they are in there, Sardoca can use his enormous resources to arrange their removal and transportation back to Nikolic in Toronto.

That's not my job. We locate that one special tin of Nikolic's, take it and go. Simple.'

'Really? I thought you would want to supervise the delivery of that caviar personally, especially as you negotiated a twenty-five per cent share of its market value.'

Instead of answering, he just raised an eyebrow at her. They were both intelligent people, and she had to know there was little chance of him ever seeing a penny of that money. Any profit he made on this job would be an unexpected bonus.

To her credit, she didn't bother to argue the point. 'So why are you doing this?'

'I have my reasons. What's number two?'

'We use the access code to get inside. We then text Dog with instructions to turn off the power. But how do we get out again? With no power, the code is useless.'

'That's a good point. Fortunately, I had a talk earlier with the office supervisor, and he assured me you don't need it once you're inside. There's a push pad on the other side of the gate, which you simply press to exit. He told me it's connected up to the main power supply, but it'll still work during a power cut. Fire regulations, apparently.'

'Fire regulations.' She sighed. 'You realise you are a very annoying man.'

Korso adjusted the bill of his cap and said nothing. He didn't want to annoy her further. Not when they had work to do. He checked the dashboard clock: 22:34. Still plenty of time. He hoped.

He inserted the ignition keys and started the engine, then pulled out of the lot and steered them west.

Twenty-Two

65 hours, 15 minutes and counting...

Natasha stopped a few feet from Ezee Self Storage's front gate and set the handbrake, leaving the engine idling.

They'd switched places a few minutes before, when Korso had parked in a side street and spent a couple of minutes taping over the licence plates. He knew he was being overly cautious, since the name on the car rental form was a fake anyway. But nobody ever got caught for being too careful.

To their right was the administration office Korso had seen on the website. It was completely dark inside. A stars and stripes hung from a pole by the main door. On the roof, two arc spotlights illuminated the whole front area. To their left was a row of twelve parking spaces, all vacant.

Next to Natasha was a three-foot-high pole with a combo keypad and intercom on top. She lowered the window, turned to Korso. He recited the number again, and she reached out and pressed 4740355 on the keypad. There was a sharp, metallic *clack* and the gate immediately began to open inward.

Korso smiled to himself. As usual, Dog was worth every penny of his fee. Even more so when it wasn't coming out of his own pocket. Natasha steered them inside.

'Make a slow circuit of the perimeter,' he said, facing front again. 'Let's see whether we have company or not.'

'And if we do?'

'I'll think of something. Let's check first.'

The entire site was awash with light, thanks to eight floodlights strategically placed around the grounds. One floodlight at each corner, with the other four placed more centrally. Natasha crawled along at five miles per hour, while Korso checked each aisle they passed. The first aisle was clear, but he spotted a pick-up with huge wheels at the other end of the second, which was the aisle directly behind theirs, according to the site plan. Korso watched, waiting for signs of movement. He could see two units next to each other that had their shutters open. But he couldn't see anyone moving over there.

'Keep going.'

They passed the third aisle, their aisle. It was empty of vehicles, which was a relief. At the next turn, they saw a small van parked outside one of the garage-sized units on the perimeter. As they passed, Korso spotted a large fat man in a Stetson pushing a huge box along the floor of the unit, then he was gone from sight. Korso also inspected each unit they passed, and noticed the standard Ezee locks were located on the left of each door, near the concrete partition, at about shoulder height. But also attached to the lower right of each door, close to the ground, was a sliding barrel-bolt lock. Some were bare, while others had padlocks on them.

Just as he'd feared.

They made a complete circuit of the site, ending up at the front gate again, but saw no vehicles other than those two.

'Do we wait for them to leave?' Natasha said.

He checked the clock. It was already 22:47. In theory, it might be tactically better to cut the power a few minutes prior to midnight, just before Ezee closed up completely. The place was guaranteed to be deserted then. But his instincts warned him off. He knew that in America, both the police and private security firms regularly patrolled these kinds of places throughout the early hours. And seeing all the floodlights turned off would immediately raise a red flag. Also, there was only one way in and out. Not a good combination.

'We could be waiting all night,' he said, finally. 'Let's make another circuit, see if either of them are close to finishing up. One I can deal with, two might be a problem.'

She nodded and started off again. They passed the pick-up in the second aisle again. Nothing had changed. No sign of movement over there. Both shutters were still open. This time, Korso made a mental note of the rotating security cameras. There seemed to be at least four cameras to each aisle. Sometimes six.

Natasha turned the corner at the end and pressed the brakes. They saw the fat guy's unit was now closed up and he was already in his van.

'This looks promising,' Natasha said.

They watched his rear lights come on, then he pulled away in front of them. He moved off slowly down the aisle, then turned right at the end and disappeared from sight.

'Stop and back up so we can see the front gate,' Korso said.

Natasha put the stick into reverse and backed the car up, stopping when she reached the corner. They both turned their heads to watch the front gate in the distance.

Soon, the van turned and stopped in front of it. The fat guy got out, slapped a palm against the push pad to the left of the gate and got back in the van as the gate opened inward. He drove through it and away. The gate immediately began to close again.

'Good enough,' Korso said. 'Now take us to Papsidera's unit.'

If the gods were smiling on them, he might not need to text Dog at all for the second stage, which would mean Natasha had paid out ten thousand for nothing. But he could live with that. It was only money, and Nikolic had plenty. *Hope for the best, plan for the worst* was a pretty good mantra to live by. It had always worked for him.

Natasha turned into their aisle, and Korso immediately checked the door of the third unit along. Of course, there was a padlock hanging off the sliding latch near the bottom. He sighed as Natasha came to a stop directly in front and killed the engine. Just in case there was any doubt, a large '27' had been painted above the yellow shutters.

'Looks like we'll have to do this the hard way, after all,' he said. He reached back into one of the Home Depot bags, rummaged around for a few seconds and came back holding one of the two heavy-duty LED flashlights in there. He checked the time – 22:53 – and opened the door. 'Wait for me in the car.'

She turned to him, her brows forming a straight line. 'I think I misheard. That sounded almost like an order.'

'More like a recommendation. I don't want to argue with you, Natasha.'

'So it was a suggestion, then. What are you planning to do?'

'Have a talk with the remaining customers. I won't be gone long.'

'Make sure of it. Don't make me worry.'

'Furthest thing from my mind,' he said, and left her.

Once outside, he immediately heard the sound of a bass-heavy car stereo playing generic country rock. Adjusting his cap so the bill was low on his face, he walked to the end of this aisle and turned right. Entering the next aisle, he saw the pick-up was still parked in the same place, with the driver's door ajar. He could also hear laughter and unintelligible conversation coming from the furthest of the open units, number 43.

He walked over to the closest one, number 44, and peered round the opening.

Taking up most of the interior space was a gleaming, bright red Pontiac Firebird Trans Am. A real brute. Korso knew a little about classic muscle cars and if he had to guess, this model had come off the factory line in the early-to-mid Seventies. It almost looked ready to start a fight. Someone next door clearly had an interesting taste in vehicles. At the back of the unit, Korso saw numerous boxes and cartons stacked right up to the ceiling.

He backed off and walked next door to 43. Two large motorcycles took up most of the floor space of this unit. One was completely covered with a greasy bed sheet, while the other was mostly in pieces on the floor. Korso wasn't so knowledgeable about bikes, but it looked like a Japanese make. At the back was a long table with instruments and parts all over it. One man in a tank top, with long, greying hair tied back in a ponytail, was working on something on the table, his back turned. He was about

Korso's height – five-eleven or so – with a bodybuilder's physique, and tattoos covering his shoulders, arms and neck.

His two associates were drinking bottles of beer as they talked to him. A stocky, overweight guy in a baseball cap, sleeveless denim jacket, vest and jeans, was perched on the table, his legs idly swinging as he laughed at something. The other was leaning against the wall, gesturing with his free hand as he said something or other. He was taller and fitter, and wore just a polo shirt, cargo pants cut off at the knees, and huge sneakers. Korso noticed an open cooler on the floor with more bottles inside, and guessed this was probably cheaper than going to a bar. None of the men had noticed him yet.

In a loud voice, he said, 'Evening, fellers.'

All laughter stopped as three heads turned to him in unison. None of them looked happy anymore.

'Who the hell are you?' the heavy guy said, pushing himself off the table.

'Yeah,' his friend in the t-shirt said, 'and what you doing here?'

'Relax, guys,' Korso said, making his manner as amiable and unthreatening as possible. This was also the other reason he'd purchased coveralls for himself and Natasha. They always made the wearer look more official. 'Ezee asked me to come over and give any customers still here a heads up that the electricity's going out at approximately 23:00 hours. They didn't want you thinking it was a power failure or anything and calling the police unnecessarily.'

'This guy.' The tattooed guy snorted as he took a few steps toward Korso. 'Like we'd ever call those shitheels for anything. So tell me, smart-ass, how am I supposed to work in here with no goddamn lights?'

'Just who are you, anyway?' the one in the t-shirt said.

'I'm a friend of Russ's, the guy at the front office. And it's only a temporary power outage. Maybe forty minutes. He said there's some emergency work being done at the AEP North substation that handles this section of Amarillo, and that a whole bunch of businesses around here will be affected. That's why they chose to do it at eleven p.m. on a week night.' He motioned toward the pick-up. 'If you guys want to keep working, you could always back your vehicle up so your headlights are facing this way. It's not perfect, but it should do for half an hour. Either that or you could call it a night and come back tomorrow. Up to you.'

'Un-friggin-believable,' the tattooed guy said.

The heavy guy took a long slug of beer. 'Goddamn power companies, always tryin' to screw you over at every opportunity. Am I right, Jonesy?'

The one in the t-shirt belched. 'Sure as shit.'

Korso thought it best not to out stay his welcome. He waved his flashlight, and said, 'Well, I got to go see if there are any other customers still here, give them the same good news. See you later.'

As he turned back the way he came, he heard one of them say, 'Not if I see you first, asshole.' He kept walking.

Back at the car, Natasha was still in the driver's seat with one hand on the wheel as she watched him approach. He got in and checked the dashboard clock: 22:58.

'Well?' she said. 'How did it go over there?'

'About as expected,' Korso said, grabbing his phone. He gave her a concise summary of the last few minutes while he keyed in three words and sent the text off to

Dog's number. He put the phone back on the dash. 'There. Shouldn't be long now.'

It wasn't.

At exactly 23:00, all the lights in the place went out.

Twenty-Three

65 hours and counting...

'Told you Dog was worth the money.'

With the quarter moon mostly hidden by cloud cover, the only illumination came from the faint light spill of the streetlights on Canyon Drive, and the pick-up's muted headlights across the way. The car stereo was still pumping out country rock at the same volume. To Korso, it sounded like the exact same song as before. He walked back to where he'd seen the nearest security cameras, and saw they were no longer rotating. And no telltale lights, either. Not even red ones. They were completely dead.

So no back-up generator.

Back at the car, Natasha was removing items and tools from the back. He opened the passenger-side rear door and grabbed the other Home Depot bag from the foot-well. From within, he pulled out a pair of safety glasses and put them on. Then the high-tension hack saw with twelve-inch bi-metal blade, which he handed to Natasha over the seat. Finally, he extracted the propane plumber's welding-torch kit. He came round the car and set the box down next to the shutter.

Natasha had already set the cordless, eighteen-volt, LED workbench light on the ground, close to the sliding-bolt latch. She switched on the light and leaned in to inspect the padlock more closely.

'It reads "Stanley",' she practically whispered. 'Is that a good make?'

'Not bad for the price,' he said, crouching down and removing the propane torch from its plastic packaging. 'The hardened steel shackle makes it better than most. Just be glad it's not a Sargent & Greenleaf. They're almost impossible to break down.'

Natasha reached back into the car, pulled out a pair of cloth-lined leather welding gloves and handed them to Korso.

'Thanks,' he said, and put them on.

Picking up the torch, Korso turned the control knob counter-clockwise to open the tank's valve and immediately heard the sound of escaping gas. Pointing the nozzle away from the car, he set the gas flow to its lightest setting and pressed the ignition button. Orange flame erupted from the chrome nozzle. Korso kept rotating the control knob until he got a soft blue flame with an even dispersal. He kept rotating until he was satisfied the blue flame was at its most concentrated.

'And this will cut through the padlock?' Natasha said.

Korso shook his head. 'Not even close. But it will weaken the shackle enough so that once it cools down I can cut through it with the hacksaw.' He paused. 'Theoretically.'

'Theoretically? You mean you haven't done this before?'

'Well, I watched a professional locksmith do it on YouTube. How hard can it be?'

'YouTube,' she muttered, shaking her head. 'Unbelievable.'

He allowed himself a small grin of satisfaction. He had done this twice before, in fact, but saw no reason to tell her that. The more he was able to keep Natasha off balance about him, the better his chances of survival in the long term.

Korso noticed Natasha had already placed the seven-inch straight-jaw locking pliers next to the lamp. He picked them up, clamped the bottom of the padlock in their steel jaws, and squeezed tight. He locked the pliers at that position, then brought the torch close to the padlock. He aimed the intense blue flame at the shackle, just at the part where it began to curve into a semi-circle. He got comfortable and let the flame do its work.

'How long?' Natasha said.

'Fifteen minutes, minimum. The longer, the better, really.'

'Is that how long the man on the YouTube video took?' Her tone was acid.

'Just watch my back. And take a look around, maybe check on those guys in the next aisle. I don't want anyone over there getting curious.'

She didn't answer. But after a few moments, she turned and moved away until she was gone from sight.

Korso kept both hands steady as the torch slowly heated up the steel, gradually altering the hardened metal's chemical composition so it would become brittle and weak enough to be cut through manually. As he worked, he thought about Natasha. His opinion hadn't changed much from their first meeting. He still found himself liking his accomplice, without ever trusting her, of course. But he kind of enjoyed baiting her too. She was so intense all the time, he found it hard to stop himself.

But the baiting also served a practical purpose. When people became rattled and discomposed, they often revealed parts of themselves that would otherwise have remained hidden. That was especially true of those who were permanently wound up tight, like Natasha. And if she were to occasionally let slip something that could prove useful to him, so much the better. Korso was happy to take advantage of any edge he could get.

About five minutes had passed when he noticed a faint orange glow on the shackle as the steel began to heat up. About another ten minutes, more or less.

As Korso watched the hypnotic flame, he began to frown. He thought he'd heard something over the soft hiss of the flame. He was just about to turn his head to look when something cold and metallic momentarily touched the back of his neck.

He froze.

'That's right, asshole,' the one called Jonesy said from behind him. 'You even think of movin', I'll take your head off with one squeeze of this trigger.'

Twenty-Four

64 hours, 53 minutes and counting...

Korso first instinct was to play dumb. It worked more often than not. 'Hey,' he said, 'what is this? What the hell's going on?'

'You tell me, man. That little fairy tale you gave us back there smelled all kinds of wrong, so I told the guys we should stick around and check things out for ourselves. Looks like we made the right choice, don't it?'

'Look,' Korso said, 'I don't know what this is about, but you've got it all backward.' As he talked, he made his right hand begin to shake. At the same time, he gently placed the small propane canister on the ground, the torch still going at full flow.

'Hey, asshole,' Jonesy said. 'I didn't tell you to stop. Pick up that torch and get back to work.'

'Sorry, but having a gun pointed at my head makes me nervous.' Still crouching, Korso dropped the pliers and raised both hands as he turned his head. Jonesy was standing about two feet away, partially leaning against the trunk, with a snub-nosed .22 revolver aimed at Korso. 'Look, if it's money you want, there's some in my wallet. It's in the car.'

Jonesy snorted. 'Shit, don't give me that. You cut the power, then warn us off calling the cops, which means whatever's in that unit is worth a whole lot more than a few measly bucks in your wallet. So maybe you should just tell me what's in there.'

Korso decided the dumb act was no longer working. 'I don't know exactly,' he said. 'I mean, not for sure. The guy paying us didn't give us any details. Just that he'd arrange a power cut at eleven o'clock sharp, and we were to break in to unit twenty-seven and grab two boxes with certain numbers printed on them, and take them back with us. He didn't tell us what was inside, and we didn't ask.'

'That ain't what your girlfriend said. She told us there's a shitload of coke in there. You sayin' she's a liar?'

Korso shook his head, thinking fast. 'We both talked about it on the drive over and decided that's what it had to be, since the guy paying us has been known to sell coke before. But neither of us knows for sure. Why would he tell us if he didn't have to?' Korso realised that at some point the car stereo had been turned off. Other than the sounds of distant traffic, the whole site was quiet. 'Hey, what have you done with my girlfriend? Where is she?'

'Oh, don't you worry about that. My buds are takin' real good care of her. She calmed down some once we relieved her of that big ol' .45, and she'll stay fine and healthy long as you keep working on that lock. Otherwise, I'll put one in you and finish it myself, then when I'm done, your little bitch'll finally get the lovin' she's always dreamed about.'

So by the sounds of it Natasha was playing the mouse routine again. Overconfidence in their own cleverness would make the other two careless, and she'd hopefully exploit that to the full. Knowing she could take care of herself, Korso put her out of his mind and looked at Jonesy. The hand holding the gun remained steady, as though this wasn't the first time he'd done this kind of thing. And he also had enough smarts to leave a couple of feet of space between them, so Korso couldn't spring a surprise attack. But maybe there was another way, although he'd need some kind of distraction.

Maybe he could force one.

'Jonesy, isn't it?' he said. 'You sure you can shoot a man in the back? In cold blood?'

'Damn right. Wouldn't be the first time I had to put someone down and then clean up the mess afterwards.' He pulled back the hammer of his .22. 'You wanna try me?'

'No, I believe you. But what I didn't tell you is that there's an alarm on the other side of this door, activated by a tripwire. The moment the shutter's raised more than a few inches, the alarm starts its countdown and you've got fifteen seconds to enter a four-digit code that only I know. Enter the wrong code and *boom*, the whole unit goes up in smoke.'

'Bullshit,' Jonesy said, curling his lip. 'You're lyin'. There ain't no code.'

'Up to you. I'm not about to argue.' Korso peeled off his right glove, wiped the back of his hand across his brow. 'But if you kill me, you'll never get ins—'

There was a sudden *crack* and something fizzed on the ground to his left. Korso froze. That was too damn close.

'That's the only warning shot you get,' Jonesy said. 'Alarm or not, you get back to work or the next one's in the back of your head. I ain't gonna tell you again.'

'Okay, okay,' Korso said. 'Take it easy, all right? I'll do whatever you want, but just point that thing away from me. I need a steady hand to burn through the shackle, and you shooting at me isn't exactly calm—'

'What the hell was that?' a voice called out.

The car was in the way, so Korso couldn't see the speaker. It sounded like the heavy guy's voice, but it didn't matter. This was exactly what he'd been hoping for.

'Just makin' a point,' Jonesy called out. 'Givin' our boy a little incentive is all. Nothin' to worry about.'

While they were talking, Korso started moving, knowing that Jonesy's attention was now split two ways. Korso's right side was away from Jonesy, so with one eye on his assailant, he bent his right elbow until his lower arm was close to his chest. Then he used his hand to unzip the chest pocket on his coveralls.

'Put one in his foot next time he gets smart,' the other one called out.

'Ha, you know it, Sy.' Korso froze as Jonesy briefly glanced his way. Then he turned back to his friend, and said, 'How's my girl doin' over there?'

Barely moving his arm at all, Korso reached into the pocket and grabbed the folding knife between thumb and index finger. He slowly pulled it out. He was glad now he'd gone for this particular model. It was one of those with a protruding tab, called a flipper, at the base of the blade, allowing a fast one-handed opening with a single press of the index finger. That would make all the difference when the time came.

'Too early to tell, man,' Sy said. 'Ask me again in a few minutes.'

'Just don't bust up her face, okay? I know what you're like. That piece in Vegas was in hospital for months after you were done with her.'

Still moving as little as possible, Korso lowered his arm and carefully slipped the knife, still folded, into the hip pocket of his coveralls. Where it would be easier to get to.

Sy gave a nasty laugh and said something Korso didn't catch. Then Korso sensed movement behind him, followed by the cold touch of the gun barrel against the back of his neck. But just for a moment. Jonesy quickly backed up, out of range.

'I told you to pick that torch up,' he said. 'Get your ass back to work. Right now.'

'Okay, okay,' Korso said, turning back to the door.

Since Jonesy's attention was back on him again, he had to assume this Sy had left them alone. Natasha was clearly occupying all his thoughts, which was fine by him. Korso wouldn't get a better opportunity. As he picked up the pliers with his left hand, he let his right hand drop to his hip.

'What did you mean about the woman in Vegas?' he said, to get Jonesy talking again. 'What happened to her?'

'Nothin'. Just a few cuts and bruises is all. She was right as rain in no time. You just forget all about her and…'

But Korso wasn't listening. While Jonesy talked, Korso inserted his hand into his pocket and grabbed the knife. With his index finger ready on the flipper, he flexed his thigh muscles and dived to his left, away from the light and the propane torch. At the same time, he pulled out the knife and pressed the flipper to release the blade, turning his body as he landed. He kept rolling, then rose to a crouch in a single fluid motion and saw Jonesy's head was still turning toward his new position, the hand holding the gun following close behind.

Jonesy was now a silhouette in front of the only available light. The perfect target.

In less than a second, Korso mentally picked a spot, aiming low. In a single motion, he grasped the tip of the blade in a pinch-grip, and with his wrist bent slightly, swung his forearm forward until his arm was straight out in front, and released the knife.

It flew from his hand and hit the target.

Jonesy grunted something and began to fall without even getting a shot off. Korso was already sprinting, and got to him before he hit the ground. Snaking his left arm round the man's neck in a tight chokehold, Korso used his other hand to grab the .22 by the barrel and quickly tore it from the man's grip. Jonesy was still trying to find his footing while making incoherent choking sounds. Korso dropped the gun and used his right hand to clasp his left.

So far, so silent. Let it stay that way.

Korso quickly increased the pressure by clasping his hands together, squeezing the carotid arteries in Jonesy's neck tightly, completely blocking the airways and restricting all blood flow to the brain. As the seconds passed, the man's struggling steadily became weaker and weaker until he was barely moving at all. After ten more seconds he lost consciousness completely, and Korso dropped his now limp body to the ground.

Picking up the .22, Korso saw it was a Taurus with an eight-shot cylinder and rubber grips. Not a bad little gun. He looked over the unconscious man and saw the blade had entered his upper left leg, just below the thigh. He was impressed. It was pretty much the exact location he'd been aiming for. Leaving the knife where it was for now, he went back to the car and grabbed the duct tape from one of the bags, and the Ruger from his jacket pocket.

Returning to Jonesy, he placed two long strips of tape over the man's mouth and used a lot more to secure his hands and arms behind his back. Pulling the knife from his thigh, he used Jonesy's shirt to wipe the blood off and put it back in his pocket, then wrapped more duct tape tightly around the leg wound. Not exactly a military-approved field dressing, but it was the best he was going to get, and more than he deserved. Korso then went round and switched off the propane torch.

Finally, a quick check of the .22 told him it still held seven rounds, while the Ruger still had a full magazine.

One down. Now for the other two.

Twenty-Five

64 hours, 46 minutes and counting…

Korso saw they had positioned the pick-up as he'd suggested. It was parked directly in front of 43, almost blocking the entrance with maybe a couple of feet to spare. Both headlights, set on full beams, illuminated the unit's interior.

He stood next to the Pontiac in 44, listening. He could hear male laughter coming from next door, along with some indistinct chatter. What he couldn't hear was Natasha screaming in pain. But then she wasn't exactly the screaming type.

Careful to stay out of the light, Korso poked part of his head round the wall and glanced inside the next unit.

The protective sheet had been removed from the other Japanese superbike. Natasha, head lowered and with her back to him, was standing at the rear of the bike, facing one of her two captors at the worktable. Korso couldn't see her face. The black cap was gone, but she was still wearing the coveralls. Her back was pressed hard against the bike's rear cowl with both wrists tied behind her with what looked like thin mountaineering rope, which was in turn connected to a metal loop on the bike's sub-frame. Meaning she couldn't sit down, or even move more than a few centimetres. And that rear cowl was no doubt digging into her spine every time she took a breath.

The bodybuilder was smiling as he leaned back against the worktable, casually aiming Natasha's own Sig at her. It looked like a toy in his huge fist. The heavy guy, Sy, stood just to the right of Natasha, well out of the line of fire. He was also grinning.

Without warning, he swung his left arm round in a flash until his fist connected hard with Natasha's right temple. Her head swung round with the impact, and a thin sliver of blood spurted from her mouth.

Natasha didn't make a sound. Not even a grunt of pain. She spat a thick globule of blood on the floor, sniffed, then raised her head again.

'What's that, bitch?' Sy said, looking into her face, clearly enjoying himself. 'Cat got your tongue? Not so stuck up now, are ya?' He turned back to his buddy. 'Hey, Bobby, you think she understands things are gonna get worse before they get better? Or maybe she really is as dumb as she looks. What do ya think?'

'I think you better go easy, Sy,' Bobby said, still waving the gun around. 'Jonesy ain't gonna be happy if you turn her face into hamburger before he gets his turn.'

'Screw Jonesy. Once we get that coke, he ain't gonna care one way or the other. 'Sides, I'm just tenderisin' her for him. Hey, wanna see something? Check this out.' Sy clenched his right fist and slowly began to pull his arm back again.

Stepping into the light, Korso aimed the Taurus at a point on Bobby's body and squeezed the trigger. The shot echoed loudly in the confined space. Bobby screamed and grabbed his upper right arm with his left hand, while the Sig clattered to the floor. Korso stepped in front of the pick-up, still aiming the Taurus at Bobby in case he grew some balls in the next few seconds. In his other hand he held the Ruger. He aimed it at Sy's head.

Sy stood staring at the gun, open-mouthed, wide-eyed, like he'd just woken from a dream. He looked ready to bolt or cry at the slightest prompting.

'On the floor,' Korso said. 'Face down. Do it now or I put one in your kneecap.'

Sy gulped once, then dropped to the floor like a sack of rocks. He lay flat on his stomach, arms out in front of him. 'Hey, don't shoot, man. Please. We were just havin' some fun, okay?'

'Sure, I understand.'

He glanced at Bobby, who was rocking back and forth and groaning, still clutching his right biceps with his free hand. Blood was seeping through his thick fingers.

Korso stepped over to Sy and casually kicked him in the left ear. Sy cried out in pain and hunched up as he pressed a hand against the damaged ear. He wouldn't hear right for days, maybe weeks. Out the corner of his eye, he saw Natasha silently watching him. He picked the Sig up from the floor and stood in front of the bodybuilder.

'Son of a *bitch*,' Bobby moaned, looking at all the blood seeping from his wound. He glared up at Korso. 'You shot me. *You shot me.*'

'And that was only a little .22,' Korso said. He showed him the Sig. 'Move and I'll ruin your other arm with this. You understand?' When Bobby didn't reply, Korso kicked him hard in the shin. 'I asked you a question.'

'*Yeah*, yeah, I understand,' Bobby said, wincing from the pain. 'Jesus *Christ.*'

Korso turned to Natasha. She had a red bruise on the left side of her face, near the eye, which was bloodshot.

Other than some oil and grease marks made by Sy's hands, he could see no other visible wounds. Her coverall was unzipped down to the waist, revealing her day clothes underneath. But no naked flesh. It hadn't reached that stage yet.

He pulled the knife from his pocket, flipped it open. As he cut her bonds, he said, 'How are things with you?'

'Fine, thank you.' She turned her head to the right and spat out more blood. This time the globule landed on Sy's head, who didn't even notice. 'I could have handled these two myself, Korso. I didn't need your help.'

He finally cut through the last of the rope. 'I know. But time's against us. I couldn't wait.'

She brought her arms round and gently rubbed her wrists as she studied him. 'Just as long as we understand each other.'

He handed her the Sig. 'Here, you dropped this.'

'Careless of me.' She checked the magazine, then rammed it home and racked the slide. 'And the other one?'

'Taken care of. I'll go get him now.'

Korso left her and jogged back to 27, where Jonesy was still in the same prone position he'd left him in, still out for the count. Korso jogged to the end of the aisle to make a check of the front gate, but saw no vehicles waiting to get in. Their luck was still holding, but it wouldn't last forever. He went back to 27, grabbed Jonesy by the collar of his polo shirt and began dragging him to 43. Briefly, he heard screams coming from that direction, but they quickly stopped.

Hauling a dead weight wasn't exactly light work. It took Korso another minute to get him back to what remained of his friends. Dropping Jonesy in front of the pick-up, he took a moment to get his breath back. He heard a muffled thumping sound and saw Natasha at the rear of the room, silently kicking Bobby with great force. He was lying on his back, his face already a bloody mess. He wasn't making a sound, so must have passed out from the pain.

Korso also noticed Sy was now huddled into a foetal position, either unconscious or dead. Either way, he wasn't moving. Also, his outstretched left hand looked less like a human appendage than a flesh-coloured rubber glove dipped in ketchup. All five fingers were broken and the man's palm looked as though Natasha had stamped on it repeatedly. And Korso had only been gone a few minutes. She sure didn't waste time.

She noticed him then, and stopped what she was doing and came over. Beads of sweat peppered her forehead, and she seemed a little out of breath. There was also blood on her hands and knuckles.

'You were right before,' she said, wiping her brow with the back of her hand, at the same time smearing blood onto it. 'A bullet is not always the best answer. Sometimes the simplest methods are far more satisfying.'

'That's not exactly what I meant,' Korso said.

She looked down at Jonesy on the floor. 'What about this one? He also lives?'

'As far as I'm aware. It's just a leg wound.' He leant down and dragged Jonesy into the centre of the room next to Sy, whom he noticed was still breathing after all. He shook his head. When Sy eventually woke up, he'd probably wish he were dead. Still, it was hard to feel sorry for the guy. 'Remind me to never get on your bad side.'

'You never will.'

He frowned. That was either a compliment or a veiled threat. 'I'm not sure how I should take that.'

'Take it however you wish,' she said, giving him that half-smile of hers.

Korso shrugged. 'Okay, let's close up and get back to what we came here for.'

'No.' Her expression grew serious again. 'I've not yet found the padlock or the keys to lock these three in.'

'Just pull the outer sliding latches across. That way they're stuck inside until someone lets them out eight hours from now, and we'll be long gone. Why complicate things?'

'Because they deserve worse.'

'And I deserve to live my life without outside interference. But we don't always get what we want, do we? Now, it's been a long day and it's not over yet, so let's go.'

She stood there for a moment, staring at him. Then she saw her black cap on the floor, picked it up and joined him.

Twenty-Six

64 hours, 14 minutes and counting...

Korso finally cut through the shackle of the padlock. It had taken him a little longer than anticipated. Placing the hacksaw on the ground, he slipped the remains of the padlock through the hasp, then pulled the door's sliding latch across. He stood up, inserted Papsidera's Yale key into the side lock halfway up and turned it clockwise. It gave easily.

Natasha was standing to his right, just behind the light. 'It seems you did know what you were doing, after all.'

'Hold the applause for now,' he said. 'Let's see what we've got first.'

They each crouched down at the same time, inserted their fingers under the bottom bar and in unison, raised the shutter door all the way to the top.

Natasha picked up the static light and held it up in front of her, partially illuminating the interior. Korso judged the size of the unit to be about ten feet wide by thirty feet deep. There were no crates, of course. Instead, the place was packed with large, heavy-duty, corrugated cardboard boxes. These boxes were all stacked against the left wall in two rows that ran down the length of the unit. Stacked together at the far end were a few more boxes of various sizes, although these looked a lot older and shabbier.

To Korso, it felt wrong. The ones on the left all looked new, but the volume didn't look nearly enough to contain the contents of six large shipping crates. But what did he know? He took the folding knife from his pocket and handed it to Natasha.

'It's your show,' he said.

She stepped over to the nearest container and placed the lamp on the one behind it. She opened the knife, looked at the box, and then slowly closed the knife again. She looked up and down the room, frowning.

'What is it?' Korso said, joining her.

She waved a hand. 'None of these boxes are sealed. Look.'

Korso saw she was right. The top flaps of the new boxes were all free of wrapping tape. Natasha opened the one in front of her and they both looked inside. And, of course, the box was empty. Completely empty.

'*La naiba*,' she said, reverting to her mother tongue.

'My thoughts exactly.' Korso had a good idea what the word meant. He opened a few other boxes, but they were all the same. Just empty containers waiting to be filled.

'All that effort. For this.' Natasha let out a long sigh. 'Just another dead end.'

Korso said nothing. There wasn't much he could say. They seemed to be at another impasse. But there had to be another approach to the problem. Had to be. There always was. It just needed a mental readjustment...

A phone began to ring.

He and Natasha looked at each other. It was one of those retro tones, similar to that of an old rotary phone, but muffled.

'Not mine,' she said.

It couldn't be his burner as he'd already destroyed the SIM card. Anyway, it sounded like it was coming from the rear of the storage unit.

Korso grabbed the lamp and made his way down to the boxes at the end. As he did so, the ringtone became louder. He placed the lamp on the floor and Natasha started hefting the older cartons out of the way, seeking the source of the noise. She'd made a space between two of the smaller boxes when they saw the cell phone on the floor next to the rear wall. It was a cheap Nokia burner, similar to Korso's, with a charger that was connected to a power socket in the wall. The screen flashed in time with the ringtone. The caller was *Anonymous*.

Natasha picked it up. Raising an eyebrow at Korso, she removed the charger from the phone. She pressed the green button, then pressed the loudspeaker option that immediately appeared at the bottom of the screen.

They each waited for the caller to speak. All they heard was white noise.

After a few more seconds of silence, a male voice said, 'Nobody going to say anything? Admit it, you both must be pretty curious by now.'

Korso turned to Natasha, inviting her to speak first. She pursed her lips and gave a single shake of her head.

'You like to watch,' Korso said, turning back to the phone. 'Does that mean you're watching us right now?'

There was a chuckle at the other end. 'Not this time, friend. All I did was set a little electronic tripwire on that shutter door to alert me should anyone try to get inside, which you've clearly succeeded in doing. Good thing I thought ahead and left this cell, wasn't it? I can't see you this time, but you can only be the same two who showed up at the house in Fort Worth.'

'Only for you to call the police on us. That wasn't friendly.'

'What did you expect? You were breaking and entering. Not that the cops seemed to trouble you all that much. So what do I call you?'

'You mean you don't know?'

'Would I ask if I did?'

Korso pondered a moment. 'I'm Jack,' he said. 'She's Jill.'

'Very droll. So, Jill, you not speaking to me?'

Pulling a stick of gum from her pocket, Natasha gave another quick shake of her head as she unwrapped it. She stuck the gum in her mouth, started chewing.

'Apparently not,' Korso said. 'So what do we call you? We know it's not Kujan. Is it Adamson? Or maybe Papsidera? Or are they both buried deep in a quarry somewhere?'

Another chuckle. 'Let's see now. You can call me... Cain. With a C, like in the Bible. Yeah, I like that. Cain.'

Natasha had unwrapped another stick of gum, which she now offered to Korso. He took it, folded it in half. 'Okay, Cain, let's get down to it. It seems you've got something we want.'

'Maybe I do, maybe I don't. I assume we're talking about a certain shipment that went missing a few weeks back?'

'What else.'

'And look at the two of you there, going to all this effort and trouble just to recover it. Why is that, I wonder?'

'I assume that's a rhetorical question. You know the kind of money that shipment's worth on the open market, so don't act all surprised that the owners hired a couple of tracers to find out what happened to it. You must have expected someone like us, or else why hide the spy camera at Adamson's place, or arrange the alarm system here?' Hoping to turn the conversation away from that line of questioning, he said, 'Tell me, Cain, you were the man Papsidera called from Kujan's apartment in Tijuana, right? The man with the plan.'

'If you say so.'

'I'm asking you.'

'And that answer's the best you'll get from me. Why should I fill in the blanks for you? If I wanted to know who gave you that information, would you tell me?'

'There's no reason not to. We located a bar girl who was present in the room at the time, that's all. She witnessed the call, but had no idea what it signified. Your turn.'

'Okay. It was me at the other end. Satisfied?'

'Not even close. So why *are* you calling us?'

'That's the real question right there, isn't it? And the answer's simple. I want to deal.'

Korso and Natasha looked at each other. He stuck the gum in his mouth. 'After all the time and effort you put into taking the shipment in the first place? Why?'

'Well, for one thing I heard some troublesome rumours about that particular cargo. Long after it went missing, of course. But the main rumour I heard, the one that concerns me, is about the possible identity of the cargo's original owner. Care to shed a little light on that for me? Because that information could make all the difference to the outcome of this discussion.'

Korso looked at Natasha. She nodded, at the same time holding her thumb and index finger close together.

'I can give you an initial,' he said. 'Saying any more over an open line would be unwise on a number of levels. But that initial should be enough.'

'That's not exactly what I wanted to hear. Okay, what's the initial?'

'N.'

'Shit.' There was a sigh at the other end. 'So it wasn't a rumour then. He actually exists.'

'When it suits him.'

'And he's really as bad as the stories make out?'

'Worse.'

Another sigh. 'Now maybe you understand why I'm willing to negotiate. Having someone like that on my ass isn't exactly what I bargained for when I got invited into this project, know what I mean?'

'I get the general idea. But let's deal with the elephant in the room first. Am I to assume you're currently in possession of the cargo in question? Because that's kind of a deal-breaker.'

'Well, I know where it's being kept, let's put it that way.'

'But it's in a place where you can gain immediate access to it.'

'Maybe not immediate, but at very short notice.'

Natasha twirled her finger, indicating Korso should get to the meat of it. Ignoring her, he said, 'So what's the story, Cain? Are you planning to simply give back everything you took, no questions asked? Is that it?'

'Not quite. I have to make a living, after all, so it's only fair I get paid at least a token amount for the return of the items. For instance, ten per cent of the market value would be more than enough for me.'

'I can see how it would be, especially now you've disposed of your partners.'

'What can I say? Loose lips, etcetera. But I'd say five hundred grand is more than fair in this situation, wouldn't you? Especially as I'm your only lead to the main prize.

So, Jack and Jill, just to clarify things, that's five hundred thousand dollars, in cash. Are you interested in my terms, or should I just hang up right now?'

Natasha gave a vigorous nod of her head.

'We're interested,' Korso said. 'Just tell us the next step.'

'The next step is for you to come to me. I'll leave a sample of the cargo in a specified spot to prove I'm everything I say I am. Once you're satisfied, we can go on from there. Sound good?'

'Where?'

'Colorado, a little place called Bilchner. It's a genuine, modern ghost town. You'll know what I mean when you get there. You'll love it.'

'I doubt that.'

Natasha touched Korso's arm and mimed steering a wheel. He nodded and motioned for her to give him her smartphone. She passed it over and he opened the browser and typed Bilchner, Colorado into Google.

'You still there, Jack?'

'I'm here. Just checking where this Bilchner is.'

He saw the town was located in the southwestern quadrant of Colorado, meaning they'd have to drive west through New Mexico on the I-40W, then at Albuquerque head north on US-550. According to Google Maps it would take around nine hours, more or less. Travelling by air would get them there in a fraction of that time, but they'd be unarmed. Making the decision a no-brainer. 'I've got the location now, so give us a time to meet. Bear in mind we'll be driving to you, and we'll also need a few hours' shut-eye first.'

'I can appreciate that. We all need our beauty sleep. How does tomorrow at three sound?'

'Reasonable.'

'That's fine. Oh, and you better take that phone I left as well, since that'll be our primary means of contact. At some point during the morning, I'll text you the sample's specific location and we can go from there. I'll be seeing you guys tomorrow.'

There was a faint click as Cain ended the call. Korso picked up the cell and turned it off so they couldn't be tracked. Any text messages from Cain would show up once it was turned on again.

'It looks like we're back in business,' Natasha said.

'Why the silent treatment with Cain?'

'Elementary survival tactics. The less the enemy knows about us, the better. Of course, you know this meeting tomorrow will be a trap.'

'I'd expect nothing less,' Korso said. 'Come on, let's go find a motel to rest up for a few hours. We've a long drive ahead of us in the morning.'

Twenty-Seven

63 hours, 53 minutes and counting...

Korso found them a place just off the I-40 called the Welcome Inn. It was an unremarkable, three-storey building shaped like a fat L from above, nestling between a huge motorcycle dealership on one side and an even bigger furniture warehouse on the other. From the south came the constant sound of heavy traffic travelling along the interstate.

He turned into the motel's half-empty lot and stopped the car just outside the main office. Through the window, he saw a young Indian guy with a goatee sitting at the front desk, working on his computer. Or more likely playing a video game.

'I'll get us rooms,' Natasha said, and got out of the car.

Korso said nothing. He just leaned his head back against the headrest, shutting his eyes for a moment. Other than an hour or so on the short plane trip from Tijuana, the last time he'd slept longer than a few minutes had been on the flight from Bermuda, over twenty-four hours previously. And that had only been for four or five hours. He was used to operating with little to no sleep, but it wasn't something he liked doing too often. The body needed a certain amount of rest each twenty-four-hour cycle. If it didn't get it, the mind started making mistakes.

And his current situation, where everyone was a potential threat, meant any minor error he made could turn into a life-threatening one within seconds. He couldn't allow that to happen. He needed rest. Just five hours would make all the difference. Four, even.

He yawned.

The sound of the door opening yanked him back to full consciousness. Natasha got in and shut the door.

'We're on the other side of the motel,' she said, 'away from the interstate.'

Korso nodded and drove them round to the rear parking lot. There were only five other vehicles parked on this side. He found an empty spot midway down and killed the engine.

Grabbing his bag from the back seat, he yawned again as he got out and locked the vehicle. He joined Natasha by the stairs, and followed her up to the second-floor landing where she came to a stop outside room 54. She inserted a key card into the slot and the door clicked open.

'Is this yours or mine?' he asked.

She said nothing, just opened the door wide and stepped inside.

Interesting. All of a sudden Korso found himself wide awake. He paused for a moment, then followed her into the room. Closing the door behind him, he switched on the lights and watched Natasha drop her overnight bag on the bed nearest the window.

She came over and took his bag and set it down next to hers on the same bed. Korso didn't miss the significance of the action. She looked over at him, that half-smile never looking more inviting than it did at this moment.

'You told me before that I was attractive,' she said.

'I did. You are.'

'So these sleeping arrangements are agreeable to you?'

'They couldn't be more agreeable.'

'Good.' Her smile widened as she reached out her hand to him. 'I want a long hot shower, Korso. I have other people's blood on me, and I will need help washing it all off.'

—

'Not that I'm complaining,' Korso said, later, 'but that kind of came out of left field.'

'Left field?' Natalie raised her head from his chest. With her body still pressed close to his, he could feel her heartbeat. 'What does this mean?'

'It's an American baseball term. It means unexpected.'

'Oh, I see. Yes. But I think it would be in your best interests not to make this more than it is. Or was.'

'And what was this, exactly?'

'A simple biological function between two consenting adults. Very pleasurable, I admit. But nothing more than that.'

Korso smiled in the darkness. She was right. From the shower to the bed, then back to the shower again, it had been very enjoyable. Not to mention draining. 'I'm not about to ask for your hand, if that's what worries you.'

'I would hope not.'

'But I am curious. What caused the change of heart?'

'I'm not sure.' She paused for a moment. 'Maybe it was that brief exchange in that storage place, after you shot the steroid man.'

Korso frowned, trying to remember, but he couldn't think of anything that stood out. 'Really? What did I say?'

'It's more what you left out. When I said I didn't need your help, you could have made me feel very foolish with a single well-chosen comment. But you chose to do the exact opposite instead.'

'It's in my nature to avoid the obvious.' He ran his index finger along the faint scar that trailed down the side of her face.

'You like this?' she said, pressing his hand against the scar. 'You kissed it many times over the past hour.'

'One of my little eccentricities, I guess. But, yes, it's definitely one of your more attractive features. I can't be the first man who's said that to you.'

'You're not. One man has… well, he told me it adds character to my face. He also offered to pay for cosmetic surgery if I wanted it removed. But I told him no. It's a part of me, and I've warmed to it over time. It's also a good reminder that we learn from our mistakes.'

'If we've got any sense, we do. It looks old. A memento from your childhood?'

She just stared at him, slowly rubbing the back of his hand along her temple. He thought she was going to ignore the question entirely, but she finally said, 'That depends on your definition of childhood. I was seventeen, so still a child in many ways. I was in basic training, and one of my instructors wanted me very badly. His specialty was hand-to-hand combat. He knew all the ways to kill a person, all the techniques. A walking encyclopedia of death. Tae kwon do, judo, karate, jiu jitsu, boxing, close-quarters knife fighting, and many others. He taught me much, but he was arrogant… and a sadist. He enjoyed suffering, more so when he was the cause of it. He was tough. As tough as they come.'

She rested her chin on his chest, looking at nothing. 'I was young and attractive, and he was not the first NCO to suggest my training would go a lot easier if I were to share a bed with him on a regular basis. Except in his case it was more like an order than a suggestion.'

'Let me guess. You refused, and he took your rejection badly.'

'Outwardly, no. For a few weeks, he trained my class and me the same as always. But soon he began to target me for demonstrations. After a while it was always me he chose. Never anyone else. One time, when he was teaching the class on the use of improvised weapons, I dared to challenge him on his constant victimisation of me in front of an audience.' She ran a finger down the scar. 'This was the result.'

'What did he use to cause that?'

'That day he was training us on the use of barbed wire as an offensive weapon.'

Korso winced. 'Jesus.'

She smiled. 'I admit I could have chosen a better moment.'

'What happened afterwards?'

'Afterwards? I was taken to the barracks infirmary where I was operated on by a surgeon who looked even younger than me. I spent a month recuperating, then when I was discharged I resumed my basic training. The sergeant responsible for my disfigurement received a verbal warning from his commanding officer, then resumed his duties as per usual. Nothing changed, except he no longer targeted me for demonstrations.'

Korso stared at the ceiling, at the odd, distorted patterns caused by the lights from the parking area outside. He listened to the faint sounds of traffic coming from the interstate. He could also make out a siren somewhere off in the distance.

'How long did it take you?'

'For what?'

'You don't strike me as the type to turn the other cheek, so how long before you paid him back?'

'Three years. Closer to four, actually. I was on a week's furlough and I travelled across the country under an assumed name and paid him a visit one night. He was still at the same barracks. I knew he liked to frequent a certain bar on Fridays, where the women were happy to head out to the back with a man for a few extra drinks, so late that night I waited at the delivery entrance at the rear. In the early hours of the morning, he finally came out the back door with a woman who was just as drunk as he was. I waited for them to get their business over with. It took a long time. When she finally went back inside, he went to one of the dumpsters and urinated against it. I wore dark coveralls and a black ski mask, so he never saw me coming. I overpowered him very easily. After that, things became… messy.'

Korso could imagine. Although he preferred not to. 'Was he still breathing at the end of it?'

'Just barely. He survived, although he must wish I'd finished him. Without going into specifics, I made sure he was no longer the whole man he used to be.'

'I wish I hadn't brought it up now.'

'Yes, it has kind of ruined the mood. But this is all ancient history and is not typical of me. As a rule, I tend not to dwell on the past. What about you?'

'I don't think about it at all.'

'Yes, I've noticed you never speak of your own history. Why is that?'

'There's no point. Any mistakes I made back then I've already filed away and learned from. The rest is just white noise. Only today and tomorrow matter.' He didn't bother adding that the less anyone knew about him, the better in the long run. Present company included. Instead, he closed his eyes and said, 'Let's get some sleep.'

Ignoring him, she ran her fingers down his neck and across his collarbone, then pulled lazily at the small hairs on his chest. It all felt very nice, and it had been a while since he could say that. The seconds passed, and he could feel himself beginning to drift when she said, 'There's an old legend circulating about you, Korso. Or Jara, as you were called back then. You must know the one. It concerns somebody or something called the Nicaraguan. You're familiar with this?'

He said nothing, just continued to let himself drift, hoping she'd get the hint. They had just five hours before the alarm call from reception at six, and he wanted to make the best use of that time by sleeping through it.

'Except not really a legend,' she said, not taking the hint at all, 'just fragments and pieces, really, with very little consistency between them. I've not found one person who knows the whole thing, how much is true, *or* how much is exaggerated.' She pulled one of the longer chest hairs, and kept pulling. 'Are you listening?'

'No. And stop that.'

She released him. 'I believe Sardoca knows more about this Nicaraguan incident than most, but he refused to admit it when I pressed him. Now that I know his feelings toward you, I can understand why. Apparently, it happened almost ten years ago, which would be around the time you were with Mr Nikolic. All I know is it concerned a cabal of Bolivian ex-secret police members who threatened to take over some of Mr Nikolic's more profitable business ventures. In the process, many of his employees ended up brutally tortured or murdered, or both. Much blood was spilled, and many properties and inventories destroyed. They say Jara was personally tasked by Mr Nikolic to end the problem once and for all, and that he did so on his own, without outside help. Except possibly this Nicaraguan, whoever he might be.'

Korso snorted. 'Who's *they*?'

'Them.'

'Ah, *them*,' he said. 'Continue. I like bedtime stories. They help me sleep.'

'There's little more to tell. Everything else is just rumour and unsubstantiated gossip. Some say Jara spent over a month researching the enemy, amassing information, and then picked off all seven ringleaders over the course of one night. Or that he infiltrated their organisation over many months and killed them all in one fell swoop. Others insist there were twelve Bolivians in all, and that Jara used this Nicaraguan in some manner to induce them to war amongst themselves until none was left standing. While others are certain these men weren't Bolivians at all, but Brazilians, and that the Nicaraguan was actually the name of a fishing trawler delivering a huge shipment of cocaine to this group, and that Jara assassinated five of the seven ringleaders when they showed up at the docks to supervise the handover.'

'Sounds like Jara was everywhere at once.'

'Only if all four accounts are factual, which is clearly impossible. One of these versions must contain more truth than the others.'

'Not necessarily. Maybe each account contains partial elements of truth.'

'That does not help.'

'It's not meant to.'

Sighing, she began to slide her hand down past his navel. 'That last account, for example, with the trawler and the cocaine and the five dead men. That one doesn't stretch credibility so much. It likely contains some basis in fact.'

'And the two missing Bolivians?'

'Brazilians.'

'Right,' he said. 'Brazilians.'

'Which is the detail that adds credibility, as it makes you out to be less than superhuman for once. Maybe those remaining two men escaped with their lives, or maybe they were dealt with later. As it stands, just one more mystery.' Her hand was still moving down there, which was producing fairly predictable results. 'Which you could solve right now.'

'Then it wouldn't be a mystery anymore.'

'Just tell me what happened, Korso.'

'We just agreed the past is dead. What difference does it make what happened ten years ago?'

She brushed her lips across his chest. 'It would satisfy my curiosity. When you brought up my scar, I told you the cause of it.'

'You didn't have to. If you'd ignored me, I wouldn't have pressed you.'

'But I didn't ignore you. So what harm is there in clarifying matters for me in this instance?'

'Not much, I guess.'

'So?'

'Let me ask you something first.'

'Very well.'

'That tin you're after contains blood diamonds, am I right? Or maybe even the rarest of the rare, blue sapphires? Tell me the truth now.'

Her hand stopped moving and she breathed a sigh. 'Why is it you still refuse to believe me? I've already told you I do not know what's inside, any more than you do.'

'Then we don't really have anything further to discuss, do we?'

She used an elbow to raise herself partway up, and looked down at him. 'Seriously? After everything we've shared, still you will not tell me?'

'*Quid pro quo*, Natasha. You tell me yours, I'll tell you mine. Fair's fair.'

She raised a fist and punched the pillows on her side of the bed. 'There's a word for you in my language that I cannot bring myself to say. It's too brutal and I don't like to swear, but you are definitely the most… *infuriating* man I have ever met.' She then moved the pillows and herself a foot away from him and lay down on her side, facing the window, breathing heavily.

Korso closed his eyes, happily letting his mind drift again. It had all worked itself out, after all. Finally, he could get some sleep.

Twenty-Eight

50 hours, 37 minutes and counting...

Korso was driving. He had been since they'd left the motel at 06:30 that morning. They were still in New Mexico, heading north on US-550, about thirty-five miles from the Colorado state border. The day was bright and sunny, with few clouds in the sky. Traffic was light. The next city on their route was a place called Bloomfield, and Korso planned to stop there for lunch, even if it was from a drive-thru. He was hungry, and had no doubt Natasha felt the same.

So far, it had been a long, uneventful journey. Not to mention a quiet one.

When the alarm call had awoken them both at six, Natasha had been first into the shower, taking her phone in with her. Korso had heard snippets of muted conversation in there as Natasha no doubt updated Sardoca on their current situation and progress. He had used the time to completely dismantle Cain's burner phone until he was satisfied there were no tracking devices hidden inside. Since then Natasha had barely spoken at all, other than the occasional one-word answer to a direct question. Clearly, whatever goodwill he'd accumulated over the past day had evaporated with his refusal to explain himself.

This was fine with him. Silence was one of his favourite sounds. Korso could go whole weeks without uttering a word. But as far as their professional relationship went, this uneasy barrier between them promised nothing but trouble if it continued for much longer.

A road sign was coming up ahead, welcoming drivers to the City of Bloomfield, New Mexico. Out the corner of his eye, he saw Natasha take note of the sign as they passed it.

'We'll grab some lunch here,' he said, 'if that's okay with you. And even if it isn't.'

She didn't reply, just looked at the road straight ahead.

'You know you'll have to talk to me sooner or later, Natasha. And the longer you keep up this silent act, the stupider you'll feel when you have to break it.'

She said nothing, just stared ahead.

'Besides, I know why you're mad. And it's got nothing to do with my refusal to give you a history lesson last night.'

She turned her head, looked at him with hooded eyes.

Still watching the road, Korso saw various business establishments start appearing with more regularity as they entered the city's outskirts. He said, 'It's because you can't help liking me. And you hate yourself for it.'

He turned to her, and saw what appeared to be the beginnings of a suppressed smile at the corners of her mouth.

'You know it's true. Admit it, if only to yourself. You'll feel much better.'

Natasha quickly turned her face to the side window, and he knew he'd won. After a while she faced front again, her expression as stern as before. The suppressed smile, if it had been there at all, was gone.

'I admit nothing,' she said. 'You're deluded.'

'Whatever you say.'

'But I am feeling very hungry now. Where do you suggest?'

'Well, we've probably still got a couple of hours to go before we hit Bilchner. But I still want to get there before three, so maybe we can get a take-out or something and eat while we drive.' He turned to her. 'That is, while you drive.'

She tilted her head at him, her brows arched. 'Ah, you are tired? Oh, you poor thing. Why, of course I'll drive. It's the least I can do.'

Actually, the least she could do was what she had been doing for the last six hours. Nothing. But Korso knew better than to mention it now they were on speaking terms again. Instead, he pulled Cain's phone from his jacket pocket and passed it to her.

'You better turn that on now, see if Cain's left us a message.'

She pressed the power button, and the usual Nokia start-up chime erupted from the speaker. 'There is one text message. Anonymous, of course.'

'Read it out.'

'It says, *Philby's Pharmacy, Main Street. Rear entrance. Left you a sample tin in the dispensary. See you soon, exclamation mark.* The text was sent at 09:34.'

'Meaning he's had plenty of time to prepare for our arrival, while we've had none. Anything else?'

'Nothing. Just that one text.'

'Okay, turn the phone off again.'

'You do not want to send him a reply?'

'Glad to see you've also got your sense of humour back.' He pointed to a gas station up ahead, with another building just beyond it. 'That looks like a KFC sign over there. I'm sure they do a drive-thru. You like chicken?'

'Sure.'

Korso slowed the car as they approached the gas-station entrance. 'If there's one thing America does better than anyone else,' he said, 'it's fried chicken.'

Following the sign for the drive-thru service, Korso ordered the eight-piece family meal with biscuits and large potato wedges and coleslaw sides, some iced tea and a bottle of sparkling mineral water.

Once they had their order, Korso steered them toward one of the empty parking slots facing out onto the highway and cut the engine. Natasha pulled the contents from the bag, and they each began to eat in silence.

Some time later, Korso was sipping some of his iced tea when he heard a double beep from Natasha's side of the car. She put down her drumstick, wiped her hands with a napkin and pulled her phone from the side door pocket and checked the screen.

She turned to Korso. 'A text from your friend. He is about to call me. A video call this time.'

'You mean I have to look at his face again? I've only just eaten.'

Natasha smiled, but said nothing. A few seconds later, the phone began ringing. She pressed the video icon, and after a brief delay, Sardoca's head and shoulders filled the screen. She positioned the phone so she and Korso were both in view. Sardoca was standing outside somewhere, wearing a black polo shirt. It looked like he was in a garden. Korso could see trees and neatly trimmed foliage in the background, but no other details.

'Natasha,' he said. 'Update, please.'

'We have just finished lunch and are on our way to the meet now.'

'About time. So how's my old comrade doing in the land of the not-so free? Natasha tells me things haven't exactly gone as smoothly as we'd hoped.'

'They never do,' Korso said. 'Still, we've made more progress in two days than you did in ten. What do you want, Sardoca? I was in a good mood before you called.'

'Well, I'm about to make your day even worse, I'm sorry to say.'

'Why do I get the feeling you're not sorry at all?'

Sardoca gave a long sigh. 'On any other day, I'd be milking this moment to the full, but it so happens I'm not enjoying this one little bit. Because in the situation we're in right now, what affects you affects me, and vice versa. And I can tell you I'm not a happy individual. Not happy at all.'

The worst part was he seemed completely genuine, which wasn't good. Korso looked at Natasha. She just shook her head, as nonplussed as he was.

'Go on,' Korso said. 'Out with it.'

'Okay. You've just lost a day from your schedule.'

Twenty-Nine

26 hours, 21 minutes and counting…

There was silence in the car. Natasha frowned at Korso while she mouthed the word, *What?*

'Repeat that,' Korso said. 'I don't think I heard you correctly.'

'You heard me just fine. But just so there's no doubt, I'll spell it out for you. Before this call, you had approximately fifty hours left to recover what we commissioned you to find. Now that's been cut by one full day to just twenty-six hours.'

Korso almost laughed out loud. It was the only possible response. 'You're actually serious. What, you figured the original deadline wasn't unrealistic enough, is that it?'

'Sardoca,' Natasha said, 'what's going on? You told me nothing of this before.'

'Hey, you think I was keeping it a secret from you? I only just found out myself. And before you even ask, Korso, that change comes straight from the top. You understand what I'm saying? Right from the *very* top. He's getting impatient, and when he gets like that he starts pissing on those directly below him. And right now, that someone is me.'

Korso let out a long breath as he leaned his head back against the headrest. It was as though all this time he'd been trudging through quicksand, barely keeping his head above the surface as he gradually made his way toward solid ground and safety. Now something down below had grabbed hold of his ankle and was doing its best to pull him under.

He turned and saw Natasha watching him without expression.

'Well?' Sardoca said.

'Be quiet,' Korso said. 'I'm thinking.'

What he was really doing was taking a moment to readjust his mindset. This wasn't exactly a new experience for him. Especially in his line of work, where clients were generally unreliable at best, and at worst, verging on psychotic. He also knew better than to waste time arguing. When someone like Nikolic made a decision, it was always final. No second thoughts. No court of appeal. Simply do it or face the consequences. Which invariably meant death... or worse.

'Tell me something. How was this news relayed to you?'

'What do you mean?'

'I mean, did your employer give you these new instructions in person?'

Sardoca snorted. 'You know as well as I do he never talks with his people one on one. Never has, never will. He relayed this to me over a highly encrypted video call, and even that's rare for him. But I can tell you he looked about as grim as I've ever seen him look, and when he told me how seriously I should take this, I believed him.'

Sardoca was wrong about Nikolic not giving orders in person. Korso could vouch for that personally. But now probably wasn't the best time to bring it up.

'So that threat of exposure you've got hanging over my head,' Korso said. 'I assume this changes things in that regard. Such as, giving me a little leeway if I don't make this new deadline to the second.'

Sardoca gave Korso his most annoying grin as he began walking, the picture moving up and down in time with his footsteps. 'This changes nothing, my friend. Nothing. Trust me when I tell you I've already got an email composed and ready to go, with all those glorious hi-res photos of you attached. It's very brief, but to the point. You go a single second over this new deadline and your former employer gets it in his inbox one second afterwards. If I can't give him what he wants most, I'll give him something else to take his attention off me. Something almost as good. And that's you.'

This surprised Korso not one iota. But he'd had to make the effort.

'And I'll tell you something else, *compadre*. Just so you don't get any funny ideas, there's something else that differentiates that tin from the others. You know which tin I mean. That faint radioactive marker on the exterior is just the first identifier. The second is a serial number on the bottom. Easy to miss, but it's there. Now I don't have to physically have that tin in my hand at the appointed time, but I'll be expecting Natasha to at least read me that serial number verbatim so that I know she's got it. If she doesn't, the email goes.'

Korso turned to Natasha. 'What was that swear word you wanted to use yesterday? Now feels like a good time.'

'Sardoca,' Natasha said, purposely not looking at him, 'can I speak freely?'

'You always have.' He sat down on a garden chair. The screen became still again. 'Why stop now?'

'I feel we've made very good progress,' she said, 'far better than I had thought possible when we first set out. Korso is doing his best under the circumstances, I can bear witness to this. And at no point has he even tried to run. Just the opposite, in fact. I believe we can succeed in our mission, but you—'

'But nothing,' Sardoca cut in. 'You don't know him like I do, Natasha. The only way he'll fulfil his obligations is if he knows I've got him in my crosshairs, ready to squeeze the trigger at any moment. That's just how it is, and how it's always been, so don't waste your breath trying to convince me otherwise.'

Natasha finally looked at Korso and gave him an apologetic shrug.

'You always were a vindictive little thug, Sardoca,' Korso said. 'It's almost comforting to know you haven't improved with age.'

'Ah, you're just bitter about being outsmarted by your betters.'

'Is that what it is?'

'What else? To be honest, I always thought those stories about you were nothing but glorified fairy tales. The more they get repeated, the wilder they get. Like that so called "Thanksgiving Party Extraction" at that senator's house in DC. All pure fantasy. I've never seen any evidence that even happened in the first place. And if by chance it did, and you were involved, I guarantee it was down to good fortune more than anything else.'

'The result of successful planning always looks like luck to imbeciles,' Korso said. 'So is there anything else, or do you want to waste more time trading insults?'

'Okay, this fellow you're about to meet with. You spoke to him, so give me your impressions. You really think he's on the level about wanting a deal?'

'It's still fifty–fifty. My instincts say it's a trap. But now he's learned who the real owner is, I can understand why he'd want to extract himself from the situation as quickly and as safely as possible. I would in his place. So he could well be genuine. We won't know for sure until we get there and see the layout. Which brings us neatly to the question of money.'

'What about it?'

'How fast can Natasha get access to half a million in cash? Because if this guy is genuine about a deal, and the sample matches up, that may be the only way to get your property back.'

'I was thinking about that, and half a million dollars is a fat chunk of cash. There are always other alternatives than paying up, you know.'

'Not when your deadline keeps shrinking down to nothing. We've got just over a day left, and you seem to forget I have a good idea of your employer's net worth, so don't start getting cheap on us now. Do we get the money or not? If the answer's no, I've got no further reason to stick around.'

'Okay, okay, relax. We've got various business accounts at all the major banks in the States, and I'm authorised to grant Natasha immediate access to any of them at a second's notice. *If* I need to.'

Korso looked over at her, and she nodded in confirm-ation.

Sardoca went on, 'And Natasha, I'll be wanting an immediate progress report on the situation, so expect another call from me at around four-thirty, your time. Understood?'

'Yes,' she said.

'That's something for us to look forward to,' Korso said. 'Let's wrap this up. We've still got a two-hour drive ahead of us.'

'So stop wasting time and get on with it.'

His face shrunk from the screen as he ended the call.

'He's a real sweetheart, your partner,' Korso said.

'None of us are angels.' Natasha shrugged. 'Not you. Not me. And especially not him. Surely you are not surprised.'

'Irritated, mostly. How do you manage to stop from killing him?'

She just smiled as she opened her door. 'Let us switch. I will drive the rest of the way.'

Thirty

24 hours, 13 minutes and counting...

At an elevation of 8000 feet, Bilchner was one of several similar towns situated in a huge valley in the San Juan mountains. Since leaving New Mexico, the two-hour drive into this part of Colorado had been both interesting and precarious. Amazing mountain scenery on one hand, sharp hairpin turns and eye-popping drop-offs on the other.

As Natasha turned off the highway for the mile-long drive into town, Korso could see Bilchner wasn't exactly booming. For a start, their rental was now the only vehicle on the road. Secondly, the welcome sign on the way in had been blasted with a shotgun at some point, so that the only letters remaining were *BIL*.

The first building they encountered was a ramshackle gas station. It would have looked old-fashioned in the Seventies, with ancient-looking pumps standing out front like sentinels. The front windows were smashed. The place looked long deserted. About half a mile further down the road, Korso could make out a large number of buildings scattered around that suggested a medium-sized town, while in the far distance, the ever-present mountains watched over everything with impartiality.

'I see what Cain meant,' Natasha said, studying the gas station as they passed by. 'It actually feels like a ghost town.'

'More like a Superfunded town,' Korso said.

'Superfunded town? What is that?'

'A place so toxic and contaminated by pollutants that it's essentially been declared off-limits by the government. I did a little research while you were driving. There's an article on the *Newsweek* site about a deserted town in Oklahoma that some time back was officially declared uninhabitable by the Environmental Protection Agency. The companies responsible for the mess were then forced by the government to begin the long process of cleaning up the place, using the resources of a federal trust fund set up in the early Eighties called the Superfund. On the same page was a sidebar listing ten similar hazardous places in the US. Bilchner, Colorado, was near the top.'

'Interesting. And how long ago was Bilchner declared a no man's land?'

'About twenty-five years ago.'

'Twenty-five years? The companies responsible seem to be dragging their feet a little.'

'Or the government is. I'd imagine much of that initial trust fund has been siphoned off into the back-pockets of various politicians. That's usually how it works.'

'So now I see why Cain chose this location. The town is completely deserted?'

Korso shook his head. 'Not completely. There are always die hards who refuse to leave their homes under any circumstances, and some who simply can't afford to relocate. I imagine a few people still live here, although I doubt they'll be too sociable.'

'Good. We leave them alone, they leave us alone.'

'From your lips to God's ears. Incidentally, don't think I didn't appreciate you trying back there.'

'With Sardoca, you mean?' She waved it away. 'We are both professionals, each carrying out our duties as best we can. But this new deadline we have been given is… ludicrous. Especially at this late stage.'

'Careful. That almost sounds like a criticism of your boss.'

'Sardoca is not my boss.'

'I didn't mean him.'

'Oh. Yes, I see.'

They drove on.

Less than a minute later they entered the town proper. If you could call it that. Korso lowered his window. The air was cool and smelled unexpectedly fresh, with a faint breeze coming in from the west. He listened hard, but could detect no sounds of birds singing. No sounds at all, in fact, other than the soft hum of the car engine.

'Eerie,' Natasha said. 'Almost like a forgotten movie set.'

'I was thinking the same.' Korso had experienced a great many weird things in his lifetime, but this was a new one. '*Dawn of the Dead*, maybe.'

'George Romero. Yes, I like that one.'

'You're just full of surprises.'

They passed a vacant lot with a huge PARKING sign above. No parked cars, of course. Just random piles of old tyres dotted around. He heard the faint bark of a dog coming from somewhere, but even that stopped after a few seconds. Off to their right, maybe half a mile east of them, he could see the top half of a water tower. Up ahead on the west side, there was a frame church with a hundred-foot-high steeple, and a large clock at the top.

Both hands were stuck on the twelve. They'd probably stay like that for as long as the building remained upright.

Natasha slowed the vehicle to a crawl as they cruised down Main Street. Nearing the centre of town, the residential properties lessened and there were more retail buildings and small businesses. All had seen better days, and none looked occupied. Some were shuttered. Others had broken display windows.

They passed a diner with a prefab steel panel over one of its two front windows. The other window was still mostly intact, but only just. There was a row of what looked like bullet holes running across the top of the thick glass and a thin crack ran all the way from top to bottom.

They passed streetlights with missing lamps and an uprooted, busted-up mailbox. Korso noticed the sidewalk on either side was cracked, with weeds and grass fighting their way through the gaps toward the sunlight. But no sign of a Philby's Pharmacy.

'Wait.'

Natasha braked immediately, and looked around in all directions. 'What is it?'

'I feel eyes on my back. Cain's had hours to prepare, so it's pretty much guaranteed he's watching us right now.'

'So?'

He turned to look behind them. 'So that's just one of a multitude of things I don't like about this setup. And those bullet holes in the diner window didn't make me happy, either.'

'That could have happened years ago.'

'Or yesterday.'

'Look at that,' Natasha said.

Korso faced front again. She was pointing at the inter-section up ahead. A large mutt with dirty grey fur stood in the middle of the road, watching them with great interest. Korso couldn't identify the breed, but it looked tough. Like a born survivor. It began to rigorously scratch its left ear with one of its hind legs, still watching them. He wondered if this was the same dog that he'd heard barking before.

'Doesn't look underfed,' he said, 'so it's obviously getting food from somewhere, or from someone.'

'Probably the former,' Natasha said. 'It looks the solitary type.'

Korso opened the door, took one step outside, and waved at the dog. He'd always liked animals, and most seemed to like him back. But the mutt just gave three loud angry barks, then turned away and casually trotted off between two buildings until it disappeared from sight.

He got back in, shut the door.

'Nice to see some life here,' he said, 'even if it's just the four-legged kind.'

'Shall I continue?'

'What else can we do? We still need to find this pharmacy.'

Natasha pressed the gas and they began moving slowly down the street again. Korso noted every building they passed, looking for anything that might resemble a drugstore. They reached the intersection where the dog had stopped. The road sign on the corner read Kendall Avenue. To the right he saw what looked like office buildings and some more retail units, with larger industrial-type buildings further on. Warehouses or factories, maybe. The water tower he'd seen before loomed large in the background. To the west, he saw some more office buildings, along with a few residential properties. None of them looked inhabited.

Natasha was also looking in all directions.

'No sign of that dog,' she said.

'It's probably keeping a close eye on us, though. Like Cain.'

She steered them onward. Soon, Korso saw a place up ahead on the right that looked promising. He pointed, and Natasha gently eased the brakes until they came to a complete stop directly outside.

Philby's Pharmacy was a single-storey stucco building with a sign above, though several of the letters were missing. Steel plates covered the display windows, but at least there were no bullet holes. The plywood front door had a glass panel taking up most of the top half, and Korso saw what looked like a retractable security grille behind it. Philby's neighbour on the right was a similar-sized building without any identifying markings, and had probably been vacant even before the town was condemned. The business to its left had once been a hair salon. Wide steel shutters covered the front windows and door.

'Wait here,' he said, opening the car door. 'I'll try the front first.'

Natasha looked at him. 'Cain said the rear entrance.'

'I know what Cain said.'

Korso stepped out and walked over to the former drug-store. There was an inch-wide gap between the steel plates on the windows. He cupped his hands against the glass and peered through, trying to make out interior details, but there wasn't enough exterior light to see anything. He went over and tried the door handle. It moved easily. He pushed the door open an inch before the security grille stopped any further progress. He looked through the gap and saw what might be a couple of display stands inside, but he wasn't even sure of that. He couldn't see much else from the tight angle.

In the car, he saw Natasha had retrieved her black baseball cap from the back seat. He watched with interest as she fixed it on her head, pulling the bill low over her brow.

'Okay, let's gear up,' he said. 'We'll leave the car here.'

'That side road is more than wide enough for our vehicle.'

'Except I've no idea what's back there,' he said, pulling the Ruger from the glove compartment, 'and I don't want to risk boxing us in with only one exit. Walking's better.'

He checked the magazine out of habit, made sure the safety was on, and stuck the Ruger in his front waistband under his jacket. He then pulled out the .22 revolver he'd taken from Jonesy. 'You want the Taurus as well?'

'Better safe than sorry,' she said, taking it from him.

'A woman after my own heart.'

He reached back and pulled out one of the Home Depot bags from the rear footwell. He pulled out a flash-light and handed it to Natasha. The other one he kept for himself. Then he unzipped his overnight bag and removed his lockpick tools, another burner phone and the larger of the two fibre-optic scopes.

Natasha was staring at the instrument. It was a Medit flexible fiberscope with a metre-long, six-millimetre-diameter stainless-steel braided insertion probe at one end, and an intricate-looking eyepiece at the other. It had cost him somewhere in the low five figures, and that had been seven years ago. The other one had a minuscule two-millimetre insertion probe and had cost him twice as much. As far as he was concerned, they were each worth their weight in gold.

'I've used fibre-optics before,' she said. 'This one looks expensive.'

'Think of a number, double it, and you might come close. Okay, I think that's everything.'

'You're sure?'

'I'm never sure of anything. That's why I overcompensate.'

They got out of the car. He pocketed his stuff while she locked the vehicle. Which made him smile. He would have done exactly the same. Even in a deserted ghost town.

They proceeded down the sidewalk, turned into the access road. At the end it opened into a small parking and delivery area for the three retail properties out front. Now there were only weeds and garbage back there. And no other exit, other than the one they'd used. To their right, a narrow path led to Kendall Avenue, the street they'd passed at the intersection.

Natasha was already standing at the rear entrance of the former drugstore. There was a steel door in the centre of the building, but no windows. She reached for the door handle and turned it. It gave easily. She pulled the door open all the way.

'Korso,' she said.

'Coming,' he said, walking over to her.

He stood at the entrance and looked inside. He saw a small utility room, containing a dirty sink and no faucets, and rusty copper piping jutting out of the cracked walls. A few coat hooks. No other furnishings that he could see. There was another door directly ahead, about six feet away. Somebody had made a huge dent in the wood panel.

She turned to him. 'What do you think?'

'That my instincts have never lied to me before. And you?'

'The same.' She paused. 'But nothing has changed since the last time we did this. We have to proceed.'

'But with extreme caution.'

He activated his flashlight and moved the light around the room, the walls, the inner doorframe, looking for wires, motion sensors, anything that might ping on his radar.

Nothing. Nothing at all. Just a room.

He stepped forward.

Thirty-One

24 hours, 2 minutes and counting...

No flashing red light anywhere to indicate an alarm had been triggered. Although that would have been too obvious. He spotted a light switch on the wall, but ignored it. The power had surely been cut off years ago. He walked over to the interior door. It was slightly ajar, with an inch-wide gap between it and the frame.

Peeking through the gap, he saw a medium-sized office-type room beyond. He nudged the door open further and shone the flashlight around. Shelving and storage units covered the walls, mostly empty, of course. Although he did see a few basic medical supplies here and there, such as packets of bandages, dressings, some medical tape, and so on. There was a large work desk on the right side. Lying on its side on the desk was a fat retro-style alarm clock, complete with large clock face and twin bells on the top. It looked as dusty as everything else in there. There was also a long, stainless-steel cabinet with two built-in steel sinks and a gooseneck faucet, and storage cupboards underneath. All of which indicated this area served as the dispensary. Despite the dust and grime, it all looked in pretty good shape, considering. The furnishings seemed mostly intact, with no obvious signs of vandalism.

There was a wall partition straight ahead to act as a barrier between staff and customers, and beyond that a service counter. Korso could also see some large gondola shelving units in the shop area out front. Probably the same ones he'd seen through the gap.

He stepped inside for a closer inspection of the office and dispensary, while Natasha slipped past and proceeded down the walkway to the front of the store.

Korso moved further into the office and shone the flashlight around, seeing nothing of interest. Then he found an alcove in one corner of the room, almost hidden behind some shelving units. He went over and shone the beam on another work desk in the corner. Underneath were some metal lockers. Rusty now.

And beside the desk, lined up next to each other against the wall, were three pharmaceutical fridge units.

They were the kind with glass display doors. None of the three were in good shape, with rusted hinges and handles. Two of the doors had large cracks in the glass. One fridge was missing the door altogether. But more importantly, while the last two units were both empty, the first refrigerator contained a circular steel tin. In Korso's opinion, it looked big enough to contain about a kilo-gram's worth of caviar.

Korso knelt down two feet away and kept the light on the interior of the fridge. He saw the words *Amicus Beluga* printed in tasteful gold script on the tin label.

'Natasha,' he said.

She was with him seconds later, looking at where he was shining the flashlight. She didn't move any closer to it than Korso.

'Amicus Beluga is the right brand name,' she said. 'And that tin is the correct size.' She crouched next to him, still staring at it. 'Do you know what I'm thinking?'

'That there's always cheese in a mousetrap.'

'A mousetrap, yes. And I don't like this repeated use of storing things in refrigerators. First, the body in Tijuana. Now this tin sample. I don't like it at all.'

'I'm glad to hear you say that.' He didn't bother mentioning that if Cain wanted to put an immediate end to their investigation, wiring an IED to the fridge door would be the perfect way to do it. Nobody would find their remains for months. If ever. He was sure the exact same thought had already occurred to her. 'Did you find anything out front?'

She shook her head. 'Only some empty shelving stands. Very little else.'

He reached into his jacket pocket and pulled out his pick tools. 'Take these and try out your new skills on that security grille out front. Being in a building with only one usable exit makes me nervous.'

Natasha took the snapgun and wrench from him. She was still looking at the fridge unit. 'What will you do?'

'Nothing yet. I'm just looking.'

'Be careful.'

Korso lowered his head until his cheek was almost touching the porcelain floor tiling. He aimed the flashlight under the refrigerator. He saw plenty of dust balls and grime under there. Lots of cobwebs too. Which indicated nobody else had been under there recently.

Still keeping his distance, he got to his feet and played the light around the floor area in front of him. The floor tiles had probably been off-white once. Now they were just a dirty grey. But on one of the tiles, in front of the first refrigerator, was something that looked very much like a muddy boot mark. He knelt down a few inches away. The print was badly smudged. He wiped part of the boot print with an index finger. The dirt felt slightly damp. Clearly Cain's. He looked around for any other markings, but saw none.

Somewhere off in the distance that dog started barking again. He could also hear Natasha triggering the snapgun in the other room.

Korso got up and moved closer. There was about an inch gap between the fridge units and the wall. He shone the flashlight behind the first one, but there was too much crud back there for him to see anything clearly. Keeping the flashlight fixed on the same spot, he used his other hand to pull the fibre-optic scope from his pocket.

'How are we doing out there?' he called out.

'Satisfactory,' Natasha yelled back. At the same time, he heard the sounds of steel shutters creaking back and forth. A few seconds later, Natasha returned. 'We now have a second exit.'

'Good. Come over here and hold this flashlight steady, will you? And avoid touching any of the refrigerator units. Just in case.'

Keeping her body well away from the units, she pressed one elbow against the wall for balance while holding the flashlight in her other hand, light aimed downward. At the same time Korso adjusted the thin, flexible probe so it was more or less straight, and carefully inserted the lens into the gap, keeping it close to the wall. He looked through the eyepiece, but all he saw was glaring white light.

'Too bright,' he said. 'Raise the flashlight higher.'

Natasha raised the light a few more inches. He looked through the viewfinder again. This time he could clearly see the steel backing cover of the unit. Or a fish-eye version, at least. It looked plain enough, with dark gaskets at the sides and corners. He moved the long probe around with his free hand, and saw nothing that looked out of place. It was just a basic steel protective panel, like you'd see on the back of any refrigerator.

Still looking through the eyepiece, he gently extended the scope further until he saw the semi-exposed area at the bottom that contained various electrical components, such as the condenser coils and fan. He moved slowly and carefully, making sure the scope didn't touch the fridge at any point. The light grew dimmer.

'Anything?' Natasha asked.

'Not yet,' he said. 'Bring the flashlight closer.'

Natasha lowered the light a little. The view immediately improved. Except all he saw now were close-ups of the floor. He carefully extracted the probe, bent the end at a slight angle, then reinserted it into the gap. When he reached the open area at the bottom, he slowly swivelled the lens to get a better view of the interior. He saw copper coils and fat diodes, along with various other components he couldn't identify. But he also spotted two thin wires taped to the side of the fridge, leading inward. He couldn't see where the wires ended, it was too dark in there. But it didn't feel right. He'd never seen electrical wiring on the back of a fridge before.

Korso slowly swivelled the lens to the other side of the unit.

The moment he saw the tiny blinking light, he froze.

Thirty-Two

'Natasha,' Korso whispered. 'Please. Don't. Move.'

The flashlight above him remained completely steady, for which he was profoundly grateful.

'Tell me,' she whispered back.

'Some kind of sensor. A tiny LED blinking at two-second intervals. Probably not a motion sensor or the probe would have triggered it already, but I can't be sure. Also, two electrical wires taped to the side of the fridge unit. They lead further in, but I can't see where.' He moved the lens around again. Stopped. 'Wait. Now I see it.'

'What?'

'A slab of putty-like substance. Plastique. Either C4 or Semtex. I can only see part of it. The rest is hidden in shadows.'

'How large?'

'Hard to tell, but I'd say there's enough to turn this building into vapour. Either triggered by opening the fridge door, or more likely by applying the slightest amount of pressure to it. Hold the light steady.'

The flashlight above remained as motionless as before. Taking only shallow breaths, Korso very slowly and very carefully withdrew the fibre-optic scope, inch by agonising inch. When he'd finally extracted the lens at the end, he backed off and motioned for Natasha to do the same. Korso walked over to the other side of the dispensary and leaned against the work desk there. He took a long deep breath, let it out again.

'At least now we know,' Natasha said, joining him.

'We already did,' he said, 'deep down. This just confirms it. The tin proves Cain's got the shipment, and the plastique proves he never had any intention of selling it back to us. He wants to keep it all. And he doesn't want us leaving this place, except in very small pieces.'

'Which means he'll be watching this building right now,' Natasha said, looking at the ancient alarm clock on the desk, 'waiting for us to trigger the detonator.'

'And when he realises we're not likely to, he'll resort to plan B. Whatever that is.'

'Maybe he'll activate it remotely.'

Korso shook his head. 'Unlikely, or he would have done it the second we entered the building. Either way, we're in a bad spot. If we somehow manage to leave town alive, we're right back to square one again. So we stay, but we still need to bring Cain in alive to have any chance of retrieving the shipment. While he simply wants to erase us completely.'

Natasha looked toward the front of the store, frowning. 'Leaving us with only one clear option.'

'Find Cain and force him to talk. The second part's easy. The first might be a problem.'

'Maybe not. If I were Cain I would find somewhere close by, in an elevated position. Somewhere with a good view of this building. We passed a number of two-storey buildings on the way here, many of them with flat roofs.'

Korso pushed off from the work desk and walked to the front of the store. Making sure he stayed in the shadows, he went over to the front door and looked out. Natasha was right. The empty retail premises directly opposite were all two-storey buildings with flat roofs. Cain could be in, or on, any one of them. Although it was more likely he'd choose somewhere outside the theoretical blast range.

He heard Natasha quietly approaching from behind, and turned to her.

'You're right. A flat roof would be a good vantage point. Our best bet is to split up and search, and just hope he's working alone. That way he can only focus on one of us at a time. And if he's not alone, our problems are only just beginning.'

'Or we could simply call him.'

Korso blinked at her.

'On the burner phone he left for us,' she said. 'If nothing else, it's another weapon in our armoury. We could even use it to feed him disinformation, confuse him.'

Korso smiled. 'Now I know why I brought you along. You have it with you?'

'No, I left it in the car. Wait here.'

He slid the now unlocked security grille across, then pulled open the front door for her. She slipped past him, and stepped out onto the sidewalk.

Korso watched her pause just a few feet from the door, her side to him, her head lowered as she felt around for the car keys in her pocket. The car was parked about fifteen feet away, almost directly in front of the shop. He noticed the sky was a magnificent azure blue, the sun still high. The air was still fresh. By every known criterion, it was a beautiful April day.

The small hairs on the back of his neck tingled.

In his peripheral vision, Korso suddenly caught a tiny flash of light somewhere off in the distance. Then it was gone. A reflection, maybe. It had been there for less than a second. It had come from the direction of the church he'd seen earlier.

But from somewhere high up. Like the steeple.

Korso's senses immediately went into overdrive.

He saw Natasha had already pulled the car keys from her pocket. As she raised her right arm to aim the fob at the car, Korso sprung from the doorway. He closed the distance in less than a second and leaped at her before she could take a single step.

Time seemed to slow down.

He heard the familiar sound as the car unlocked itself. He saw Natasha starting to turn her head his way, and then he crashed into her, wrapping his arms around her waist. They both went down in a tangled heap. He saw and heard the car keys clatter to the ground. He felt Natasha's elbow connect with his left cheek. He heard a sharp *crack* behind him, like a stone hitting ice.

'*Sniper*,' he yelled, quickly disentangling himself. 'Back inside. *Quick*.'

Korso swivelled his body round as he got to his feet, grabbing Natasha's left arm and pulling her up with him.

'*Wait*.' She ducked down quickly, grabbed the keys she'd dropped, then rose and ran with him toward the shop front. He got to the door first, dived inside and rolled his body to the right. Natasha scrambled in after him and dived to the floor to his immediate left. Twisting his body round until he was facing the doorway, he kicked out with his foot and slammed the door shut.

There was another faint *crack* sound and he saw a puff of dust erupt from a floor tile close to Natasha's head.

She instinctively rolled her body away until she was in the shadows again. Korso was still looking at the glass panel in the door. There was a small hole in the top left corner of the glass that hadn't been there before. That's where the *crack* had come from. Using just elbows and feet, Korso scrambled back until the shadows concealed him as well.

He looked over at Natasha and their eyes met.

'Now we know what plan B is.'

Thirty-Three

23 hours, 46 minutes and counting...

They remained perfectly still for a few more seconds, neither of them wanting to draw attention to themselves. But there were no more shots.

Korso rose to a crouch, and kept his head down as he carefully made his way back to the dispensary area, safely behind the partition wall. Or as safe as anyone could be with a slab of C4 sitting right next to them. Natasha joined him seconds later.

'Are you okay?' he said.

She nodded. 'That was far too close for comfort. You saw where the shots came from?'

'There was a glint from that church spire, west of us. You were right about Cain finding an elevated position. We just didn't think high enough.'

'I heard no shots.'

'He's using a suppressor. Ghost town or not, there's no point attracting unwanted attention from any locals who might still live here.'

'Meaning he can pick us off at his leisure,' she said, disgust written all over her face. She pointed the key fob to the front of the store, pressed the button. Outside, the rental made its *chirp-chirp* sound as it relocked itself.

Korso just looked at her.

'My way of giving Cain the finger,' she said, shrugging.

He couldn't argue with that. 'At least we know where he is. Although for how much longer, I don't know.'

'He will almost certainly relocate eventually.'

'But right now he's got the best view in town, and he's not about to give up that advantage. Not unless he starts getting impatient.'

'So we split up and move fast before that happens,' she said. 'We each travel by foot to the church, making sure to always keep cover between ourselves and him.'

'It's about all we can do. We'll exit by the rear. You head to the left, northward, then veer back in a westerly direction toward the church. I'll go south, then do the same.'

She was already nodding her head. 'A pincer movement.'

'And just to be clear, when we find Cain, we shoot to wound, not to kill.'

'I'm not stupid.'

'I never said you were. But when your blood's up it's often easy to lose sight of what's in your best interests.'

She gave a deep sigh. 'Very well. I will only shoot to wound. Satisfied? Or would you like me to swear on my mother's grave?'

'That shouldn't be necessary. Can I assume you brought your own phone along?'

'Of course. And you?'

'Right here.' Korso pulled it from his pants pocket. He switched it on and recited the new number for her. Once she had it memorised, he said, 'Progress updates as and when, either by voice or text.'

'Agreed.'

'Let's not waste any more time, then.'

They made their way to the rear of the store. Natasha paused in the doorway, peering at the water tower half a mile east. 'If Cain has an accomplice,' she said, 'that tower would make another perfect vantage point. They would have eyes on us at all times.'

'Nothing much we can do about it either way.' Although that very same thought had already occurred to him.

Natasha turned to him. 'Korso—'

'We're all out of time, Natasha.'

She made a face. 'In more ways than one.'

Then she turned and sprinted back the way they'd come. Korso didn't watch her go. He was still peering at the water tower, but saw no telltale flashes of light up there. If it was only Cain they had to worry about, there was a fair chance they might actually get through this alive.

He turned to his right and ran across the small parking area, then down the narrow pathway toward Kendall Avenue. At the end he came to a stop, using the shop on his right as cover. Directly across the street was another long, single-storey office building. There was a long driveway at the side, no doubt leading to more parking at the rear. On its right was a building that faced out onto Main Street. They must have passed it in the car, but Korso couldn't remember whether it was a store or not. He saw another long building, seemingly split up into smaller commercial units, to the left of the offices. Whatever they were once, it was hard to tell now. Beyond those and further back, he could make out a few vacant lots and a number of large warehouses and industrial-type buildings.

But it was the disused building opposite that he wanted.

Cain had already proven he was more than adequate with a long-distance rifle, but in Korso's experience even experts had a tough time when it came to a fast-moving target.

Without another thought, he leapt from cover and sprinted across the street. During the few seconds he was exposed he kept waiting for the shot that would take him down. But no shots came. Or if they did, he didn't hear them.

He reached the driveway safely, but didn't stop. He carried on running, using the building on his right as cover from the church spire. When he reached the area at the back, he slowed to a complete stop while he searched for the best exit. The rear yard was much the same as the one he'd just left, only larger, with space for ten parking slots. There were two ancient-looking dumpsters back there, with large piles of old garbage stacked up against them. A five-foot-high wooden fence separated the parking area from the adjoining property it backed onto. Beyond the fence, Korso could see a backyard and a one-storey clapboard building that looked like a private residence. It was also the only exit route.

Korso was just about to step forward when he suddenly spotted movement near the dumpsters. His right hand twitched, preparing to reach for the gun, but he saw it was just the mutt he'd spotted at the intersection. Its head was buried in the garbage, its dirty grey fur almost indistinguishable from the trash. It was also a lot larger up close.

The dog somehow sensed Korso's presence. Its haunches tensed up as it raised its head to appraise the intruder on its territory. Korso saw clearly it was a male.

The dog bared his teeth, and a low menacing growl started from back in his throat. Those teeth looked very sharp.

'Easy,' he said, showing both palms to the dog. 'Just passing through.'

The dog still glared. The growling grew louder, more intense.

Palms still up, Korso began edging his way toward the wooden fence. If the mutt suddenly launched himself at him, Korso would have little choice but to shoot him. For all he knew, the thing might be rabid. But he wanted to avoid that if he could. Besides, the gunshot would surely alert Cain to his whereabouts.

He kept sidling his way across, his eyes never leaving the dog's for a second. Never showing fear, but not displaying aggression either. As he kept backing away, the growling faded until only the glare remained.

His back suddenly made contact with the fence. The mutt barked twice, and then returned to the business at hand by dunking his muzzle into the trash again.

'Good boy,' Korso said. He turned, grabbed hold of the top of the fence and heaved himself up and over, landing on both feet on the other side.

Still crouching, he looked to his right and was glad to see the neighbouring building on that side shielded him completely from the church. He ran toward the house, looking for walkway access on either side of the property that would take him to the street out front. There was a narrow crawlspace on the right of the house, but the owner had dumped a pile of heavy firewood in there, blocking it completely. On the other side was a garage that met up with the fence, with no space at all in between. The property on the other side of the fence was another low building that ran the whole length of the backyard. So the only way out was through the house itself.

Korso jogged over to the back door and reached for the handle. It was unlocked. He pulled the door open. The interior was dark, but it looked like a kitchen area. He was about to step inside when he heard a sound he knew all too well.

The unmistakable *click-clack* of a pump shotgun being racked.

He dived to the ground just as the blast erupted from within the house.

Thirty-Four

23 hours, 37 minutes and counting...

Korso expected to feel stinging sensations from stray buckshot, but he felt nothing. He just kept rolling his body instinctively away from the danger area, and then leapt to his feet, pulling the Ruger from his waistband, all in the space of a second, without conscious thought. The old training never let him down. It was too deeply ingrained.

His gun was already aimed at the doorway, his hand completely steady.

A man with a pot belly stood there, aiming a Winchester pump directly back at him. His face was lined and weathered, his hair long, grey and unwashed. Dark stubble covered his cheeks and mouth. He didn't exactly look like someone Cain would recruit, but the possibility couldn't be discounted.

'Drop it,' the man said. His voice was low, raspy. As though he didn't use it much.

'You first,' Korso said.

'I ain't kiddin', brother. Drop the piece right now or I put you down.'

'I'm as serious as you are,' Korso said, watching the man's eyes rather than his trigger finger. 'Maybe more so. Why do you want me dead?'

'Dead? Shit, rock salt ain't gonna kill you, boy, though it'll mess you up some. As for the why, I don't abide trespassers and I always protect what's mine. So back the way you came.'

Rock salt, Korso thought. *Not even proper buckshot.* So he was just another citizen thinking he was protecting his rights.

'What trespassers?' Korso said. 'We're in a ghost town. There's just you, me and a stray dog back there.'

'I don't give a shit. This here's still my property, and you're on it.'

'Look, this is a real gun with real bullets. And lead beats rock salt every time. All I want is to get through to the next street, so put the gun down.'

The man shook his head. 'Better find yourself another route, sonny boy. 'Cos you sure as hellfire ain't comin' through my place.'

'I don't have time for this. I could shoot you right now. You'd die.'

The man gave a tobacco-stained smile, his shotgun still aimed at Korso's face. 'We all die, brother. Better pull that trigger if you're gonna. Or get goin'. Your choice.'

Korso could see he wasn't bluffing. The eyes never lied. He was crazy. He'd clearly been living out here alone for far too long. Korso could simply end the argument with one shot, but while he'd committed many immoral acts in his life, cold-blooded murder was one he consistently tried to avoid. He could always put one in the guy's leg, but without medical assistance he'd probably get a terminal infection and the end result would be the same.

He sighed. Dealing with fools really wore on a man's patience.

'All right,' Korso said finally, backing up. 'I'm leaving.'

'You're a lot smarter than you look, sonny,' the man said, his Winchester following Korso every step of the way.

Korso reached the fence and stuck the Ruger back in his waistband. The man nodded and lowered the shotgun. Korso turned round and climbed over, dropping down again on the other side.

The dog was gone. No doubt the sound of the shotgun had encouraged it to try safer pastures. Korso ran back to Kendall Avenue and came to a stop on the sidewalk. He looked west. The church steeple was just out of shot. Which meant as long as he stayed on this side of the path, he'd be okay. He turned the other way and ran east down Kendall, still irked at wasting two minutes. And also by the fact that he was now travelling in completely the wrong direction.

He ran past the building that had been split up into smaller units. The next structure was a low flat building that looked like a deserted warehouse. But before that was a large vacant lot surrounded by a seven-foot chain-link fence with numerous *No Trespassing* signs affixed to it.

Approaching the fence, Korso felt his phone vibrate in his pocket. He pulled it out and took the call without looking. There was only one other person who had the number.

'Problem?' he said.

'I was about to ask the same.' Natasha was breathing heavily, as though jogging while she talked. 'I called you before. I thought I heard the echo of a shotgun blast.'

'You did. Just one of those die hards I told you about. He wasn't exactly rational. Watch out for them.'

'So you dealt with him?'

'Not exactly. I've had to make a slight detour.' He decided now wasn't the time to go into details. 'What about you? Making decent headway?'

'Reasonable. There is not much cover here, so I also had to make various detours. Progress is slow. Speak again soon.'

She hung up and Korso pocketed the phone. He climbed over the fence and landed on the other side. About a hundred yards ahead was another chain-link fence. Past that was a building with clear access on both sides to the street that he wanted. From there, he'd change course and finally start making his way toward the church. Keeping close to the right side of the lot, using the adjoining building as cover, Korso began jogging.

He'd only covered a few yards when he heard a faint buzzing sound coming from somewhere nearby. Like the sound of a swarm of hornets in flight, only a little too regular to be natural. Korso slowed his pace and peered into the sky, listening hard as he looked in all directions. As the humming grew more distinct, he decided it was coming from the west, the direction from which he'd just come. The more he listened the more it sounded like a toy plane.

He stopped and turned to the building to his right, using a hand to shield the sun from his eyes. Then he spotted the source of the sound.

A drone.

A small, black quadcopter, with four little rotors, one at each corner, appeared over the roof fifty yards away and began making its way directly at him. There was also something hanging under its belly. The sound of the electric engine remained subdued as it closed the distance, which told Korso it was one of the high-end 'stealth' models with built-in noise dampeners.

It also meant Cain wasn't working solo after all. There was no way he could keep track of them through a telescopic sight *and* remotely pilot a drone at the same time. It was impossible. So there had to be an accomplice somewhere. As the thing got nearer, Korso instinctively started backing away toward the factory building behind him. He squinted, and now saw the mantis claw grabber under its belly. Used to drop items, and also to recover those dropped by mistake. In its clutches was a small dark object. Korso knew it wasn't a camera. Most drones came with them already built in. But whatever it was carrying, it couldn't be good.

Still backing away, Korso pulled the Ruger from his waistband and aimed it at the drone. Just as he fired, the drone yawed quickly to the left. He fired again just as it pitched itself forward. Another miss. The thing kept coming at him. He knew it was pointless shooting again from this distance. Thanks to the four propellers, any half-decent operator could alter the direction of those things almost at the speed of thought.

Korso turned and sprinted for the factory. He spotted a large open entrance to the right of the building and aimed for that. Aware that he was now in the sight of the church steeple and running across open ground, he also began zigzagging, making his trajectory as unpredictable as possible, thus preventing Cain from guessing his next move and getting a lead on him.

He could still hear the muted buzzing behind him, and knew most commercial drones had a standard top speed of forty to fifty miles per hour. Obviously, it could overtake him at any time, but would it? With the sun at his back,

Korso watched the ground in front of him as he ran for the building, waiting for the telltale shadow of the drone as it crept up on him. But the shadow didn't appear. It was just keeping pace with him for some reason.

He finally reached the factory grounds. The long building was constructed from grey brick with no visible windows on this side.

Korso passed through the entrance and immediately darted left, slamming his back against the wall. He crouched down, then quickly swivelled his body round the opening and aimed the gun at the point where the drone should be.

It wasn't there.

Nor was there any buzzing.

Ever conscious of that church spire in the distance, Korso quickly looked in all directions without seeing any sign of the drone then ducked his head back out of sight.

He faced front and quickly surveyed his immediate surroundings. The factory was a huge empty space, except for some old machinery parts piled up in one corner and the rusted husk of a flatbed truck set against the opposite wall. Whole sections of the roof had collapsed. A few windows were dotted around, the safety glass either smashed or missing. There were also two fire-exits on opposite ends of the building. The door on the far left was wide open, while the steel door on the far right exit had been completely removed.

And still no sign of the drone.

Standing up, Korso risked a peek round the open entrance. At the same time he reached into his pocket for his phone, in order to warn Natasha. Suddenly, there was a fizzing sound and a tiny chip of brick erupted two inches from his face.

Korso immediately dropped to a crouch as he ducked back out of the line of fire, aware that he'd just narrowly escaped a bullet in the head. He reared back again as another bullet took out a small chunk of the concrete floor two feet from his position. Since he was already out of the line of sight, that one had to be Cain showing off. After a brief pause, a third round took out another chunk of concrete two inches to its right.

There were no accompanying gunshot sounds, of course. Just random pieces of the earth suddenly vanishing in front of his eyes.

Very impressive, Korso thought. *Just what are you trying to prove?*

He frowned as another tiny piece of the floor suddenly disappeared forever, this one midway between and slightly above the previous two shots, the bullet holes now forming a loose triangle. Dust particles floated lazily in the air.

It didn't make sense. There had to be a point to all this, something more than simple grandstanding.

Then he noticed the muted buzzing was back. He would have heard it before if he hadn't been distracted by the target practice.

Korso looked up and saw the drone was almost directly above him now. It must have flown through one of the many gaps in the roof. The grabber underneath was still carrying its consignment, but he couldn't see what it was.

But he could make a good guess.

He leapt away from the wall just as the claw suddenly opened and released its load. Korso ran a few more steps and dived to the ground and flattened himself against the floor, hands wrapped over his head, making himself as small as possible, waiting for the inevitable explosion a dozen feet behind him. He heard something briefly roll along the floor, then stop. Nothing else happened. Cautiously, he raised his head and turned and looked at the object. It was a small, fat, black tube with a steel casing. Korso glanced up and saw the drone still hovering ten feet above his previous position. Then he noticed the pull ring still attached to one of the claws.

Korso barely had time to turn his face away when the grenade detonated.

Thirty-Five

23 hours, 23 minutes and counting...

The world flashed white. The accompanying blast was deafening in the enclosed space. An intense blast of heat momentarily hit the back of Korso's neck as he rolled away, both hands covering his ears. He'd clamped his eyes shut as the thing detonated, but it hadn't helped much. Everything was still a featureless white.

All his senses were skewed.

He felt nauseous, and there was a high-pitched ringing in his ears. It felt as though somebody had hit him in the face with the side of an anvil. He forced himself to remain calm, knowing the worst would pass in a few seconds. He'd employed flashbangs himself and was well aware of the side effects. Already, he could feel his vision starting to return. Everything was still blurred, but he could now make out basic shapes and textures. His hearing was still useless, though. The temporary tinnitus simply overrode everything.

Slowly and carefully, Korso climbed unsteadily to his feet, only for the world to start spinning wildly like a psychedelic nightmare. Fighting the disorientating effects, and keeping well away from the light of the entranceway, he stumbled like a drunkard until he made contact with the brick wall. He knew the blast had badly affected the pressure in his inner ear, causing a complete loss of coordination and balance. That was how stun grenades worked. He just had to wait patiently for the effects to reduce in intensity. Whether he was permitted to was another story.

He looked up and saw the drone without hearing it, still hovering there in the same position. At this point, the drone was more a dark shape than anything identifiable. But the built-in video camera was no doubt recording his every move. Korso pulled the gun from his waistband and aimed it at the shape. Or tried to. Everything was wobbly, swaying in different directions, his eyes one way, his hand the other. The gun barrel kept circling before his eyes, like water swirling down a plughole.

'Quit that,' he said.

And for a brief moment, it did. The swaying stopped. The world stabilised. Korso steadied his aim at the indistinct hovering object. If in doubt, always go for centre mass.

He squeezed the trigger. The gun recoiled. He heard only a muffled *thump*.

But the drone was no longer there. With luck, he may have hit one of the rotors and rendered the thing useless. He couldn't see it anywhere, but that didn't mean much. He couldn't see much of anything at the moment.

He shook his head, which only made things worse. He looked at the ground, focusing his eyes on nothing. At the same time, he relaxed his mind and tried to think things through in a logical manner. That always helped. And one thing became immediately obvious to him. Cain and his partner had driven him here deliberately, where the confined space would only intensify the already powerful effects of the flashbang. But the bigger question was why employ the flashbang at all? After all, it was a non-lethal weapon. And the answer to that one was also obvious. In order to weaken and disorientate Korso. So he could be finished off up close. Quietly, and with minimal effort. It was time to move.

Korso raised his head and looked around. His hearing was still a mess, but his vision was improving. He could already see things with much more clarity. Like the details on the rusted flatbed truck opposite him. Carefully, he pushed off against the wall and smiled when he no longer felt any dizziness. Normality was finally returning.

Deciding against backtracking a second time, Korso ignored the fire exit to his left and turned to the one at his far right. He ran past the large entranceway before Cain could get a bead on his position. Once past the opening, he kept going at a steady jog as he aimed for the beacon of light from the fire-exit doorway.

He was still ten feet away from it when he sensed, rather than saw, something strike the brick wall in front of him.

Hearing nothing, but immediately aware he was being shot at, Korso dived to the ground to his left, away from the light of the doorway. Rolling along the ground, he raised his head to look behind him and saw a male figure crouched near the ancient flatbed truck, seventy or eighty feet away. He had a gun in his hand, the barrel still aimed at Korso. He must have gotten in through the other fire exit. If Korso had chosen to head that way instead, it would have been all over.

Korso quickly raised his own pistol, aimed quickly, and squeezed the trigger.

The sound of the shot echoed in the vast space.

The shooter disappeared behind the hood of the truck. Korso had no idea if he'd scored a hit, but he had to assume not.

At least this time he'd actually heard his own gunshot, which meant the stun grenade's effects were wearing off. It also meant the other man had to be using a silencer. Rising to a crouch, Korso ran over to the wall at his right, his gun aimed at the spot he'd last seen the shooter. Sticking close to the wall, he began walking toward the old truck, gun before him.

He'd covered about thirty feet when the shooter's head and right shoulder appeared above the hood, his gun aimed near the spot Korso had occupied before. Aiming for the fleshy part of the man's shoulder, Korso squeezed off two shots. The gun bucked twice in quick succession. There was a loud yell, and the man went down like a sack of flour.

Korso sprinted the rest of the way to the truck. When he reached it, he squeezed around the rear flatbed next to the wall until he saw the man on the ground on the other side. He was turned away from him, facing the main entranceway with his side against the vehicle, clutching his right shoulder with his left hand while the other hand still held the gun. There was a small puddle of blood next to him, getting larger. Other than some deep, heavy breathing, he barely made a sound, though he had to be in great pain.

But Korso was more concerned with that large open entrance. If he moved up a few feet and crouched, he'd be able to clearly see the steeple of the church. And Cain would be able to see him just as clearly. As it was, Cain must already have a good view of his wounded accomplice on the floor. That wasn't exactly ideal. Not wanting to expose himself any more, Korso kept his distance, staying close to the wall, still partly covered by the flatbed.

'Drop the gun,' he said. 'I don't need to kill you, but I will if I have to.'

The man didn't argue, or even turn his head at the sound of Korso's voice. He just did as he was told and gently let go of the gun. Korso clearly heard it clatter to the floor. The ringing was still there, but his hearing was improving with every second.

'Look, don't shoot, okay?' the man said in a muffled voice, his head lowered to his chest. 'I'm no hero.'

'Wise man. Now slowly turn until you're facing away from the entranceway.' That way, with any luck, Cain wouldn't be able to see the man's lips moving. If he thought the man was talking, Korso had no doubt he'd kill him in a heartbeat.

Still clutching the wounded shoulder, the man carefully turned his body until his back was flat against the vehicle. Then he turned his face to Korso.

Korso recognised him now. The large eyes, the pronounced cheekbones, the widow's peak. He'd seen three versions of that face before.

'Adamson,' he said.

'Yeah, so?'

'We've got a lot to discuss. I thought you were dead.'

Adamson coughed. 'I will be if I don't get to a hospital fast. I'm bleeding like a stuck pig here.'

'Talk to me and I'll dress the wound, then take you out of here.'

The man hawked, then spat on the floor. 'Yeah, right.'

'I've got nothing against you, Adamson. All I want is information. You give it to me and I'll drop you at the first hospital we pass. They'll probably call the police when they see the gunshot wound, but they'll still patch you up. That's the deal. You want that, don't you?'

Adamson glanced at his shoulder again, before turning back to Korso. 'Yeah, I want it. What do you wanna know?'

'First off, is it just the two of you? Or are there more to worry about?'

'Man, I wish there were.' He coughed again. Spat again. 'Nah, just the two of us. Jesus, this hurts like a bitch.'

'Next question. Where's the shipment?'

'The caviar? Damned if I know, man, and I ain't lying. The original plan was to stick the crates in some storage unit down in Texas, but that idea was scrapped early on. Now only my friend upstairs knows their exact location, and he sure as hell ain't letting me in on the secret.'

'You mean your partner up in the church tower?'

'Partner?' The man snorted, then winced in pain. 'Guys like that don't partner with nobody, man. He makes the decisions and gives the orders. Me, I'm just the lowly worker ant. I wasn't even there when they took—'

But Adamson didn't have time to complete the thought before a bullet took out his right eye.

Thirty-Six

There was barely any blood. It was all too fast. Korso had instinctively ducked at the slight movement, but he knew it didn't matter. He was out of Cain's range.

Adamson was still staring at him with his one remaining eye. It might as well have been made of glass; the brain behind it was already dead. Korso watched as his head flopped lazily to the left, then the rest of him slowly slithered down the side of the truck until the body collapsed on the floor in a lifeless heap.

So much for getting some answers.

Korso carefully backed off the way he'd come, toward that fire exit he'd been aiming for before. Still keeping close to the wall, he clicked his fingers next to his right ear to test his hearing. Confident it was close to normal again, he pulled out his phone and speed-dialled Natasha's number.

She answered on the fifth ring. 'Where are you in relation to the church?' she said in a distracted voice. Her words echoed, as though she was on speakerphone.

'No closer than I was before. But I did just have a run in with Cain's accomplice. He used a drone initially. I'm still feeling the effects of the flashbang it was carrying.'

'A flashbang? You are all right, though?'

'More or less. It was Adamson, by the way.'

'Adamson. Huh, so he *is* alive then.'

'Was. Cain put one in his brain before he could tell me anything useful. But on the plus side, we only have one of them to worry about now.'

There was a pause, as though she was busy doing something else. 'Yes,' she said, finally, 'I suppose that is good news.'

'Something's wrong. What is it?'

'Cain shot me.'

Korso came to a sudden halt a few feet from the fire exit. 'Are you serious?'

'Of course. But don't concern yourself. I'll live. The bullet merely grazed the bone in my upper left arm, although the furrow's quite deep.' She made a grunting sound. 'It bled heavily. But at least my old first aid training finally came in useful. I'm working on the wound as we speak.'

'Where are you?'

'Some house. I'm not sure of the street name, but it's two blocks away from the church.' She grunted again, then let out a long breath. 'There. At least the bleeding has stopped now.'

'You're lucky. When did all this happen?'

'About six or seven minutes ago.'

Korso thought that seemed feasible. It had only been about five minutes since Cain and Adamson had worked in unison to corral him into this damn warehouse.

'So you are on your way now?' Natasha said.

'I will be. Listen, does Cain know which house you're in?'

'Yes, I'm sure he saw me break in here. Why?'

253

'Because with Adamson out of the picture, his attention's now split in two directions. And he can only concentrate on one of us at a time, right?'

'Right.'

'So this might be a good time for one of us to keep him occupied by making themselves an irresistible target, while the other slips in through the vestry door and disarms him. Sound like a plan to you?'

'When you say one of us...'

'I mean me, obviously,' Korso said. 'I'm too far away to do much else other than draw attention away from you.'

Silence on the line. 'You keep surprising me, Korso. He is a very good shot, you know.'

Korso was all too aware of that. But while he didn't particularly relish putting his life on the line for anyone, especially someone he didn't really trust, he knew the risks better than most. And they weren't as bad as they might seem at first glance. Back in the distant past there were occasions when he too had been in a highly elevated position, just like Cain, peering through a telescopic sight. He knew how hard it was to hit a moving target from distance. Even more so when that target was both aware he was being tracked, and not moving in a straight line.

'We've no other choice,' he told her. 'You said it yourself. We have to move fast before he gets impatient and decides to move on. You all patched up and ready to move?'

'I'm ready.'

'Good. Once I hang up, wait at least sixty seconds before you leave the house. We want to make sure I'm the one he's focused on. And move quickly. So even if he does spot you, he won't get a clean shot.'

'Understood,' she said. 'Good luck.'

Pocketing the phone, Korso took a deep breath as he stepped over to the nearby fire exit. He placed a hand on either side of the open doorway, looked through. Beyond was a wide open space that had probably been a large employee parking area once. Now it was just a bare lot with direct access to the empty road ahead, which would take him west. Toward the church, and toward Cain.

And whatever else might happen along the way.

He pushed himself through the doorway and started running.

Thirty-Seven

23 hours, 12 minutes and counting...

Moving perpendicular to the church, Korso ran in a straight line across the road ahead. He wanted to make himself visible to Cain as soon as possible. The moment he reached the empty street, he veered right and headed west, jogging at a steady pace, not wanting to wear himself out needlessly. He focused on the church steeple half a mile away, still with its clock hands forever stuck at twelve.

If Cain was keeping an eye on this general area, he'd have spotted Korso the second he came into the open. And it wouldn't take him long to figure out Korso was acting as bait for his partner. But that didn't matter. Just as long as Korso's presence kept him occupied for the next few minutes.

Korso began zigzagging again at random moments, whenever the feeling took him. If he had no idea what he was going to do, there was no way Cain could predict his movements either. Nondescript commercial buildings passed by on each side. Korso barely paid them any attention. He focused on the church spire over half a mile away. And his pace and rhythm. He breathed in through both nose and mouth in order to maximise his oxygen intake.

Jogging five miles every morning back in Bermuda meant he had a good idea what his body was capable of. Half a mile usually took him a little less than five minutes, but that was running more or less in a straight line. Zigzagging would add at least another minute to the journey. Just as long as he got there in one piece.

He avoided thinking about Cain peering at him through his rifle sights. There was no point musing on the unknown. And with the suppressor, there'd be no gunshots to warn him anyway. The first he'd know of it would be if he took one in the chest. Then he wouldn't be worrying about anything anymore.

When he reached the intersection to Main Street, he jogged straight through without pausing. This one was called Campbell Avenue. He felt like he was in one of those movies about the last man on earth. The sun was still high in the sky, but behind the steeple now. Perfect conditions for Cain, assuming he was keeping Korso in his sights. He heard distant barking and wondered if it was the same mutt from before. More empty buildings passed by on either side of him. Some retail units. A few more shuttered stores. More neglected houses.

The seconds passed, turned into minutes.

He'd covered about half the distance when his thoughts turned to Natasha. If she was only two blocks from the church, it would only take her about sixty seconds to reach it on foot. Then maybe another minute or two to climb the stairs and overpower Cain. Maybe she already had, and the danger was over.

Pointless speculation.

Another block passed by. Another intersection. Then another. More neglected houses, along with plenty of vacant plots. Korso ran past them all, seeing nobody. The clock tower grew ever closer.

Jogging down the middle of another nondescript street, this one called West Burlington, he reached a count of 220 in his head. He figured he was about five blocks away from his destination now. His breathing was still regular, but his thigh muscles were feeling the strain from all the rapid changes of direction. He zigged left again, and thought he saw something strike the concrete a few inches to his immediate right. But he couldn't be sure. It could have been anything.

Seconds later, he was passing a streetlight when he heard a sharp *TTINNG* as something ricocheted off the steel lamppost.

All doubts vanished. Cain was now using him for target practice.

Breaking into a sprint, Korso zagged to the right-hand side of the street toward a row of single-storey clapboard A-frames, leaped over the overgrown hedge of the nearest, and kept going. He heard a brief rustle behind him as another bullet struck the hedge he'd just cleared. The front yard was bare, with no trees to use as cover. He increased his pace, aiming for the house directly ahead. They were all on small plots, with hardly any space between them. So it was through the house or nothing. He saw two large windows, one on either side of the front door. Both glass panes were still intact, and he wasn't about to cut himself to pieces trying to get in that way. That just left the wooden door.

He leaped onto the porch, tried the handle. It was locked. Taking one step back, he raised his right leg and with his full weight behind it, launched a powerful, horizontal front kick at the weakest spot, just beneath the lock. The moment the heel of his boot connected with the door, there was a loud splintering sound as the lock separated from the frame, leaving a slight gap. Korso shouldered himself inside and immediately dived to the floor, slamming the door shut with his foot.

The house was in semi-darkness, all the drapes drawn, but he was able to make out that he was in a living area with two more doorways leading to other parts of the house. Other than an old table set against one wall, all the furnishings had long since disappeared. The wooden floor was grimy with dust and dirt.

The door on the left was ajar, and through the gap he saw part of on an old bed. No good. Getting to his feet, Korso ran over to the other door, pulled it open, and entered another empty room with another doorway leading back. He ran straight through and into a kitchen area. Out the rear window he saw a very long backyard, overgrown with grass and surrounded by six-foot-high wooden fencing on all three sides. Good cover, at least. The house backing directly onto this one was almost two hundred feet away.

Korso assessed his options for a moment. As he'd hoped, he now had Cain's full attention, and he only needed it to stay that way for a little longer.

He could run down the yard and make his way through that house down there, but then he'd be back on the streets again, right out in the open. He wanted Cain to be on the hop instead, trying to guess where he'd next appear. So the better option was to make his way toward the church via the backyards of the other two properties on this block, using whatever was available for cover. And the trick was to let Cain see him just enough to keep his attention focused, but never long enough to get a precise fix. He only needed to keep himself in view for another minute or so, allowing Natasha enough time to do her part. Once he reached the next intersection he could go back to zigzagging. It would only take thirty more seconds to get to the church, by which time she should have taken care of business.

In theory.

From his position, he was unable to see if the neighbouring properties had similar fences, but over the top of this one he could also see three evergreen spruce trees in next door's backyard, and a small cottonwood in the last property. They'd have to do.

Korso unlatched and opened the kitchen door and ran out of the house, aiming for the fence at his left. Grabbing the top of the planks with both hands, he jumped up and heaved himself over, landing on both feet on the other side. Staying low, he saw another wooden fence facing this one, fifty feet away, but it was only four-foot high. Korso now had a good view of the church spire in the distance… which meant Cain had the same view of him.

Glancing to his right, he saw the three evergreens, all bunched together. Sprinting toward the nearest spruce, he heard a sharp splintering sound behind him, and figured he'd just avoided getting one in the head. Reaching the trees a second later, he made his way between them using the pine needles as cover. Once he was in the open again, he was close enough to the fence to crouch-walk the rest of the way. Staying low, he repositioned himself twenty feet to the left, which was about where he'd seen the cottonwood.

He jumped up and vaulted over the low fence. The cottonwood, dense with yellow leaves, was just to his left. Beyond the tree was another boundary fence, but six-feet high this time. He stayed in the open for another half-second, letting Cain get a look, then ran to the tree.

Standing behind the trunk, under the cover of the leaves, he took a breath. About a minute had passed since he'd left the first house.

After a few more moments, he pushed off and sprinted at the fence, reaching it seconds later. Staying low, he moved ten feet to the right, just in case. After thirty more seconds, he figured enough time had passed for Natasha to make her play. As far as he knew, he hadn't been shot at for a while now. He jumped up, hauled himself over the fence, and landed on the sidewalk of the next street along.

Without pausing, Korso ran back to West Burlington, turned right and just kept running. Back on his original course. He kept his speed up and continued zigzagging constantly, just in case. No point in taking any more unnecessary chances. Not now he was so close.

It took Korso another forty-three seconds to reach the street he'd been aiming for. He quickly ducked behind a tree in the front yard of a nearby house, using it as cover to look the place over while he got his breath back.

The church grounds took up the entire block. The church itself was a large two-storey clapboard building with plenty of space around it, the area probably serving as a huge parking lot back when the town was populated. The concrete spire was set at the far right of the building, rising to a point about a hundred feet into the sky. The shaft was about eighty feet high. Above it, the belfry. Then the attic, which bore clock faces on all sides. After that, the spire itself, with a cross on the very top. Toward the edge of the property was a much smaller, tan-coloured, clapboard building with a broad porch around it. Possibly the living quarters of the local pastor, back when there had been one. Both buildings had the look of long neglect and disuse.

Korso didn't let that fool him. Cain would be in the belfry, just above the shaft, with those ornate arched openings that were just perfect for a sniper.

He felt his phone vibrate and pulled it from his jacket pocket. The same number as before, so clearly Natasha's phone. But was it her, or Cain? He took the call and pressed the phone to his ear, hoping the next voice he heard would be female.

After a short silence, a faint, slightly muffled voice said, 'Are you there?'

'That depends. Who is this?'

'Who do you think?' Natasha said, in a much clearer voice. 'Where are you?'

'Within spitting distance of the church,' he said, allowing himself a brief smile. 'And you?'

'Inside the clock tower. In the room with the church bells.'

'The belfry.'

'Yes, the belfry. I've been trying to call you for over three minutes.'

Korso checked the screen and saw the missed call icon at the top left corner. 'With good news, I hope.'

'Just the opposite. Cain is gone.'

Thirty-Eight

22 hours, 57 minutes and counting...

When he finally reached the top of the spiral stairwell, he saw Natasha crouched on the east-facing side of the belfry, peering at the town through the arched openings. She still wore her dark baseball cap with the bill pulled down low, and there was now a dark material tied around her upper left arm in a makeshift field dressing.

She turned at the sound of his footsteps. 'Korso, you're all right? No injuries?'

'Still in one piece. How about you?'

'I've suffered worse. Come over here and look at this.'

The cramped room was only ten feet square, and Korso had to stoop to avoid banging his head against the two large church bells above him. He went over to Natasha, and immediately recognised the rifle lying on the floor next to her. It was a Bergara B-14 HMR, a popular bolt-action hunting rifle with a five-round AICS-style magazine. Capable of shooting over a distance of a thousand yards, or just over half a mile. They were fairly common and inexpensive, but Cain had clearly been in a hurry if he left it behind. Although he'd had the presence of mind to take the bolt lever, so nobody else could use it.

'I entered through the rear door several minutes ago,' Natasha said. 'He must have beaten me by seconds, or exited via the front.'

'No sign of him at all?'

'None.'

'No stray shots after you left the house?'

She shrugged. 'None that found its target, thankfully. He may have tried and missed, but how would I know?'

'Good point.'

Korso thought about telling her of his being shot at, but decided against it. He studied the bandage around her arm. It looked like she'd used an old t-shirt. It was flecked with her blood, but not too much of it.

'How's the pain?' he asked.

'Bearable. But it keeps me focused. Cain could be anywhere now, Korso. Maybe even watching us as we speak.'

'Possibly, but he's lost the height advantage now, along with his rifle.' Korso raised his foot and brought his heel down hard on the long barrel, then down again on the scope, completely misaligning the gun's aim. 'Just to be sure.'

He knelt down next to Natasha, and looked out through the arches at the deserted town beyond without really seeing it. He was looking inward, trying to think like Cain, in order to second guess his next move. After mulling various possibilities over, he said, 'I don't believe he'll try and kill us again. Not here, anyway.'

Natasha turned to him, her brow furrowed. 'What makes you say that?'

'Two things. The C4 he left for us in the drugstore, and his continued attempts to pick us off from this eagle's nest. Or three things, if you count his using Adamson against me. That all tells me Cain prefers to kill from a distance, not up close and personal. Also, he's seen us both in action, so he now knows for a fact that he's dealing with trained professionals. And it's now two against one in our favour, don't forget. So he's not about to suddenly change character and try to take us out at close quarters. That's not his modus operandi. Too much risk of things going wrong. And he's far too careful for that.'

'A fair assumption. So what do think he'll do?'

'Probably what I'd do if I were in his shoes.'

'Which is?'

'Disappear.'

She blinked at him. 'Seriously?'

'Why not? As far as he's concerned, he's still holding all the winning cards. He dragged the two of us out here and made a decent effort to take us out of the game permanently, and failed each time. What does he gain by trying again? Nothing. Not when he can simply disappear off the face of the earth, with no chance of us ever finding him again.'

She breathed out a sigh. 'I was afraid you might say that. Do you really think we've no chance if he chooses to run?'

'No.'

'But you said—'

'I'm trying to think like Cain, and that's simply how he would see things. I don't give up so easily. I've been in this business long enough to know there's always more than one way to solve a problem. You just have to find it.'

She looked at him. 'You have a talent for finding the positive in every setback.'

'There's no secret to it,' he said with a shrug. 'I'm just used to doing things the hard way, that's all.'

'And do you have any ideas on our next move if he does decide to vanish?'

'Not yet. Let me think on it while we head back to the car. And I also remember seeing some unused bandages and medical tape in that pharmacy, so you might want to change that dressing while we've got the chance.'

They made their way down the stairwell in single file, and left the building the same way they'd entered, by the rear door. Once they reached the road out front, they headed east toward the drugstore, each lost in their own thoughts.

It was eight minutes later when they arrived at the section of Main Street they'd started from, the Chevy Impala still parked where they'd left it. Korso had used the walk to give Natasha a brief account of what he'd gone through, and she updated him with her side of the story. The drugstore looked the same as when they'd first arrived in town, except for the front door, which was now ajar. He turned his attention to the vehicle and groaned inwardly when he saw the rear tyre on the driver's side. It was completely flat.

'Probably caused by Cain when he was shooting at us earlier,' Natasha said.

'Or more recent than that,' Korso said. 'A little parting gift to remember him by. It also means his trail will be that much colder by the time I get it fixed. Let me have the keys.'

Natasha pulled them from her pants pocket and lobbed them over. Korso caught them and knelt down next to the wheel. He spotted the bullet hole straight away. It was hard to miss. The rifle round had entered the bottom part of the tyre, pulling the rubber apart to leave a hole the size of a dime.

Getting up, he pressed the unlock button on the fob and the car chirped back at him. He stepped over to the rear and popped the trunk, pulled up the false floor, unscrewed and removed the spare wheel and then placed it on the ground. As he was reaching in for the jack and wrench, he heard Natasha open one of the car doors. He saw her in there, rummaging around for something. He slammed the trunk lid down and set to work.

He was just starting on the second wheel nut on the flat when Natasha joined him. She was holding out the burner phone Cain had left them.

'He left us a sweet message,' she said.

Korso looked at the display. It contained two words: *Sayonara, assholes.*

'As succinct as ever,' he said. 'Sent when?'

Natasha pressed some buttons. 'Ten after four. Six minutes ago.'

Korso nodded as he went back to loosening the nut. Hard to believe it had been just over an hour since they'd entered this godforsaken town.

'How long will it take to change this tyre?' she said.

'Not long. Five or ten minutes.'

'Good. I will go and change this dressing.'

'Stay alert. He could still be nearby.'

'The same goes for you.'

Korso thought that was sound advice. He pulled the Ruger from his waistband and set it down on the ground next to him. He grabbed hold of the wrench and was about to turn it again when he stopped. He felt something nagging at him. He stood up, saw Natasha walking toward the front door of Philby's. The partially open front door. She pushed it open further and took a step inside.

'*Wait*,' he called out.

Natasha stopped immediately. She turned back to him. 'What is it?'

'That door wasn't open before. After we dived inside to avoid the gunfire, I distinctly remember kicking it shut behind us. And we left by the rear exit.'

Natasha looked at the door as though it might hold a clue. 'You're sure?'

'Absolutely.'

'So Cain has been here since then.' She slowly pulled the Taurus from her waistband, pulled back the hammer. She took another step inside.

'Natasha, I said *stop*.'

She halted again, turning to him. 'What now?'

'Close quarters, remember? It's not his style. He likes distance between himself and his quarry.' He thought for a moment. 'Do you hear or see anything in there that you didn't before?'

Without taking another step, Natasha pushed her head into the store. After five or six seconds, she pulled back and said, 'I see nothing different in there. What am I listening for?'

'I'm not sure. Look, forget about those supplies in there. You can buy some fresh bandages at the next Walmart we see.'

'It will only take a second to check.'

'Natasha, I'm asking you not to go in there. I don't like it.'

She looked at him again. Then she shrugged, turned and began walking back. 'Very well,' she said. 'But only because you asked so nicely.'

Natasha reached his side of the car, and said, 'I still think you are overreac—' when the building exploded behind her.

Thirty-Nine

Korso instinctively dived to the ground, knowing the Chevy would protect them from the worst of the shock-wave. The noise of the blast was tremendous, like the world was coming to an end. An intense wave of heat briefly washed over him as he clamped both hands over his head. He felt the weight of Natasha's body as she landed on his legs.

All around, the sounds of glass shattering. Glancing up, he saw large chunks of masonry landing in the street, and heard something land on the roof of the Chevy. Smaller pieces of rubble landed on his hands and his neck and the back of his head. The sound of thunder quickly died down to just the ringing in his ears. Then nothing. He felt Natasha shift her weight and freed his legs. Glancing over, he saw she was in the same position as him, both arms protecting her head.

'You okay?' he said, a little louder than necessary.

She raised her head, looked at him, and nodded once.

Korso slowly raised himself up, using the side of the car for support. He looked at what remained of Philby's Pharmacy. The roof was completely gone, as was much of the roofing of the adjoining properties on either side. The outer walls had collapsed in on themselves. The whole property was engulfed in flames, and dark smoke writhed and billowed into the sky. It looked solid enough to reach out and grab.

He used a hand to wave smoke away from his face. He'd witnessed the effects of C4 many times, but its destructive capabilities never failed to impress.

Natasha was now standing next to him, staring open-mouthed at the devastation. She turned to Korso with a fierce look in her eyes, then suddenly grabbed him by the back of his neck and clamped her lips hard against his. Seconds passed, he didn't know how many. Just as suddenly, she released him and turned back to the destruction before them.

'You're welcome,' he said, once he got his breath back.

She raised a finger. 'Not another word.'

He saw a smoking brick had landed on the car roof. Or half of one. He reached over and picked it up. It felt hot in his hand. It had also left a dent in the roof. Throwing it to the ground, he walked round the car, inspecting it closely. Other than the roof, he saw very little external damage. Black soot and dust covered every inch of the vehicle on one side, but all the windows were intact. More importantly, so were the other three tyres.

Returning to the one flat tyre, he began to work the wrench as fast as he could. The sooner they were out of there, the better.

'I think you can say goodbye to your deposit,' he said.

Natasha snorted. 'The least of our problems. Somebody *must* have heard that explosion and called the police, meaning further complications we can do without.'

'Only if we're still here when they arrive.' Removing the last nut, he inserted the jack under the car and began raising the vehicle.

'Can I help at all?' Natasha said.

'Not really. This is a one-person job.'

As he worked, she said, 'If Cain could detonate the plastique remotely, why didn't he when we were both in there earlier?'

'I don't think he did detonate it remotely.' Once the flat tyre was an inch off the ground, he removed it and fitted the spare in its place. 'I'm no explosives expert, but if the trigger device was pressure-sensitive, then a small vibration against the fridge could have been enough to set it off. And then I remembered that ancient-looking alarm clock on the work desk in there. The one with the huge bells.'

'I remember seeing that now,' she said, nodding. 'And you were asking me before if I could hear anything in there. You were thinking of a ticking noise?'

'It was just a thought.' Korso began replacing the wheel nuts, tightening each one as he went. 'Cain gets back here before us and puts one in the tyre to delay our departure just long enough. He winds up the clock, sets the alarm for ten minutes and places the bells against the refrigerator. Boom. Sayonara.'

'Well, you were right on that point. Although you also thought he wouldn't try to kill us again.'

'I never said I was perfect.'

After lowering the vehicle to the ground again, he removed the jack, and tightened each of the four nuts further until he was satisfied the wheel was solid. Meanwhile, Natasha dragged the old wheel to the sidewalk, and slammed the trunk shut.

'Still no sirens,' she said, opening the passenger door.

'Yet.'

Neither of them spoke until Korso got them out of Bilchner and safely back onto US-550. Fortunately, they didn't see any police cars during their exit from town. Or any other vehicles for that matter. He continued heading south, aiming them toward the city of Durango, located fifty or sixty miles from their present location.

Now they were out of the woods, so to speak, Korso reduced his speed to a respectable fifty-five miles per hour, matching that of the other vehicles on the road. After everything they'd faced, it would be dumb to get pulled over for speeding. He checked the dashboard clock. It was 16:34. A little over two days since this had all started. By rights, he should have had another forty-seven hours to work with, but instead he had less than a day. He turned to see Natasha swiping a finger across her phone display. He also noticed the specks of blood on her arm dressing hadn't gotten any worse.

'The bleeding seems to have stopped,' he said.

'Hmm,' she said, still focused on the screen.

With both eyes on the road, Korso pulled his own phone from his pocket and keyed a number. He raised it to his ear and waited. At the voicemail prompt, he left his name and number and hung up. He placed the phone on the central partition.

'That strange Dog person again?' Natasha said.

'The same.'

'What exactly can he or she do for us now?'

'Probably nothing. I won't know until I ask.'

Natasha returned her attention to her own phone. 'I assume you are making for that city that we passed through on the way here?'

'Right. It's the nearest place with an airport. I remember seeing some signs for it when we drove through town.'

'Yes, I was just checking it on Wikipedia. It is called the Durango-La Plata County Airport, located twelve miles southeast of the city. And I believe it is now time for our two pilots in Texas to start earning their pay.'

She pressed a few buttons and raised her phone to her ear. After a few seconds, she said, 'This is your client. You are both awake and sober? Good. We are currently in southwest Colorado, and so I want you to bring yourselves to the Durango-La Plata Airport as soon as humanly possible, where you will refuel the plane for the next trip. We're still figuring out our next destination, and will provide you with that information once you're here. How long will it take you? Not good enough. I want you at this airport within two hours. Do that and you will each receive a thousand-dollar cash bonus… Yes, I thought you might.' She ended the call, placed the phone on the dash.

'Cash bonuses,' he said. 'You've changed your tune since Tijuana.'

She shrugged. 'One must adapt to the circumstances, and time is now of the essence. Was I lying?'

'About what?'

'About being able to provide them with a new destination when they arrive.'

'Well, you were a little premature, but the pilots don't need to know that. And they'll wait for as long as we want them to. Once we get to Durango, we'll figure out our next move in more detail. And on that subject, can you get your source in the SAA investigative unit to email you their official and unofficial findings so far, so I at least know what to ignore? And while you're at it, anything from their CAA counterparts in Guyana would be—'

His phone began trilling. 'Put it on speaker,' he said.

'Hello again, Korso.'

This time, the modulated voice filling the car was a generic robotic voice of indeterminate gender, totally void of inflection or emotion.

'Dog,' Korso said. 'What are you now, the Terminator?'

'Funny. So did everything work out at that storage place in Texas?'

'Not really, but through no fault of yours.'

'Naturally. I mean, how could it be? So what can I do for you this time?'

'We have a burner phone here. Totally anonymous. It was left to us by the person we're tracking, and any information you could glean from it would be greatly appreciated. And before you say it, I don't expect miracles.'

'Very wise. Still, I guess I can try. Is the phone switched on now?'

Korso turned to Natasha with a raised eyebrow. She pulled Cain's burner from her pocket and pressed a key. The display lit up. 'Yes, it is,' she said.

'Give me the number and I'll take a look-see. If there's nothing there, consider this a freebie. Anything else will cost you.'

'Understood.' Korso recited the number from memory, then just concentrated on the road while Dog worked.

Less than a minute later, Dog said, 'Nothing. That phone's cleaner than a nun's browser history. I'm looking at the call log now, and all I can see is a single incoming call and two incoming texts. All completely anonymous and untraceable. And I do mean John Doe anonymous, with cut-outs and everything. If your guy was the one making those calls, he's clearly no dummy.'

'That much we already know. Thanks for checking, though.'

'No sweat.'

'Well, it was worth a try,' Korso said. He pressed the button to lower the window, and threw the phone out.

'Was that wise?' Natasha said. 'That phone was our only means of contact with Cain.'

'I have trust issues with people who continually try to kill me. Also, he might be able to track us through it. It's not worth the risk.'

He drove in silence for the next few minutes, figuring out the best approach from which to come at the problem. He figured they had enough time for just one more throw of the dice. If he got it wrong, it was game over and he'd be on the run for the rest of his natural life. For however long that might be. Still, he knew there was always an answer to any given problem. He just had to find it.

Another phone began ringing, pulling him from his thoughts. Natasha's this time.

She grabbed it, checked the screen. 'Care to guess who?'

'Not really. Just let it ring.'

She ignored him and took the call. 'Three, four, seven, one. I am here... No, it went badly. We still do not have it.' She moved the phone away from her ear as Sardoca yelled garbled obscenities. Once he'd calmed down, she brought the phone to her ear and said in a calm, deadly voice, 'You would do well not to take that tone with me. I am not one of your lackeys.' There was a pause as she listened to his no doubt apologetic reply. 'Very well.'

She hung up and went into her menu.

'Not a happy camper, I take it,' Korso said.

'Did you expect him to be? I'm to call him back via Skype. A video call again.'

'Like it isn't bad enough just listening to his voice.'

Natasha said nothing as she pressed more buttons. Korso just drove.

Shortly, she raised the phone so it was in front of her face, holding it in landscape mode. 'Ah, there you are,' she said. 'How's the audio? Can you hear me?'

'I hear you just fine,' Sardoca said. 'Move the phone around, Natasha. Let me see everything.'

Out the corner of his eye, Korso saw Natasha panning the phone slowly around the car interior in a semi-circle, then back again.

'Good,' Sardoca said. 'Now angle it so you're both in the frame.'

'Interesting choice of words,' Korso said.

Natasha placed the phone against her door's armrest, then sat back in her seat. Korso took a brief glance at the phone, and saw Sardoca from the waist up, sitting at what looked like a breakfast bar. He wore a sweatshirt with the arms cut off, and a blue baseball cap. He held a bright green smoothie in his right hand.

'So what went wrong, Korso?'

'I'm driving,' Korso said. 'Natasha can tell it far better than I can.'

'I want you to tell me.'

Korso smiled. 'This may come as news to you, Sardoca, but I don't care what you want. Natasha, be so kind as to give your associate a recap of events so far.'

Natasha turned to the screen and started talking, giving Sardoca a concise account of their long hour in Bilchner. Mostly her side of events, of course. She finished with the explosion in the drugstore, mentioning how Korso had warned her away from entering the building moments before it went off.

'Well, I wouldn't read too much into that,' Sardoca said. 'With you gone, Korso would know the instant I found out I'd feed him to the sharks, so it's far better to keep you alive in the long run. He always looks out for his own welfare first. Am I right?'

'Aren't you always?' Korso said.

'So let me see if I've got this straight now. With time fast running out, you're telling me you still don't have a clue who this Cain might be, or where the shipment is, and that our only lead has now flown the coop to god only knows where. Have I missed anything out?'

'That's actually a pretty faultless summary,' Korso said. He was almost enjoying this. It was always good to see Sardoca sweat.

Sardoca gave a weary sigh. 'Except I know you, Korso. And you've never been the type to simply give up on an assignment. Which means you've already got something else in mind.'

'Of course I do. It's not rocket science. If one trail goes cold, you simply come at the problem from a different angle. So that's what we'll do.'

'And what angle is that?'

He noticed Natasha was also looking at him now. 'We tried the direct approach, which was to track down the shipment itself, which in turn led us to those responsible for the heist. That looked promising for a while, but now Cain's decided to take himself off the grid that trail's dead, as are most of the men behind it all. So instead we'll go after the aircraft itself. Find the plane, find the shipment. In theory, of course.'

'Theories? I don't have time for theories, Korso. Which means you don't either.'

'Well, if you hadn't wasted ten days of your original deadline we'd have exhausted all manner of possibilities by this point, crossing each one off as we went along. But we no longer have that luxury, do we? So unless you've got a sure-fire lead you've been keeping from us, this is the best you're going to get.'

'He has a point,' Natasha said. 'We're fast running out of options here.'

Sardoca said nothing, but sipped at his smoothie. Korso drove, more than comfortable with the silence. After a moment, Sardoca said, 'Okay, tell me what you need.'

Finally, something constructive. 'Tell him, Natasha,' Korso said.

'Contact our man in the SAA,' she said. 'It will sound better coming from you. Instruct him to email PDFs of their findings so far, both official and unofficial, in order that we can discount those areas already investigated. The same goes for their counterparts in Guyana. Do we have someone in that organisation able to supply us with that kind of data?'

'The lead investigator, as it happens.' That smug smile of his filled the screen. 'Since a week ago. The moment he heard the figure we were offering him, the guy was like a dog in heat. I'll have them both email the relevant documents to you within the next thirty minutes.'

'Good,' Natasha said.

'Anything else?'

'Not right now,' Korso said. 'Once I've had a good look at their progress, we can start formulating a definite plan of action. We may need further intel, but I'll let you know when we do. Or Natasha will.'

'Fine. Now that we're getting down to the wire, I'll also be wanting more frequent progress reports from you two. And Natasha?'

'Yes?'

'Never let your guard down with this guy. I mean it. Not for a second.'

Sardoca's face shrank to nothing as he ended the call.

Korso gave Natasha a sideways glance. 'If only he knew.'

Forty

21 hours, 35 minutes and counting...

Forty-five minutes later, Natasha flashed her Platinum Visa at the card reader next to the cash till. It beeped back and a green tick flashed up on the display. The large, bespectacled cashier gave Natasha a wide smile as she handed her a receipt for their food.

'Thanks for visiting Harlequin's,' she said. 'You two have yourselves a great evening now. And don't forget to check out the bestsellers section downstairs before you go. We got some new arrivals just in today.'

'We will,' Natasha said, smiling back. 'Thank you.'

With his laptop under his arm, Korso picked up the full tray and carried it to one of the empty tables by the window. At 17:25 on a weeknight, the cafeteria had plenty to choose from. They sat facing each other. Natasha took her coffee and bagels from the tray, leaving him with his tea, mineral water and toasted ham and cheese sandwich.

They'd entered the city of Durango ten minutes earlier. Korso had been driving through the downtown area, looking for a quiet place to lay low and make plans, when he saw the large bookstore. Nestled between a franchise hardware store and a sports bar, it was an unassuming, two-storey building with an eye-catching black and white logo out front. It also boasted its own cafeteria on the second floor. Since he always gravitated toward the literary, the place immediately appealed to him. After parking the vehicle, Natasha had picked up some fresh bandages and other supplies from a nearby drugstore, after which they made their way to the bookshop. Upon entering, Korso had nodded with appreciation at the first floor's eclectic layout of displays, as handmade signs with too many exclamation marks promised unbelievable delights behind every book cover. Korso got a kick out of the writer's obvious enthusiasm. And also the irreverence. Under different circumstances, he could have spent a whole afternoon in there, just browsing.

Natasha sipped at her coffee while Korso set his laptop on the table. Muted conversation came from the few other patrons dotted around the cafeteria. Some were quietly reading the paperbacks they'd just purchased, occasionally sipping their drinks or munching on their snacks. An elderly man at a nearby table was happily paging through a collection of Edgar Allan Poe's short stories. The numerous bookshelves taking up the background gave the place the feel of a library reading room.

'Time to see if Sardoca's kept his word,' he said.

Natasha pulled her phone from her pocket and swiped the screen a couple of times. After a few seconds, she said, 'As promised. I'll forward it to you now... There, done.'

'Thanks.' Korso opened his laptop, logged on to the store's free wifi service and accessed his email account. He had three new messages in his inbox. The first was from an existing client, the second from a potential one, the third from Natasha. He opened it and checked the address of the original sender. It was from a standard Gmail account. The username was *sarfra* followed by what looked like ten random numbers, but probably wasn't. There was no text in the email, just two PDF attachments, labelled *Ukr1* and *Guy1*.

'This Gmail address of Sardoca's,' Korso said. 'Is that the account he usually uses to communicate with you?'

She bit into a bagel. 'And everyone else he deals with, for all I know. Why? Are you planning to put it on a spam mailing list?'

'I'm not that small-minded.'

Putting down the bagel, Natasha replaced the lid on her coffee cup, reached for her shopping bag and got to her feet. 'In the meantime,' she said, 'I will be in the restroom replacing these bandages.'

Korso nodded distractedly as he double clicked on the first attachment. It opened up to reveal a sixty-seven-page document. There was no contents listing, since the final official accident report hadn't yet been filed. What he was reading was clearly still a work in progress, consisting mostly of preliminary reports and third-party testimonies submitted by the individual FAA investigators. Therefore, no title page or synopsis at the beginning, and definitely no 'analysis and conclusions' section at the end. But that was fine. He was less interested in their theories or hypotheses than he was in their specific areas of research. Fortunately, this wasn't like some assignments when he'd had to wade through pages and pages of ancient photocopies, with much of his time spent deciphering mostly unintelligible handwriting. These days everything was keyed straight onto an iPad using the industry standard Times New Roman or Helvetica, thus making his job that much easier.

He slowly scrolled down the document, speed reading through all the technical wording to make sure he didn't skip anything vital. Since it was all written in their native

Ukrainian, he was sure he had missed things. Korso was fluent in Russian, so he could understand most of it since they both used a similar form of the Cyrillic alphabet. But there were numerous differences in the languages. Whole paragraphs flew by where he barely understood a single word. Most obstacles of that type could be solved by using the surrounding text as context for the problematic passages, enabling him to make some sense of the whole. But it was a hard slog.

Part of his subconscious noticed Natasha return to the table at some point, but his attention remained squarely focused on the screen in front of him.

As he neared the end of the file, he finally reached the appendices. This was more like it. Among other things, these sections listed the various locations checked by the investigators, and the results of their findings there. All were still at the bullet-point stage. Later, a technical writer would integrate all these disparate elements into a single cohesive report that would make sense to the average layman, whereupon it would then be released to the media. But for now, bullet-points were just fine.

He looked through it all carefully, methodically. He figured the SAA must have a fairly substantial expense budget. Assuming this appendix was up to date, in the last six weeks their investigators had travelled to a total of seventeen countries in order to follow up leads, not including the Ukraine itself. Half of those trips were to smaller islands in the Caribbean, such as Trinidad and Tobago, Barbados and Grenada, as well as Jamaica and Puerto Rico. The rest were devoted to Guyana and its closest neighbours, Suriname, French Guiana, Venezuela, and a few others.

He looked through it all, then sat back in his chair and stared out the window, digesting what he'd read, while adding his own conclusions to the mix. He caught sight again of the elderly guy reading Edgar Allan Poe, and as he did so, the germ of an idea began to form in the back of his mind.

Coming back to the present, he noticed it was almost twilight outside. Checking the clock on his laptop, he saw almost an hour had passed in the blink of an eye. He didn't have many of those left.

Natasha looked up from her phone. She was wearing a completely different shirt than before, with only a small bulge on her upper left arm to indicate that she still wore a bandage under it.

'Your tea is cold,' she said.

'How would you know?'

'I tried some. Disgusting.'

Korso picked up his cup and drank down half of the cool liquid in one go. 'Nothing wrong with cold tea. Where did that shirt come from?'

'I went out and bought it thirty minutes ago. You didn't notice me leaving.'

Korso reached into the paper bag for his sandwich and took a bite. Although cold, it still tasted good. 'So what else happened while I was away?'

'The co-pilot called me a few minutes ago to say they'll be landing shortly. I told him once they're on the ground they should refuel the plane and just wait for us, and that we'll give them our new destination once we arrive. Assuming we have one by then.'

'I remain optimistic. Anything else?'

'I've also been looking over this Guyana document,' she said, waving her phone. 'I tried the other one, but soon gave up. My Russian is only adequate.'

'It's Ukrainian, and it was tough going for me too, though informative. But Guyana's an ex-British colony, so I'm assuming their reports are in English, right? I haven't looked at them yet.'

'They are, but you may not want to bother. The GAA are clearly not as thorough as their Ukrainian counterparts. The PDF document contains only eighteen pages.'

'They're probably just understaffed,' Korso said as he leaned forward and opened the document himself. 'Guyana's still what they term a developing country, although that could change anytime. I read that they struck oil in the Atlantic several years back.'

'How fortunate for them.'

'Only for those in power. The country only benefits if that wealth trickles down to the populace, which seems doubtful with all the corruption over there.'

She smirked at him. 'Cynic.'

He shrugged. 'We both know how the world works.'

Using the touchpad, he slowly scrolled down the document. Natasha was right. There wasn't much to it. As far as he could see, they only had three people assigned to the case, and all their investigative work was based in Guyana itself. He speed read through it all fairly rapidly, and saw nothing of any real consequence. Although that was kind of interesting in itself. The investigators had searched the countryside for wreckage or tracks, as well as interviewed farmers or anybody who might have seen or heard a low-flying plane on the specified date, with no results. But he also knew that Guyana was one of the more sparsely populated countries in South America, with rainforests covering much of its land mass. So on the face of it, those results didn't really mean much.

Except, that little germ of an idea was now starting to grow in his mind. Time to see if there was any weight to it. Exiting the document, Korso opened his browser and went to Google and typed three words into the search field.

The results that came up were less than satisfactory. Each of the top hits contained two of those words, but never all three. He went to Yahoo instead, tried the same thing again, and got essentially the same results.

So he tried one of the less well-known search engines instead. That had sometimes worked for him in the past, giving him results he hadn't been able to find elsewhere.

This time, he got a hit on the third page of results. Some user on Reddit had posted some photos, and even given the latitude and longitude coordinates. He read the user's comments with steadily mounting enthusiasm. He'd always assumed these kinds of places were confined to just the wealthier countries. Which just went to show there were still things out there that could surprise him. Korso wondered if Cain had seen this very same site, and gotten the very same idea. It was an intriguing notion.

Wanting to exhaust all possibilities, he spent the next few minutes trying the same thing with a number of other countries. He got no hits at all. Not on any of the search engines. This was about what he'd expected, but it was good to have it verified.

'You found something,' Natasha said. 'I can tell by your expression.'

'So much for my poker face,' Korso said, closing the laptop. He grabbed the paper bag containing the rest of his sandwich, and got to his feet. 'Clock's ticking. I'll tell you all about it on the way.'

Forty-One

The airport was only twelve miles away, so the drive would be a short one. Just long enough for Korso to explain what he had in mind. Once downtown Durango was behind them, Natasha took the left fork that got them back onto US-160 and headed southeast, with the Animas River running parallel to them for part of the way. Sunset was less than an hour away, and the sky was slowly darkening. Other drivers were already employing their side lights.

'So do we now have a destination we can give our pilots?' she said.

'We do,' Korso said, wiping the last of the breadcrumbs from his lips. 'Whether it's the right one or not, we'll only find out once we get there.'

'Where?'

'Guyana.'

'Guyana? Those reports provided you with the inform-ation you needed then?'

'Partly. The rest I figured out for myself. While I think about it, you'd better pull into the next rest area you see along here.' He pointed to the right. 'Preferably while this river is still within spitting distance.'

'To get rid of these weapons, you mean.'

'That's what I mean.'

'Korso, I should warn you I have no contacts in that region who can provide replacements. Which means we will be going in essentially naked.'

'Don't put images like that into my head. And anyway, I imagine guns aren't too hard to find over there, assuming we have time to look. We'll survive somehow.'

'So, back to the subject at hand. Please explain to me how you arrived at Guyana as our final destination.'

'Okay. Now from what I can see, the Ukrainians have been pretty thorough in their investigations, checking all the things I would have checked if I was starting with a blank slate. As have the Guyanese, in their own way. The SAA investigators have spent their time following up leads in all the neighbouring countries, while the GAA have been concentrating on their own patch, which actually makes sense. Guyanese locals are far more likely to talk to their own people than strange foreigners.'

'But?'

Korso smiled. 'There's always a but, isn't there? *But* neither party have made any effort to really think outside the box. These official investigations all have tried-and-tested procedures that can easily become formulaic and confining if you let them. Added to which, we possess vital information that they're not privy to, so we've got an immediate advantage over them from the start. We *know* who took that plane, and we know *why* he did it. They don't. So they've done exactly what you'd expect them to do in that given situation, which is talk with air-traffic officials, local pilots, the police, taxi drivers, farmers etcetera. They've gone down their list of procedures and ticked every box, and everyone's given them the same answer. Nobody saw or heard a thing. And on top of that, they've searched and found no trace of the plane anywhere. Net result? That aircraft of yours has vanished into thin air.'

'Which is impossible,' Natasha said.

'Which is impossible. Planes don't just disappear, unless you believe in those old Bermuda Triangle stories.' He pointed at a sign up ahead. 'Rest area coming up in half a mile.'

Natasha signalled right and pulled into the narrow slip road. Less than a minute later, she came to a stop outside the small rest-stop building. It was a low cinder block structure containing a women's toilet on the left, a men's on the right, and an open portico in the centre, through which Korso could see a chain-link fence and the river beyond. There were no other vehicles parked. No other people in sight.

He held out his hand. Natasha passed him her Taurus and Sig Sauer without a word. He got out and entered the portico, passing four vending machines until he reached the fence. Checking again to make sure nobody was watching, he threw the two handguns over the fence and into the flowing water. He pulled the Ruger from his waistband, and threw that in too. He returned to the vehicle and got in. Natasha pulled away and soon rejoined the traffic on the highway.

'When we first talked about this,' she said, 'you suggested that after the pilots dropped under the radar, they could have simply flown onto a pre-arranged site in one of the neighbouring countries. Or maybe even to one of those small islands in the Caribbean. What makes you believe they doubled back instead?'

'Well, I discounted those smaller islands straight away. I've been living on one for the past two years, so I know how quickly news travels in such places. Everybody knows everybody, and as a result secrets don't stay secrets for very long. I can guarantee that if a low-flying aircraft, even a relatively small one like your turboprop, flew over one of those islands in the middle of the night, somebody would have heard it. And you can bet the moment an SAA investigator showed up asking questions about a missing aircraft, somebody would have mentioned that little fact. But according to those reports, nobody did.'

'In that case, why not fly to a neighbouring country, such as Venezuela or Suriname?'

'Because both those options involve far too many risks, and we know Cain goes out of his way to avoid unnecessary risks if he can help it. That's one thing we agree on, actually. See, for the last couple of hours I've been trying to get into Cain's mindset and think like he does. Why try sneaking into the controlled airspace of another country and risk being shot down as a hostile, when I can just as easily double back and re-enter the country I've just left? Far better to stick with what you know in such cases. If worse comes to worst, and Guyana air traffic control somehow spots me, I can always tell them one of the main engines started misfiring badly and we risked going down into the Atlantic if we didn't get it looked at immediately. Which also explains why we kept the aircraft at a low altitude, just in case we needed to make an emergency landing.'

'And you think air traffic control would believe that?'

'Why not? I'm sure situations like that have happened. Besides, what am I possibly trying to gain by returning to Guyana just minutes after leaving it? No reason makes sense other than the one I've given. But that's just a worst-case scenario, just something Cain would have considered in depth at the planning stages.'

'But you're still guessing, Korso. You don't *know*.'

He stared at her. 'What do you think we've been doing the last couple of days? From the moment we met, we've been acting on a combination of hunches, guess work and old-fashioned gut instinct. And that's not out of choice, but because we haven't had the necessary facts at hand to pave the way. Added to which, there's this ever-shrinking deadline that's also been forced upon us, which naturally places limits on the decision-making process.'

Natasha just nodded in response. The car was silent for a while. Korso simply waited for the inevitable question to come.

Finally, 'What's the flight time to Guyana?'

'From here, approximately nine hours. But Durango airport's for domestic flights only, so we'll have to make a stop at an international airport with immigration facilities before we can exit the country. Denver's the closest. So add another hour for that, if we're lucky... better make it two.'

She paused for a moment as she made calculations. 'Which means once we land, we have only nine hours left with which to locate the shipment.'

'If the wind's with us, it could be a little more than that. But nine sounds about right.'

'Nine hours, then. And you said Guyana is a small nation?'

'Only comparatively. It's actually well over two hundred thousand square kilometres. Smaller than your homeland, but only just.'

'So since we're not in any position to scour the entire country, either by land or air, that suggests you already have a good idea where our aircraft might be stashed.'

'I think so. See, it occurred to me that since it's impossible to dismantle or demolish a plane like that quietly, why even bother trying? The better and easier option is simply to hide it. Have you ever read *The Purloined Letter*?'

She shook her head. 'But I've heard that title, I think. Who wrote it?'

'Edgar Allan Poe,' he said. 'After inventing the modern detective story with *The Murders in the Rue Morgue*, he used the story's hero, C. Auguste Dupin, in two sequels. The last of these was *The Purloined Letter*. It's all about this stolen royal letter which, due to its content, can grant its possessor great powers. The only real suspect behind the theft is believed to keep the letter in his home, in an accessible place, since the letter's power depends on his being able to destroy it at a moment's notice. But after eighteen months of extensive searching, nobody's been able to find it. That scenario sound familiar at all?'

'I notice a vague resemblance. Go on.'

'So, after plenty of to-ing and fro-ing, Dupin comes in and eventually explains that the best way to conceal the letter from those looking for it, while also keeping it readily available to destroy if necessary, is to simply not conceal it at all.'

'Hide it in plain sight, you mean.'

Korso nodded. 'In this case, creased and folded to hide the royal seal, then inserted between a bunch of other similarly creased letters nobody would ever look twice at. You see where I'm going with this?'

'So the best place to hide our plane,' she said, 'is right out in the open, among other planes nobody wants, or even cares about.'

'Exactly.'

She was smiling now. 'Like a boneyard.'

'That's one term. Aircraft graveyard is another. Essentially, a place where planes and helicopters go to die, and sometimes to be recycled. But whatever they call it, I believe that's where we'll find your missing plane. And if I'm right, there's a fair chance we'll also find your missing shipment there.'

'But in Guyana? I was always under the impression aircraft boneyards were a specifically American custom.'

He shrugged. 'Most of the largest boneyards *are* here in the US, especially in the southwest. But there are similar sites all over the world, often in places you'd least expect. Australia's got one, for example, along with England, France, and quite a few others.'

Natasha slowed as they approached the intersection that would take them onto US-172, and from there to the airport. The lights were red. She took the far right lane and waited.

'Now that I think about it,' she said, 'I'm sure I've also seen photos or footage of Russian boneyards filled with old military helicopters and planes. From what I saw, none looked in airworthy condition.'

'Russia definitely has more than its fair share of sites,' Korso said as the lights turned green and Natasha pulled away again. 'I know of one in Vozdvizhenka, and there's a vast boneyard at Rossokha, in the Chernobyl Exclusion Zone. Naturally, that one doesn't get too many visitors. There are several in South Asia too. Most of those are kept secret from the public. I know first hand of one in Afghanistan that you definitely won't find on Google Maps, no matter how hard you look. But the difference between them is that the American bases are basically expensive storage facilities for mostly redundant aircraft, while those in Eastern Europe and Asia are really nothing more than salvage yards for enterprising opportunists. The aircraft in those places are in no condition to fly to begin with, so scavengers sneak in and recycle whatever parts they need until all that's left is husks.'

Ahead, he saw a sign notifying them the airport was just three miles away.

'And you claim there's one of these places in Guyana,' Natasha said.

'According to one user on Reddit, there is. I'll show you the photos once we're on board. The place is a fraction of the size of the others, of course, since the poorer countries don't exactly have a surplus of unused aircraft lying around. Apparently, it's in a hard to reach rural location mostly surrounded by rainforest, so most of the planes there haven't been turned into skeletal husks yet.'

'So how did this person on Reddit find it?'

'Purely by chance, according to him. The guy says he was over there working as a volunteer for some world health charity, and had two weeks' vacation coming up. So he rented himself a jeep and drove around those parts of the country not usually found in the guide books. This was one of the places he stumbled onto. He says he was there for a whole afternoon feeling like a kid who'd discovered the forbidden kingdom, and that he didn't see another soul the entire time.'

Natasha pursed her lips. 'Still, it seems a huge gamble. And even if you're right, what are the chances of a brand-new aircraft being overlooked in what is essentially a scrapyard? It would stick out like a sore thumb.'

'Remember *The Purloined Letter*? The thief hid it in plain sight, sure, but he wasn't above using a little protective colouring as well. Such as folding the letter to hide the royal seal, then adding a few creases so it matched up with his other private letters. In our case, don't expect to see a gleaming new aircraft among all the detritus. Cain would have made sure to camouflage it so it fits in perfectly with its surroundings. He and his crew had all night ahead of them, remember. More than enough time to remove one or both of the wings, the tail, the windows, then scatter them all around the site. As long as you've got the manpower and the right tools it's not that hard, and the ATP is only twenty-six-metres long, which is a fairly small plane for its type. Once that was done, they could have easily added some dents to the hull and then pasted enough mud and dirt to the body that the plane would have looked as though it had been there for years.'

'But even then, there's still the possibility of a local chancing upon it by accident and then discovering the crates inside. Assuming they *are* still in there, of course.'

'Granted,' Korso said. 'That is unless Cain found a way to make the plane's interior inaccessible to all but the most determined. But we won't know for sure until we're actually onsite and can see for ourselves.'

Natasha was silent as she digested this. She signalled right for the turn-off onto Airport Road.

'There's also another reason I like it,' he said.

'And what's that?'

'This place isn't pasted all over the internet, so nobody else really knows about it. I had to use one of the lesser-known search engines to find the link, and even then I had to go through three pages of results to get to it. I can guarantee Cain would have done his research on this, and if this idea occurred to me it likely occurred to him too. With most people, if they can't find something on Google, they give up and move on. But I prefer to exhaust all avenues for any given problem, and I think Cain's probably the same. And I can just see him coming across this same search result like I did, and a light bulb suddenly going off above his head. He would have felt like this graveyard was just there waiting for him, too good an opportunity to pass up.'

'Very well,' she said. 'It seems logical on the face of it. And since we have no other options anyway, I guess we're going to Guyana. Which airport will we land at?'

'The main one. Cheddi Jagan International, in Timehri. About forty kilometres south of the capital.'

'And is that the closest one to our destination?'

'Well, it's a little closer than the one your pilots used. But all the others are nothing more than tiny domestic airports with dirt tracks for runways. We show up in an upscale business jet at one of those, and we might as well take out TV ads to announce our arrival. Best to play it low-key, I think.'

'So how far away is the boneyard?'

He saw the main terminal building coming up ahead, surrounded by a huge parking lot. 'A hundred and thirty kilometres west of the airport,' he said. 'Most of it on small dirt roads. Meaning we'll need a four-wheel drive, and a driver to go with it. I want someone who knows the lay of the land. They shouldn't be too hard to find.'

'You seem to have it all worked out,' she said, giving him her patented half-smile as she turned into the access road.

He felt he had worked out a large part of it, at least to his own satisfaction. Only time would tell if he was right or not. Wanting to veer away from that particular subject, he said, 'You know, I'm kind of looking forward to seeing how you handle Hertz, once they see the state of this vehicle.'

'I'll try to keep the bloodshed to a minimum,' she said.

Forty-Two

They were an hour into their flight to Guyana when Natasha's cell phone started ringing. She picked it up off the table between them and checked the display. Korso, dozing in the same seat as before, didn't have to ask who it was.

They'd made pretty good time at Durango Airport, managing to board the Cessna just ten minutes after entering the terminal. Natasha's Platinum Visa had made short work of the Hertz rep's issues with the Chevy. She simply paid for the car outright and told him to replace it with a new one. That was the end of that little obstacle. Once on board, she handed the two pilots their cash bonuses, after which they were more than happy to step up their pre-flight checks and get them up in the air as soon as possible. Money might not be the answer to all of life's problems, but it sure sped things up when you were in a rush.

Unfortunately, they'd landed at Denver International Airport during a particularly busy period and it took them over an hour to get processed through immigration there. And that was using a VIP Fast Track service. Meaning his initial estimate had been about right. Once they arrived in Guyana, they'd have about nine hours of their deadline left.

It would be tight, that was for sure.

Korso listened as Natasha recited her current four-number code. Then she said, 'I'm fine. We're in the air now, one hour out of Denver. Our destination is Guyana.'

'Guyana?' Sardoca said, his voice sounding loud over the speakerphone. 'What the hell are you going there for?'

'To recover what we were sent to recover, of course,' Natasha said in a patient tone. She lowered the phone's volume and set it down on the table. 'Is there a problem?'

'You tell me, Natasha.' His voice was quieter, but no less annoying. 'Just what makes you think Guyana holds the answer to our dilemma?'

Natasha told him, offering a condensed version of everything Korso had told her in the car, making it all sound a lot more certain than it actually was. Sardoca wasn't fooled.

'And that's it, Korso?' he said. 'You decided to fly all the way to Guyana on nothing more than a *hunch*?'

'More than one, actually,' Korso said, stretching his arms. 'And I believe I already forewarned you about that likelihood, or have you forgotten?'

'I remember it all too well. I just hoped I'd imagined it.' There was a loud sigh. 'None of this is going as it should. Aircraft graveyards in the jungle. Jesus. You better pray this works or I guarantee I'll make you sorry you ever met me.'

Korso arched an eyebrow at Natasha. 'Seriously?'

'So I assume you've got some kind of plan of action when your plane touches down,' Sardoca said, 'or are you just going to wing that too?'

'It's very simple,' Korso said. 'We find ourselves a driver who can take us to this boneyard. We go there.'

'And then?'

'Then we'll see what we'll see. Or do you want me to guess what happens next?'

'Natasha,' Sardoca said, 'tell me Korso isn't doing all of this on purpose just to aggravate me. Answer me honestly, is he in full command of his faculties?'

'He's given me no cause to worry, if that's what you mean. We're doing the best we can within the time constraints. What else do you want us to do? We made our choices and are now acting on them. Only time will tell if we made the right ones.'

'That's not what I wanted to hear. Shit.' There was a long pause on the line.

Natasha said nothing, just picked up a bottle of mineral water and took a sip.

'Call me again once you're on the road,' Sardoca said. The line went dead.

Korso looked at Natasha without expression. She shrugged back. Nothing else needed to be said.

Natasha turned to the portside window and yawned as she looked out at the blackness beyond. Korso got up, ambled over to the galley area and grabbed a small bottle of sparkling mineral water from the refrigerator. Returning to his seat, he drank some of the cool water and placed the bottle on the table. Natasha was still staring out at nothing.

'A small sample of a deadly, bio-engineered virus,' Korso said, slowly rotating the bottle, 'possibly developed by, and liberated from, the infamous GosNIIOKhT research institute in Moscow. Along with a sample of the antidote, of course, since one's worthless without the other. With the right bidder, Nikolic could practically double his fortune in one fell swoop. It's that, isn't it? Or something like it.'

Natasha turned from the window and gave him her most withering look. 'You never stop, do you?'

'Never.' He smiled. 'Regarding Guyana, though. There's one more reason to believe we're on the right trail. Just a small one, but they all add up.'

'I'm listening.'

'Loose lips sink ships.'

'What?'

'During that phone conversation in Amarillo, Cain gave "loose lips" as the reason for eliminating the others. I don't think he was joking. I think he always had it in mind to keep the cargo stored in Guyana, but since his crew also knew the plane's location that meant their days were clearly numbered. Certainly neither pilot could be trusted, and the same goes for Borozan. We both saw how Kujan ended up, and it's a sure bet Papsidera is landfill somewhere.'

'So far, so good. Except you have forgotten someone.'

'Adamson? No, I remember him very clearly. Especially his last words.'

'Which were…?'

'He told me he was just a worker ant following orders. That he wasn't even there when they took…'

'Took what?'

'The conversation was cut short at that point, but I think his next words were going to be "the plane". Which would explain why he wasn't killed with the others. Since he had no idea of the ATP's ultimate location he posed no real danger, and he still had his uses. For all we know, Cain may even have planned to give him a small share of the profits. But that all changed when he started talking to me in that dilapidated factory. He may have been ignorant

302

of the cargo's true location, but he still knew too much. Hence, the bullet to the brain.'

'That all sounds reasonable enough,' she said, taking another sip of her own water. 'Not that it matters now. Our course is already set.'

'In more ways than one.'

'So perhaps now might be a good time to show me those photos that put us on this path in the first place.'

'Why not?' Korso said, and reached for his laptop.

Forty-Three

8 hours, 56 minutes and counting…

They landed at Cheddi Jagan International Airport at 08:23, passing through customs thirty-five minutes later. They exited the main terminal building along with the other arrivals, mostly families or members of group tours. The sun was high in the sky, the morning already warming up nicely. As he breathed in the fresh air, Korso recalled with a certain sense of irony that Guyana and Bermuda shared the same time zone.

It was the last day. They had until 18:00 to produce the goods. Less than nine hours.

If he failed, things would very quickly become uncomfortable. Sardoca would make sure of it. And take great pleasure from it at the same time. And that was enough to spur Korso on.

Natasha was scanning the kerb out front, where a long line of official-looking yellow cabs waited. Korso doubted there was anything official about them. Most of the drivers stood by their vehicles, calling out to the luggage-laden tourists and doing their best to coerce them into their cars. Few of them paid attention to Korso or Natasha. Any cab driver worth his salt could sense where the real money was, and neither Korso nor Natasha looked like tourists. For a start, neither of them carried any luggage. Natasha

304

had left her overnight bag on the Cessna, while Korso had used a luggage-forwarding service in the arrivals lounge to transport his bag to a PO box in Lichtenstein. The box belonged to a virtual mailing address service with a very exclusive clientele. Very expensive, but completely trustworthy. He figured whatever else happened today, he wouldn't be seeing the inside of that Cessna again. So all he had now was what he carried in his pockets: some of his own cash, his passport, the last burner phone and a few other odds and ends.

'What now?' Natasha said.

'Let me have some money. Say five hundred dollars.'

Natasha didn't ask why. She just reached into her fanny pack and pulled out a wad and handed it over.

'Thanks.' He stuffed the cash in his pocket without looking. 'Now let's find a cab.'

They walked toward the rear of the taxi line, away from the other exiting passengers and loud cabbies. Many of the drivers here were just sitting inside their vehicles, making the most of the air-conditioning as they waited for the line to start moving. One of these saw Korso and Natasha approaching, and lowered his window, grinning at them with big teeth.

He looked in his late twenties and wore a thin goatee. A silver hoop hung from his left ear. Korso heard the unmistakable sound of chutney music coming out of the stereo.

'Where you headed, friends?' he called out in a sing-song voice. 'Wherever it is, I'll take you.'

Korso walked over to his car, a bright yellow Honda station wagon, walked round the front and opened the front passenger door and got in. Natasha got in the back.

The air-con was on low, making it pleasantly cool inside. Korso noticed there was no meter. A good sign.

'So where to?' the driver said, turning to Korso. 'Georgetown? I know all the best hotels. And some not so good, if that's what you want.'

'Let's talk first,' Korso said. 'What's your name?'

'Troy. And you?'

'Jack. My friend back there is Jill.'

'Hey, just like the nursery rhyme.' He glanced at Natasha in his rear-view. 'Hi, Jill.'

'Hello,' Natasha said.

'Okay, Troy,' Korso said, 'now you've probably already guessed we're not tourists, but we will be needing a driver for the rest of the day. We're also in kind of a rush.'

The grin grew wider. 'Hey, I'm your man, Jack.'

'Not in this vehicle you're not. What we actually want from you, Troy, is a recommendation. See, we're planning to journey west, inland, where the roads aren't so good, so what we really need is someone with a four-wheel drive who also knows his way around his own country with ease. Someone who drives fast *and* safely. And I figure if a cab driver like yourself doesn't know someone like that, he's in the wrong business.'

Troy's smile had faded only a little. 'Hey, I know all kinds of people around these parts.'

'Good. That's exactly what we're counting on. Now I read somewhere that taxi drivers here make on average about sixty thousand Guyanese dollars a month. Is that about right?'

The driver gave an exaggerated shrug. 'Something like that. Why?'

Korso pulled three notes from his pocket, checked the denominations, and showed them to him. 'A hundred and fifty dollars, US. Which I believe works out to thirty thousand Guyanese dollars. So that's half a month's pay right there. And it's yours if you can take us immediately to someone who fits the bill.' He clicked his fingers. 'Quick. What's the first name that comes to mind? Speak now.'

'Yannick,' Troy said, without hesitation.

'And who's Yannick?'

'My brother-in-law. He used to work as a courier for DHL, out of Georgetown. But once he married my sister, he quit that job and opened up his own auto shop in Mocha Arcadia, a village fifteen kilometres north of here. He's the best driver I know, and he's also got a sweet 2010 Toyota Tacoma pick-up that he tuned himself. No promises, but you make him a good offer and he'll take you where you want to go. And in good time.'

Korso turned to Natasha in the back. 'What do you think?'

She gave a single nod. 'Call this Yannick, see what he says.'

Korso turned back to Troy. 'You heard the lady. Call him up. Tell him we'll pay him well for his services.' He handed over the three fifties. 'If we like what we see, you also get another three of these.'

The wide grin returned. Pocketing the cash, Troy turned down the radio and grabbed his cell phone from the dash. He scrolled through his contacts, found the one he wanted and pressed the screen. He brought the phone to his ear.

After a few moments, he said, 'Hey, bro. It's Troy. How's Ana and Lily? Good. Look, I got a couple of new arrivals here in my cab. Fresh off the plane. But serious people, you know what I mean? They want a driver for the rest of the day, and they're giving me good money to recommend the best one I know.' There was a pause. 'No, it's in-country, so you'll need your pick-up. But it's *real* good money, bro. Believe me on that. They say they're in a rush and need to move quick. You interested? Want me to bring them over?' Another pause, then he said, 'Sure. You got it.'

He hung up the phone, and grinned at Korso. 'He's interested, and wants to meet you both at the house.'

'So what are we waiting for?'

–

'Troy told me you're offering good money for one day's work,' Yannick said, handing Korso and Natasha each a bottle of Coke. 'Was he telling the truth? And if so, what kind of money are we talking about?'

Troy got them to the town of Mocha Arcadia in less than twelve minutes, and they were in front of his brother-in-law's auto shop two minutes after that. It was a fairly ramshackle building just off the main street, with an open workshop out front. Inside were a number of vehicles, all in various states of disrepair. Parked outside was the dark green Toyota pick-up in question. Korso thought it could do with a paint job, but other than that it seemed to be in good shape. Yannick was waiting in the yard out front, along with a large mixed-breed dog that constantly scratched himself. Connected to the auto shop was a two-storey timber house. A pretty, dark-skinned young woman sat on the steps leading up to the front door, nursing a baby with a bottle. Once Troy had spoken with Yannick, he went over to chat with his sister, while Korso and Natasha stayed with the man they'd come to see.

'He's telling the truth,' Korso said, taking a sip of the lukewarm Coke. 'And the money we're offering is one thousand US dollars. In cash.'

'One thousand dollars?' Yannick's eyes widened as he looked from one to the other. He was wearing just a tank-top and jeans. He was a big man, maybe six feet tall, with a powerful-looking physique. His head was shaved almost to the bone, and he wore rimless tinted spectacles. 'For one day's work? Are you serious?'

'Very much so,' Natasha said. 'We want an able, experienced driver who knows his way around the more rural parts of this country. Troy recommended you. Was he correct?'

Yannick snorted. 'Miss, you won't find a better driver anywhere around here. Where is it you want to go?'

'A place a hundred and thirty kilometres west of here,' Korso said. 'You know Issano?'

'Sure. It's an old airfield, basically just a large scrap of open land not much used anymore, and a small village nearby. Nothing else around there, though, other than farmland, bad roads and rainforest.'

'You'd be surprised. About fifteen kilometres south of Issano, there's a little-known aircraft graveyard that interests us.'

Yannick's brows formed a straight line as he scratched his cheek. 'An aircraft graveyard? Near Issano? Are you sure?'

'Just a small one, but it's there.' He turned to Natasha. 'Show him.'

Pulling her phone from her fanny pack, she spent a few seconds swiping and scrolling before passing it to Yannick. He looked at the screen, then slowly swiped a finger across the images Korso had found on Reddit, pausing occasionally to read the user's comments. After a minute, he gave the phone back to her.

'You learn something new every day, I guess,' he said, adjusting his glasses. 'I never even heard of that place before.'

'Very few people have, it seems,' Korso said. 'And there's nothing on Google Maps either. But the guy who posted those shots also provided the exact coordinates of the site. Can I assume your Toyota's equipped with a GPS?'

'Not at the moment, but it'll take me less than a minute to connect one up.'

Natasha said, 'So will you drive us? Because the sooner we leave, the better.'

'Sure. A married man with a new baby can't turn down that kind of money. But why the big rush?'

'My associate Jack and I are on a very tight schedule. That's all you need to know.'

Yannick smirked at them both. 'So he's Jack and you're Jill?'

'As far as you know.'

He shrugged. 'Okay, Jack and Jill, it looks like we're in business. I'll take the cash up front, of course. You can give it to my wife, Ana, over there.'

'You'll take half up front,' Korso said, 'the rest on our return. And don't bother arguing. That part's non-negotiable.'

Yannick shook his head. 'Sorry, folks. I like you guys, but I have to insist you pay the full fee first. Otherwise you'll just have to find yourselves another driver in the short time you've got left. Best of luck with that, by the way.' He grinned in triumph.

'That's unfortunate.' Korso turned to his right, saw the cab driver still talking to his sister on the steps. 'Troy,' he called out, 'it looks like we're going to Georgetown after all.'

'Really?' Troy began walking back to them. He looked distinctly unhappy.

'You're wasting your time, Jack,' Yannick said, no longer smiling. 'You won't find another driver half as good as me anywhere in these parts.'

'Maybe not,' Korso said. 'But the deal on the table is half the fee now, half later. Since that's not acceptable to you, we'll take our chances.'

'Nice meeting you,' Natasha said.

They both began walking back to the taxi.

'Hey, wait,' Yannick said after a few seconds. 'Listen, maybe I'm being too hasty. Tell you what, half up front is fine.'

Korso stopped and turned back to him. 'You know, I thought it would be. Jill, pay the man, please.'

While Natasha reached into her pack for the cash, Troy came over to Korso and said, 'Are we still good?'

'It looks like you'll get your final payment, if that's what you mean.' He turned to Yannick, who was watching Natasha count out some bills. 'Yannick, we'll also need you to bring some of your tools along, just in case.'

'Sure, no problem.'

'Five hundred US,' Natasha said, offering him the ten bills. 'As agreed.'

'Much obliged. Please give it to my accountant sitting on the steps over there.'

Natasha walked over to Ana, while Yannick turned to Korso. 'Okay, Jack, come into my workshop and tell me what you need.'

Forty-Four

3 hours, 11 minutes and counting...

Yannick slipped the gearstick into second, accelerated again, and the Toyota bucked suddenly as the front wheels finally made their way over the tree root growing out of the uneven road. Or what passed for a road in these parts. Most weren't much more than tiny dirt tracks, and that was being generous. Once they were over the root, Yannick stepped on the gas until they were moving at a steady thirty again, until the next obstruction.

They'd been travelling for over four hours, and had barely seen another living soul all day. The journey so far had been arduous, infuriating and monotonous, often at the same time. With just the GPS to guide them, Yannick would often get them onto a path, only to come across an impenetrable obstruction like a downed tree or huge root, and then be forced to backtrack and find some other way to get them through. Despite all the detours, Yannick had still made good time. Korso had to admit he was an excellent driver. Without him the entire journey would have been impossible.

He watched the clock display change to 14:50. Just three hours and ten minutes left.

As Yannick drove on, the surrounding trees and plant life became steadily denser again, their immediate environment became gloomier and darker, and the track they were on quickly became rockier, with fallen branches to negotiate every few yards. Yannick reduced their speed to ten kilometres per hour.

It had been like this from the start. Korso barely noticed anymore. Besides, he had no shortage of things to look at. No matter in which direction he turned he spotted movement of some kind as the jungle's natural denizens busied themselves with their daily chores. So far he'd seen enough different species to fill a book. Giant anteaters, otters, skunks, fruit-eating bats, toucans, opossums, armadillos, tapirs, and just about every lizard species you could think of, and then some more you couldn't. Most of them barely gave the vehicle a second look.

Yannick tapped the brakes, and the vehicle came to a gentle stop as a large jaguar emerged from the dense foliage to their right, maybe fifteen feet in front of them. It strolled casually across the dirt track, paused for a moment without looking at the vehicle, yawned, then carried on until it disappeared into the trees to their left.

Nobody spoke. By this point, the sight was almost commonplace. They'd already seen four just like it.

Yannick started off again.

A few minutes later, he said, 'You guys don't really talk much, do you?'

'You're driving,' Korso said. 'We don't want to distract you.'

'Impossible. Driving is a natural thing for me, like breathing. I hardly think about it at all. Besides, who can I possibly hit out here?'

'I'm less concerned with whom than I am with what.'

'Are we near our destination yet?' Natasha said from the back.

'According to the GPS, we're close now,' Korso said. 'Another kilometre and we should be able to—'

'Hey, look.' Yannick pointed ahead. 'Over there on the right. You see it? A glimmer of something. Looks like sun shining on metal.'

Korso looked where he was pointing. There was definitely a glint of something over there in the trees.

Natasha leaned forward for a better look. 'Stop the vehicle.'

Yannick pressed the brakes and the vehicle came to a gentle halt.

Although they were no longer in deep rainforest country, the trees were still plentiful in all directions. They were particularly thick on the right-hand side, but Korso was sure he could make out something in there, on the forest floor. Something metallic.

'Wait here,' he said. 'I'll take a look.'

He got out of the vehicle and studied the ground as he shut the door, watching for bullet ants, or snakes. He saw none. Although it was late afternoon, the humidity was still high. All around him, bird calls, cricket whines and screeching mammals combined to produce an almost ear-splitting cacophony. He stepped off the path and passed between two fat tree trunks into the woods. Although there was plenty of sunlight shining through, the ground was still mulchy under his feet and he looked before stepping anywhere. He saw the object in question was maybe twenty feet in front of him, just lying there in the dirt. It glinted again as he got closer.

He recognised what it was immediately. A rotor blade from a helicopter.

It was about twenty-foot long and looked old. He crouched down for a better look. The steel of the shaft was discoloured and the grip end had signs of rust, but it was still in fairly good shape. He scanned the immediate area, but saw no other machine parts lying around. And no other visible tracks. He returned to the vehicle and got back in.

Yannick was munching on a star apple. Before they left, his wife had kindly assembled a hamper of food for their journey ahead, containing cassava bread, chicken foot, egg balls, a wide variety of fruits and numerous other snacks. And plenty of bottled water. Thanks to her, at least they wouldn't go hungry.

'So what was it?' Yannick asked, finishing the fruit.

'A rotor blade from a chopper,' Korso said. 'Looks like someone planned on taking it home for whatever reason, but finally just gave up and left it where it fell. Those things aren't exactly light.'

'Where there is one,' Natasha said, 'there will be others.'

'Let's continue down this path and see what's at the end of it.'

'You're the boss,' Yannick said. Lowering his side window, he threw out the apple remains, then started off again in the same direction.

Yannick kept the vehicle's speed at a steady fifteen kilometres per hour. Soon, the track they were on began to curve round to the right and the going got a little rockier.

When the track finally straightened out again, Natasha said, 'There. In the distance.'

Korso and Yannick had already spotted it. It was hard to miss. About five hundred yards ahead, the track opened out into a large area of flat land containing few trees. The savannah seemed completely out of place in comparison to its surroundings. Beyond the area, in the far distance, they could see a continuation of the woods and forest. Korso looked for signs of machines or anything else man-made over there, but saw nothing yet.

They kept on going, while Korso carefully scanned the woods on either side of them. They'd covered about two hundred yards when he said, 'Stop here.'

Yannick immediately pressed the brakes.

'What is it?' Natasha asked.

'Nothing concrete. I just don't like the thought of leaving our only means of escape out in the open. Anything happens to it and we're done for. To our immediate left there's a fairly large opening leading into the woods. I think we should leave the pick-up in there, partially undercover, and go the rest of the way on foot.'

'I don't understand,' Yannick said, frowning at them. 'What is there to be afraid of?'

'Probably nothing. But I'm a careful man, and the aircraft we're searching for might be under surveillance.'

'Surveillance? Out here? By who?'

'By someone who doesn't like us too much.' Korso looked at Natasha. 'At the very least, I'd say he deserves to know what we're doing here.'

'Agreed.' She turned to Yannick, and gave him a capsule version of their mission to find the stolen shipment, and their belief that the plane that carried it might be up ahead.

Once she was finished, Yannick said, 'And there are others who also want to find this shipment? Or who want to stop you from finding it?'

'No to the first,' she said. 'Yes to the second.'

Yannick sighed. 'This news does not make me happy, people. I'm a father now, with a family to provide for. What's in this shipment? Drugs? Weapons?'

'Caviar,' Korso said. 'Black market sturgeon caviar.'

He'd expected to have to explain what it was, but Yannick just nodded. 'Ah, caviar. Now I understand. Back when I was a courier I had to deliver caviar to the Russian Embassy in Georgetown. The chef there told me they were always short of stock. *Very* expensive. Yes, Jack, I think we'll do as you suggest.'

Yannick reversed, then carefully steered them into the woods to their left. He managed another twenty feet before coming to a stop before a pair of juvenile palm trees. Since the trees were barely ten feet high, the hanging palm leaves provided natural cover for the vehicle. That the Toyota was already dark green only helped. He manoeuvred the vehicle around them until it was completely screened from the dirt track.

'Perfect,' Natasha said.

'Thank you,' Yannick said, switching the engine off.

'Before we go,' Korso said, 'I don't suppose you happen to own a gun, by any chance?'

Yannick looked at him for a few seconds. 'In this country,' he said, 'a man must be able to protect both himself and his family.'

'So that's a yes?'

Instead of answering, Yannick reached under his seat and pulled out a small revolver with a two-inch barrel. Yannick didn't point it anywhere, just held it for them to see. It looked like an old Colt Cobra .22. It had clearly seen better days. One of the wooden grips had cracked badly, and both barrel and cylinder were covered in grime.

But a gun was a gun. Even a .22.

'My associate here is holding a sizeable amount of money in her pack,' Korso said in a light tone, as though discussing the weather. 'You could kill us both right now, bury our bodies out here, then go back to your family and nobody would be any the wiser.'

'True,' Yannick said. '*If* I were a murderer and a thief.'

Korso nodded. 'I'm glad we've got that out of the way. Is it in working condition?'

'I don't know. It's mostly for show. I haven't practised in years, or cleaned it even. My wife would kill me if she ever found it.' Yannick passed the gun over to him. 'Do you think we may need it?'

'It never hurts to be prepared for the worst.' Korso inspected the gun closely. Part of the front sight had been filed off at some point, but at least it was still in alignment with the rear sight. He pushed the release and flipped open the cylinder. It contained three .22 rounds. He showed the open cylinder to Yannick. 'Only half full. Have you got any extra ammo?'

Yannick shook his head. 'I always meant to buy more, but never got round to it.'

'Of course.' Natasha smiled. 'That would have been too easy.'

'But I have two machetes in the back, if you want. We should take them anyway. There are many snakes in these parts, and all of them deadly.'

Korso opened his door. 'In that case, we'll definitely take them.'

Forty-Five

It took them just a few minutes to get to the savannah by foot. As soon as they reached the end of the track, they had a clear panoramic view of the whole site. They each just stood there, staring in amazement at what lay before them.

The flat plain was about the size of two football fields joined together. The ground was a combination of dirt and clay, interspersed with large patches of thick grass every few feet. There were still clumps of trees here and there, just standing on their own, but the rest was open space. Or it would have been, had not parts of it been taken up by the numerous aircraft skeletons dotted around, in seemingly random locations. Korso estimated there were over thirty in total. Maybe forty. And not all crammed together like most boneyards, but spread out. Some were on their own, looking as though they had simply dropped out of the sky and landed where they fell, while others were grouped together. Some in pairs, others in groups of three or four. The obvious similarities to an elephant graveyard were hard to ignore.

Natasha tapped her machete lightly against a leg. 'Incredible.'

That was the word, all right. Korso could imagine how the guy on the website had felt when he came upon this vision, ostensibly in the middle of nowhere.

Yannick, holding his equipment bag in one hand and the second machete in the other, just stood there, slowly shaking his head.

The nearest wreck was about thirty feet away. It was a small, single-prop plane, decayed and rusty, missing both wings along with the front propeller. It looked like it had been a Cessna Skyhawk in its past life. The tricycle undercarriage was also missing, giving it the appearance of something slowly sinking into the earth. To the right of that was the remains of a small, single-engine helicopter, possibly a Bell. He recognised the shape of the main body, which was about all that was left, along with part of the tail boom. It was lying on its side, with both landing skids visible. The main rotor blades were gone, as was the tail and tail rotor. Korso thought he knew where one of the main rotors had ended up.

To their left, situated close to the woods bordering the site, the remains of two larger planes had been placed alongside each other. One looked like a Learjet 45. It still had its wings, but both turbines and part of the tail were gone. The other one was a slightly larger turboprop, possibly a Beechcraft Super Air from the Eighties. Both wings were missing from this one, and it lay on its side like a beached whale. From what Korso could see, none of the remains in the boneyard approached the size of a standard commercial jet airliner. Although he did see several in the distance that could be classed as regional jets, meaning they contained a hundred seats or less.

Still holding the Colt in his right hand, Korso began walking toward the nearest aircraft, vaguely aware that Natasha and Yannick were both following.

Over to the east, Korso also noticed a sizeable gap in the bordering trees and forest, and he could make out a long, crooked, narrow strip of open land that could just about serve as a landing strip for a plane coming in. If the pilot was feeling particularly brave that day. It looked anything but safe during daylight, so he could only imagine how terrifying it would have been in the middle of the night. There had to have been someone already onsite waiting for the ATP, with makeshift landing lights ready and prepared. There was no other way.

'What kind of plane are we looking for?' Yannick said from behind him.

'A British Aerospace ATP,' Korso said. 'It's a turboprop cargo jet, about twenty-six metres long. At least, it was. It'll probably be all dirtied up and missing a few essential parts, so as to blend in with the rest of these relics.'

'And what colour is it?'

'Good question. I never asked.'

'White,' Natasha said. 'Or off-white. It was a private plane so there were no other markings, but I think the rear rudder was a navy-blue colour. It was dark, anyway.'

Korso scanned the area again. Most of the tail fins that he could see, at least those still attached to the main bodies, were painted a dark colour. So that wasn't much help.

'Let's split up,' he said. 'I'll continue down the middle. Jill, you check those planes on the left side. Yannick, you take the right.'

'Keep to the clay and try to avoid the patches of thick grass,' Yannick said. 'Snakes like grass. And there are no hospitals and no doctors out here.'

'Understood,' Natasha said.

They each split off without another word while Korso carried on. Over the ever-present sounds of bird calls all around them, he could make out the faint whine of a jet somewhere off in the distance, although there was no sign of it in the clear azure sky.

Slowing as he neared the Skyhawk remains, Korso sniffed at the unmistakable aroma of animal faeces coming from somewhere close by. He thought he heard a dry, raspy sound coming from inside the plane, too. He knew from experience that it was the noise made when a large snake rubbed its scales together. Very few things put him on edge, but there were some animals you steered clear of at all costs. Like poisonous snakes in dark, confined spaces. He moved on quickly, passing the hull of the chopper with barely a second glance.

Thirty feet further on, there were two small crabwood trees nestled together, on either side of which lay two more aircraft in varying states of ruin. One was another Learjet type in two pieces, as though it had been cut through with a giant scythe. The other was a larger turboprop aircraft. It was still in one piece, although a wing was missing, as was the tail fin, the nose and the second propeller. Like many of the aircraft here, both could be classed as off-white, although it was hard to tell under all the grime. Once he reached the shade of the trees, Korso ignored the Learjet and inspected the larger turboprop plane.

Close up, the thing looked as though it had been there for years. Decades, even. Standing on tiptoe, Korso checked the cockpit. It was missing its windshield, and the remaining bits of glass at the edges had been smoothed over through exposure to the elements. Crouching down, he peered under the machine and noticed layers of thick rust around parts of the undercarriage. Things like that couldn't be faked. It wasn't the one.

A high-pitched whistle brought him instantly to his feet. Then another right after, longer this time.

Korso came out from the cover of the plane and saw Natasha about two hundred feet away to his left, standing in the shade of a nearby clump of trees. Behind her were three aircraft arranged in a loose group: the remains of an old military-grey helicopter lying on its side, another business jet, and a much larger turboprop.

Once she spotted Korso, she waved broadly with one arm, while pointing at the turboprop with the other.

Korso ran over, reaching her seconds later. He noticed she wasn't smiling, which gave him pause.

'Good news or bad?' he asked.

'Both,' Natasha said, leading him past the other aircraft.

The chopper was a twin-engine model lying on its side, and looked about thirty or forty years old. All that was left was the main cockpit and part of the tail boom. The main rotors, the tail rotor, the engine, the doors, the windows had all been salvaged long ago. Even the landing skids were gone. The business jet was a model Korso didn't recognise. It's nose, windshield and undercarriage were all missing, and both of its wings had been sawed away, while the main cabin door had been torn from its hinges.

They reached the turboprop, the rear half of which was still under the shade of the trees. Korso quickly looked it over, mentally ticking off boxes as he went along. The plane was the right size, about twenty-six metres long. It was in a poor state. The port side wing was completely missing, along with the nose and tail fin. The starboard wing was still attached to the main body, although it looked badly damaged, with the end broken off. It was also missing its propeller. As with the other aircraft they'd seen, there was no undercarriage. The cockpit windshield was gone, and the main fuselage was covered with mud, leaves and indentations, but little of it looked random to Korso's eyes. It all seemed artificial, as though done on purpose. Which fitted perfectly with their current theory.

Yannick finally joined him, still carrying his equipment bag and machete. He must have jogged, yet seemed barely out of breath. But then he was used to the climate.

'So this is the plane you want?' he asked, dropping the bag on what was left of the starboard wing. It landed with a *clunk*.

'We're about to find out,' Korso said.

Natasha was waiting for them by the crew door on the port side, just behind the cockpit. Like the rest of the plane, the door was covered in dried mud.

'Locked, I suppose?' Korso asked.

'Naturally,' she said. 'The same with the cargo door behind us.'

He stepped back for a better look at the rear of the plane, and saw the larger cargo door back there. Also shut.

'But I can confirm this aircraft is a British Aerospace ATP,' she said. 'Without any doubt. This model matches the photos on my phone almost exactly.'

'So what's the bad news?'

'Knock on the door and find out.'

Korso and Yannick exchanged a glance. Then Korso stepped forward and rapped his knuckles against the thick steel door.

An eruption of rattling noises greeted them from within the plane, and he took an instinctive step back.

'Sounds like a nest in there,' Yannick said. 'This is bad, people. Very bad. Still, it could be worse.'

Korso snorted. 'How?'

'There could have been labarias in there instead. Quiet, nervy, lethal, and very common here. They also move like lightning. One can strike you five times before you even know what's happening. A school friend was once bitten by one when we were playing football. It took less than an hour for him to die. Rattlers are better. They always announce their presence first, to warn off predators.'

Korso turned to Natasha, and smiled. 'Like us.'

'What is so amusing?'

'This is exactly what I would have done in Cain's shoes. I can't think of a better deterrent for potential scavengers than a cockpit full of lethal snakes.'

Korso stepped forward for a closer look at the crew door, and tried the handle. No give at all. It was sealed tight, obviously locked from the inside. The cargo door would be the same. The might even be welded shut for all he knew. He remembered the tools they'd brought along from Yannick's workshop. Specifically the oxyacetylene tank and cutting torch in the back of the pick-up.

'Yannick, how long would it take to cut through this door?'

The other man slapped the door with his palm, receiving more rattles in response. 'Thick, hardened steel. A car is child's play with the torch, but something like this? I don't know. If I had to guess, maybe two hours? Maybe a lot more.'

'And the time now?'

Yannick checked his watch. 'Quarter past three.'

Korso pursed his lips. Less than three hours to play with. And even if they got through in that time frame, they still had to clear that cockpit before they could enter. They could always cut through the cargo door at the other end instead, but the time factor still applied.

'Of course, there is a faster way,' Yannick said, and pointed at the open windshield above the nose.

'A faster way to die, maybe,' Korso said. 'The thought of blindly dropping down into a nest of rattlers from above doesn't exactly fill me with optimism.'

'I can do it,' Yannick said, with a shrug.

Korso and Natasha both turned to him at the same time.

'I believe you,' Korso said. 'But why would you?'

'For money.' He grinned. 'Why else?'

'How much?' Natasha said.

'Two thousand dollars US. In cash. For that, I will clear the cockpit for you.'

'Deal.'

'Excellent. And that will be half upfront, as before?'

'Of course.'

'Good. Let me go grab my bag from the wing.' He left them.

'I would have paid him twice that amount,' Natasha whispered once he was out of earshot. Despite the heat, she gave a brief shiver.

Korso could guess why. 'A bad encounter in your past?'

'A small garter snake bit me when I was five.' She reached into her side pack and began counting off notes. 'They are not especially poisonous, but it was enough to put me off snakes for a lifetime. How about you?'

'I'm not a big fan, particularly, but I don't have anything against them either.' He shrugged. 'That might change very soon.'

Yannick returned with his bag. He dropped it on the ground, unzipped it and rummaged around inside. He pulled out a pair of long, thick, leather gloves and placed them on the ground. They were the kind that reached almost to the elbow, and looked old and well-used. He also pulled out two telescopic snake tongs and a heavy-duty flashlight.

'I assume you've done this before?' Natasha asked, passing him the cash.

'Many times,' Yannick said, pocketing the bills without counting. He picked up the left glove and patted the leather. 'I double layered these myself. Nothing gets through.'

He passed the glove to Korso. 'Here, try it on for size.'

'Why?'

'Because you will be helping me.'

Forty-Six

2 hours, 23 minutes and counting...

They counted a total of five rattlesnakes currently using the cockpit as living quarters. Five that they could see, anyway. All adults, all in plain sight. Two big ones on the co-pilot seat, the other three in various spots on the floor. It was only a small space, so there was plenty of light to see by. Korso and Yannick were lying on their stomachs above the nose of the plane, the upper parts of their bodies almost protruding through the open windshield as they attempted to extract the first one.

It wasn't a straightforward job. With enough ammo it would have been all over in seconds, but they could only work with what they had. It had taken Yannick almost twenty minutes until he was able to get a solid grip on the first snake. They were slippery and hard to pin down. Yannick carefully pulled the current prospect up with his tongs, the spring-loaded jaw tightly gripping the rattler's neck just behind the head. In support, Korso used the second set of tongs to grip the lower part of the serpent's body. The large snake kept thrashing around violently, its tail rattling constantly, which made the job doubly difficult.

'Shh, shh, relax, my slithery friend,' Yannick said soothingly. Both men carefully rose to a crouch as, in unison, they pulled the snake out of the plane's interior and into the open air. 'You must find a new home now, that's all.'

Korso was sweating, and not just because of the day's heat. Making sure to keep the rattler well away from both of them, Yannick rotated his body and extended the tongs until the snake was hanging over the starboard side, Korso mirroring his every move with the support tongs. He looked to the port side and saw Natasha watching them from the shade of the trees, well out of range, with the other machete at her side.

'Safe?' Yannick asked.

'Safe,' Korso said, loosening his jaw's grip until the snake was able to writhe its lower body free. 'Drop it.'

Yannick released the lock on his own tongs, the jaw opened, and the snake dropped the seven feet or so to the ground. It quickly slithered under the damaged wing and away.

Korso breathed out, wiped the sweat from his forehead, and took a long swig from the water bottle beside them. The water was hot, but he didn't care.

'And that's all there is to it,' Yannick said, grinning. He took a quick swig from the bottle before passing it back. 'Not so hard.'

'Sure.' He checked Yannick's watch and saw that the whole operation had taken them twenty minutes. Better than expected. He hoped it would remain so.

'Plenty of time left,' Yannick said as he lay down on his stomach again. 'Come, my friend. One down, only four to go.'

Once the last of the rattlers dropped to the ground below and slithered off to parts unknown, Korso checked Yannick's watch and saw it was 16:27. It had felt longer. He returned to the open windshield and moved the flashlight around the cockpit for what seemed like the hundredth time. Looking for any they may have missed. But as before, he heard no more telltale rattles, saw no movement of any kind.

There was an inner door at the rear of the cockpit, so he couldn't see anything beyond. He was about to ask for Yannick's machete, when the man pushed by him and quickly lowered himself down, feet first, to the instrument panel directly beneath them.

'What are you doing?' Korso said.

Yannick grinned back at him. 'Earning my two thousand dollars US. Hand me my machete and the flashlight.'

Korso handed him the flashlight, then looked behind him and saw the weapon lying next to the now empty water bottle. He grabbed the machete and passed it down.

'What's happening?' Natasha called out from below.

'He's checking for stragglers,' Korso said, watching as Yannick crouched down with the flashlight, poking with the machete to check every nook and cranny of the cockpit floor.

'Nothing here,' he said, finally. 'I'll see if I can open the outer door from my side.'

He opened the cockpit door and stepped through, quickly disappearing into the darkness beyond. Korso saw a light beam moving around back there, but not much more. A few seconds later, Yannick called out. 'There are shipping crates back here.'

'How many?' Korso yelled back.

No answer.

Then, 'The door is not welded shut or anything.'

Grabbing both tongs, Korso slid down to the ground and joined Natasha, standing in front of the crew door and looking as anxious as he'd ever seen her. Then the door slowly opened outward, to reveal a grinning Yannick.

'Man, it's an oven in here,' he said. 'Any water left? I'm dying of thirst.'

'Sorry, I just finished the last of mine,' Natasha said.

Yannick stepped out and handed her the flashlight. 'I'll get some more from my vehicle.' He crouched down next to his bag, reached in and pulled out an old iron crowbar and handed it to Korso. 'Here, you may need this.'

'Thanks,' Korso said. Yannick got up and left.

Korso turned back to see Natasha flicking on the flashlight. She looked up at him.

'The moment of truth,' she said, taking a deep breath. 'Let's see what we've got.'

Forty-Seven

Even with the waning sunlight coming through the doorway and cockpit, the cargo area remained mostly in darkness, especially toward the tail. It was a very tight fit inside. The fuselage was only six feet in diameter and because of the floor, less than five feet at its highest point. They each had to stoop. The cargo took up the majority of the available space. Each timber crate was six-feet long, three-feet high and three-feet wide, leaving just enough room for them to shuffle in single file down the right-hand side.

Standing beside Korso, Natasha played the flashlight over the cabin, all the way to the end. 'Six crates,' she said.

'That's a promising start,' Korso said. 'Keep the light on this one, will you?'

She cast the light over the surface of the crate directly in front of them. He saw about a dozen nails embedded in the wooden lid. He handed her the .22, which she stuck in the back of her waistband. Then he wedged the chisel end of the crowbar into the seam between lid and crate, near the corner. He pushed down with all his weight, and the sounds of creaking wood filled the interior as the top corner slowly lifted away from the main body. He repeated the process all the way down that side, then the same on the other side. Once he was done, Natasha placed the flashlight on top of the next crate down. Then they each got a hold of one end and opened the crate lid all the way back.

The interior was filled with wood shavings and straw. Korso reached into the packing materials and felt what could only be a circular steel tin, with more alongside, and more underneath. He grabbed the tin and pulled it out.

The silver aluminium container he held was exactly the same as the one they'd seen in the refrigerator unit back in Bilchner. Six inches in diameter and two inches deep. *Amicus Beluga* was printed in tasteful gold script on the top. The tin was sealed all along the sides, and weighed about a kilo.

'I believe I owe you an apology,' Natasha said as she looked over her own tin.

'What for?'

'For ever doubting you. The shipment was exactly where you said it would be.'

'Before we start celebrating, maybe you can bring out that Geiger counter and see if the tin we really want is in here. Otherwise we're no better off than we were three days ago.'

'Yes.' Natasha lost the smile and reached into her side pack. She pulled out a narrow, light-grey instrument, about five inches long and one inch wide. There were five buttons on the front and a small display screen at one end. She switched it on, then studied the figures on the display.

'There's no cell phone coverage in the jungle,' Korso said. 'So I assume you've got a way to contact Sardoca once we find the damn thing.'

'I have a sat phone in my side pack.' She inserted the detector into the wood packaging, and began moving it very slowly around the crate.

'What kind of radiation did they coat your tin with?' he said.

'An extremely diluted form of Beta radiation. Not nearly enough to affect us, but if this counter picks up the slightest trace it will immediately start beeping.'

It didn't.

They moved on to the next crate, and went through the same procedure. No beeping sounds. When they got to the third crate, Natasha said, 'This one's already been partially opened. Look. The lid is loose at one end.'

'This must be where Cain took his sample from.'

Korso removed the rest of the nails, and flipped the lid open. Natasha passed the Geiger counter over the interior. Nothing. Same with the next one. They moved on to the fifth crate, which was right in front of the main cargo door. That left only one more crate after this, which would probably contain the Geisha coffee, and therefore would be of no use to them.

'Time check,' he said.

She pulled her cell from her pocket, looked at the screen. 'Sixteen fifty-four.'

Which meant they'd been at this for over twenty minutes. He didn't like it. 'Yannick should have been back by now.'

'Maybe he's taking a bathroom break. Come on, we have more important things to worry about.'

He turned back and spent the next two minutes opening the lid of the last crate of caviar. Natasha inserted the Geiger counter into the container, moved it around slowly at the top left before dragging it diagonally across the bottom right...

Beep, beep, beep, beep...

Natasha raised her head and looked wide-eyed at Korso. She was beaming.

Korso began to smile back, but stopped when he heard a familiar sound coming from the tail of the plane, beyond the last crate. He'd heard the same sound when he'd passed the Skyhawk. The sound of scales being rubbed together.

'*La naiba,*' Natasha whispered, also recognising the sound. She carefully backed off down the narrow passage, toward the front of the plane.

Korso grabbed the flashlight and aimed it at the darkness at the rear. The light caught the head and neck of a snake back there, its tongue flicking in and out of its jaws as it checked for new odours. The rest of it was behind the last crate. He couldn't see how big it was. He couldn't tell the species. But it wasn't rattling, and he recalled Yannick's earlier warning about the lethal labaria, and how common they were in these parts.

Whatever it was, they had to get rid of it. Which meant *he* had to get rid of it.

He turned to see Natasha had paused halfway down, and was now watching him, gun in hand. 'I could shoot it,' she said.

'It would take more than one shot, and we might still need them. Get me one of the protective gloves and a set of tongs. And a machete.'

Without a word, Natasha quickly backed up the rest of the way and disappeared through the doorway. She

335

reappeared seconds later, holding all three items. She came within reach of Korso and handed them to him, one by one.

Placing the machete on top of the fourth crate, Korso inserted his left hand into the thick leather glove and pulled it up over his lower arm as far as it would go. Then he set the flashlight down on the floor, the beam still aimed at the tail of the plane. The snake was still in the same position, the tongue still flicking back and forth like a water diviner. Korso gripped the tongs in his gloved hand and carefully inched his way down the passage.

The snake chose that moment to languidly uncoil itself from its darkened corner and emerge into the open. Korso's heart skipped a beat. It was as big as a rattler. Except if this was a labaria, it was about ten times more deadly. Not that it made much difference. One bite from either and he was a dead man. For real this time.

Standing just behind the flashlight, Korso used both hands to extend the tongs toward the head of the snake, the jaw grip open and ready. Six feet, seven feet, eight feet, until the grabber was just a few inches away from the snake's head. The snake looked at it curiously, still flicking its tongue. It hissed once, then in a flash, darted its head at the shaft just above the grabber. Korso barely saw it move, but he felt it connect three times. He'd never seen a snake move so fast. A labaria then.

The snake glared at this new enemy and hissed again. Korso kept the tongs steady, knowing that if the snake decided to dart at him at the same speed, there'd be no way to move out of the way in time. Korso slowly began to rotate the tongs in a figure of eight formation, hoping to hypnotise the thing like a snake charmer. It seemed to have an effect. The snake watched the jaw grip cautiously as it moved around, its head moving in time with the stick. On the fourth go round, Korso held his breath, and suddenly lunged with the tongs until the grabber encircled the snake's neck. Without conscious thought, Korso released the trigger and the jaw snapped shut, instantly trapping the creature.

Korso breathed out again. The snake hissed as it writhed and struggled, but to no avail. Korso kept the thing planted on the floor as he grabbed the machete in his right hand. He stepped over the flashlight and moved in closer. But not too close. Just so he was out of the way of the cargo door.

'Come down here and open this,' he said.

'Why don't you just kill it?' she said.

'I'm about as close now as I ever want to be. Open this door so I can throw it out.'

Sighing loudly, Natasha edged forward while Korso kept his attention on the trapped snake. Its agitated writhing was easing off a little, which helped.

The cargo door was three times as wide as the crew door, the thick red door lever currently in the down position. Natasha placed the .22 on the fourth crate, then grabbed hold of the lever and raised it up ninety degrees. She pushed. The door section opened partially. She then grabbed hold of the frame on the right side and slid it all the way to the left.

Outside, four armed men stared back at them.

They were standing in a loose semi-circle about fifteen feet away. Three of them looked to be Guyanese nationals, probably local thugs. Two held pump-action shotguns, while the other gripped a large revolver. The fourth was an unshaven white man of medium height and build, with short dark hair that was greying at the temples. He wore cargo pants and a polo shirt. A bandolier around his waist held what looked like three smoke grenades and three flashbangs. He gripped a semi-automatic in his right hand. He was also smiling.

More specifically, he was smiling at Natasha.

'Well, look who it is.'

Forty-Eight

58 minutes and counting...

'Of all the people I expected to see here,' the man said, 'you were the very last. How's tricks, Natasha?'

'You should know, Jonas.'

Korso smiled inwardly. This Jonas was Cain, of course. He'd placed the voice instantly. And their open familiarity could only mean Natasha had to be the original leak that had started all this. And far more than just a simple leak, at that, each of them double-crossing the other in the process. Korso had suspected as much when she refused to speak with Cain, or Jonas, on the phone back in Amarillo. Those suspicions gained further weight just prior to the supposed rendezvous in Bilchner, when she'd donned that baseball cap, pulling it low over her face. And the reason was clear. Jonas would recognise her face in a heartbeat. Same with her voice. And she couldn't allow that to happen. Not then.

Jonas turned to Korso and motioned with the gun.

'And the last time I saw *your* face was through a telescopic sight. You can drop the machete now.'

Korso opened his right hand. The machete fell to the floor with a loud *clang*.

'Good.' Jonas said, lowering the gun. His eyes were dark orbs under heavy brows, and two deep ridges ran from the edges of his nose to the mouth's outer corners. 'You know, I was just departing Bilchner when I heard that C4 go off behind me. I was hoping you two had gone up in smoke along with that drug store, yet here we all are again. Was it a close call, at least?'

'You wouldn't believe how close,' Korso said. 'I suppose you've already killed our driver.'

Jonas shrugged. 'Never met the fellow. We heard what sounded like a jeep drive off about five minutes ago, so he could have spotted us as we were approaching. If he's got any sense he's on his way back to Georgetown. So how did you like my little sentries in the cockpit? They cause you any problems at all?'

'I've faced worse. You've got yourself some new friends, I see.'

'You mean the guys? Just some local talent I brought along.' Jonas turned to the similar-looking pair to his right, probably brothers. Both had shaved heads and beards, and wore faded t-shirts and jeans. 'Alvaro there with the Remington, Miguel next to him with the .357.' He turned to the similarly attired older man on his left. 'And Hector here.'

'Hazor,' the man said in a thick rasp, taking a drag on his cigarette.

'Hazor. Right.' Jonas turned back to Korso. 'I wasn't sure what I'd have to face up here, so I thought it best to come prepared.'

'Have they any idea how your associates usually end up, or are you planning on surprising them later?'

Jonas's eyes narrowed. 'Be very careful with your next words, Jack, or whatever your name is. They could well be your epitaph. Do we understand each other?'

'I think so.'

'Don't think. Be sure.' He turned his attention back to Natasha. 'Now you. If you've got a piece, bring it out nice and slow.'

'I'm unarmed,' she said, raising her hands and turning full circle. She wore a close-fitting shirt, so it was pretty obvious she wasn't carrying. 'We didn't have time to seek out a source for weapons, not if we wanted to get to this location while it was still light.'

With Jonas's attention now on Natasha, Korso quickly took stock of the situation. It was bleak, but not entirely hopeless. Before Natasha had slid the door open, Korso had moved to the left to allow space for her, which meant his left side was now partly in shadow. The four men were still too far way to notice the snake on the floor behind him, or his hand holding the tongs keeping it there. Natasha placing Yannick's .22 back on the fourth crate, just out of view of the visitors, was another bonus.

So one peashooter with three rounds against four armed men. It wasn't much, but if Natasha could just keep the guy talking for a little longer…

'Interesting,' Jonas was saying, 'that you thought reaching this place today was more important than gearing up properly.'

'It was a matter of prioritising one need over the other,' she said. 'It seems we chose poorly. Speaking of which, just how did *you* get here, Jonas?'

'I rented a helicopter. Didn't I tell you I have a pilot's licence?'

'It must have slipped your mind.'

'Just like it slipped yours in mentioning the identity of your employer when you recruited me into this little scheme of yours. Or that it was his personal property we'd be liberating. Those were two fairly huge omissions, weren't they? You manipulative little bitch.'

Natasha risked a glance at Korso, who looked back at her without expression. He'd always believed her own agenda was quite different to what she claimed. Jonas was merely verifying it.

'And if I had mentioned it,' she said, turning back to Jonas, 'would you have accepted?'

'Unlikely. I'm not the suicidal type.'

'Yet you chose to double-cross me instead. That's just as high-risk.'

Jonas smirked. 'Do unto others, I say. Only make sure you do it first.'

'A dangerous mantra to live by. But I'm still curious about a few things, such as how you persuaded Borozan to help you in this scheme of yours.'

'Borozan? You mean that Russian lunkhead on the plane? I never even tried. Not worth the effort. Once I boarded with that sixth crate, one simple tap on the back of the neck was all it took.' Jonas made a diving motion with his hand. 'Into the sea he went. Food for the fishes.'

'And what of the other pilot, Palma? Was he part of it, too?'

A shrug. 'Briefly. Let's leave it at that.' He turned to Korso. 'But I'm also intrigued. Because I can't believe Natasha would have told you about me and her, yet you don't seem too surprised about any of this.'

'I'm rarely surprised by human nature,' Korso said.

'So if you knew about her involvement, why go along with her?'

'I didn't know. I only suspected.'

Natasha was also watching Korso now. 'Since when?' she said.

342

'Since shortly after we met. When you originally briefed me, you spent over an hour supplying me with every piece of relevant information, no matter how small, without ever referring to notes. And nobody's memory retention is that good. But it could be explained if you were heavily involved in the planning of the heist, and made a habit of repeatedly going over and over every facet of the job, making sure nothing had been missed or overlooked. The devil's in the details, after all.'

She frowned. 'Circumstantial at best.'

'Sure. But there were other red flags. And they soon began piling up until there was only one possible answer to explain them all.'

'What red flags?'

'Now's probably not the best time to go into all of them, but one big giveaway was your refusal to talk to Jonas during that phone call in Amarillo. Another was when you fitted that baseball cap low on your head in Bilchner, so he wouldn't be able to recognise your features.' He shrugged. 'You showed me the signs. I simply paid attention.'

Jonas grinned at Natasha. 'Looks like you weren't quite as smart as you thought, sweetie.'

Natasha made a move to step outside the plane, but Jonas raised the gun again and she stopped. 'Uh, uh. Stay right where you are. I much prefer seeing the both of you in that enclosed space, where you can cause the minimum of trouble. But what really interests me at this moment is what the hell you two are doing here at all. I know I didn't give you any clues to this location, and I didn't leave anyone else alive who knew. So how did you manage to find it?'

'By thinking like you,' Korso said. 'It was a process of elimination. I won't bore you with the intricacies, but I figured the best way to hide a stolen plane would be amongst other aircraft nobody gives a damn about. And when I found that page on Reddit, showing a boneyard in the jungles of Guyana that hardly anyone knew about, that kind of sealed the deal for me. You must know which web page I'm referring to.'

Jonas gave a sigh. 'That damned Reddit page. I have to admit, though, everything pretty much fell into place the moment I landed on that site. Practically by accident, if you can believe it. I'm just amazed anyone else found it. Then again, I'm assuming you do this kind of thing for a living, and were brought in especially for this job?'

'Against my will, but essentially correct.'

Jonas looked at Korso with more interest. 'Which means you must be fairly successful in your profession.'

Korso shrugged. 'I get by.'

'I'd say you do a little more than get by, if your presence here's any indication. But right now I'm wondering what is so goddamn important about a few measly crates of black-market caviar that Nikolic assigns you two to travel halfway round the world to find and recover them, at no expense spared. And not even the fresh stuff, but pasteurised no less. Now why is that, I wonder?'

'You asked that same question before,' Natasha said, 'back in Amarillo. And we told you why.'

'And the answer I got was as unsatisfactory then as it is now. I get that a man of Nikolic's status would want to know what happened to his shipment. But what doesn't make sense is the two of you going to such lengths to recover a few crates of expensive fish eggs, especially as they can be replaced easily enough with money and the right contacts, both of which Nikolic has in spades. And things that don't make sense trouble me. Which is why I thought it might be a good idea to make my way down here pronto, and take a closer look at my investment. See what I might have missed the first time round.'

He opened his arms wide. 'And who do I find when I finally show up out of the blue but you two assholes. Looks like I was right to trust my instincts. Now, Natasha, how about you toss that side pack of yours over to me, nice and slow.'

'My pack? All it contains is some petty cash and my phone.'

'Toss me the pack right now.' Jonas raised his gun again. 'I won't ask twice.'

With a shrug she reached down and unlatched the pack's belt strap. Korso saw one of the brothers whisper something to the other as they leered at her. It didn't take a genius to figure out the subject under discussion. Natasha lobbed the pack underhanded to Jonas, who caught it with his free hand. Tucking the gun into his waistband, he unzipped the bag and looked inside.

While he was occupied, Natasha turned her attention to Korso again. He'd been waiting for her to re-establish eye contact. He moved his gaze toward the .22 on the crate at her right, then back to her again. She gave him an almost imperceptible nod in return. Good. They were on the same page.

Korso saw Jonas extracting the cash from the pack and passing some to Hazor on his right. Natasha was still watching Korso, who made a slithering motion with his right index finger. She noticed it, and frowned. Korso then lowered his eyes to his left, looking intently at the labaria he had trapped in the shadows. She lost the frown and gave him another barely noticeable nod. So she understood what he was trying to say. After three days in each other's company, a few eye movements were now all that were needed to get his message across. All they needed now was a secret go signal. It was essential. If they weren't in absolute synchronicity on this, they were both dead.

'Now look at this impressive piece of kit,' Jonas said then, pulling out a smartphone Korso hadn't seen before. It had a full screen display, and was twice as thick as a normal cell, with a stubby antenna on top. 'Satellite phones get smaller and smarter every year, don't they? This one looks expensive. Just a finger tap away from your boss, no matter where you are in the world. Very useful.' He put the phone back and pulled out the compact Geiger counter. 'And what do we have here? Forgot to mention this little item, didn't you?' With a frown, Jonas dropped the pack and switched the instrument on. He checked the display at the top for a few seconds.

Then he looked up at Natasha, and grinned for the second time that day.

'So I was right. There *is* something else in that plane, something far more valuable than a few crates of caviar. My guess is one of those little tins in there is coated with a radioactive marker, and this device is the only way of identifying it. How about it, Natasha? Am I close to the mark?'

'Right on the money,' Korso said, before she could answer.

'Thought so,' Jonas said, turning his attention to Korso. 'So what's in the tin?'

'That's a very good question, and one I've been asking her for the last few days.'

'You mean you don't know?'

'I'm just a contractor. That information's above my pay grade.'

'Okay, I'll buy that. And what was her response?'

'She says she doesn't know either, but I'm not sure I believe her. Not entirely, anyway. But based on what I know about Nikolic's business interests, along with a few clues I was able to pick up along the way, I finally narrowed it down to three possibilities.'

Jonas's eyes were boring into his. Same with the other three. People always want to know what's in the box.

'Which are?' Jonas prompted.

'Three,' he said, glancing at Natasha, who didn't nod this time. But her expression made it clear she understood what he was doing. 'It's a prototype of a new synthetic designer drug Nikolic's been secretly developing. A very effective and highly addictive drug. Potentially worth billions.'

In his peripheral vision, Korso saw Natasha adjust her position slightly.

'Two. Another prototype.' Korso adjusted his grip on the tongs in his left hand, and felt the snake on the floor writhing around in response. 'But this one for a chemical agent that attacks the central nervous system, killing the victim immediately before evaporating, leaving no trace behind. Again, conceivably worth a fortune to someone with the right connections.'

Jonas was chewing his cheek, clearly enraptured by the imagined riches just a few feet away from him.

Korso mentally prepared himself for what was coming, knowing that everything came down to the next few seconds. Maybe his last seconds on this earth.

'One.'

Forty-Nine

50 minutes and counting…

As the four men waited expectantly for his next words, Korso edged to his right as he tensed his left arm, then yanked up the tongs in an underhand throwing motion, pulling the angry snake up with it. In his peripheral vision, he noticed Natasha already reaching for the gun just behind her. The three thugs were still in the same positions, the two brothers to the left of Jonas, the other one to the right, all unsure what was happening in front of them. Jonas was different. He'd been caught off guard but his reactions were a little faster. He was starting to bring his handgun up in Natasha's direction.

Korso stayed focused on his own situation. He was already swinging his arm down and up in an underhand throw, tensing every muscle. Feeling every ounce of the six or so kilograms of lethal snake at the end of the tongs, he aimed for the two brothers; the biggest targets. He saw the long, curving, writhing body of the labaria as it passed his left leg, and as his arm continued along its upward arc, he pressed the button that unlocked the jaws of the grip. The moment the tongs were pointing horizontally at the brothers fifteen feet away, the snake finally came free and flew toward them at speed, like something out of a horror movie.

He heard a shot to his right and saw Jonas stumble. Down, maybe, but not out. Not from a .22. Another shot immediately followed, and Korso saw the one called Hazor dive or fall to the ground. Directly ahead he saw the snake land right at the brothers' feet. They both yelled in terror and backed away, but the snake was faster. It darted straight for the legs of Alvaro and struck his naked ankle repeatedly. Dropping the Remington, Alvaro fell to the ground, holding his leg and still screaming as he desperately scrambled away. His brother, Miguel, was yelling something as he pointed his gun at the ground, trying to zero in on the rapidly moving snake as it slithered around in the dirt.

Tossing the tongs, Korso launched himself out of the cabin and sprinted for the brothers. The best defence was an effective offence, especially when the enemy was otherwise occupied. As he ran, he noticed flashes of movement to his right, but ignored them, trusting Natasha to take care of her own problems. The sound of a shotgun blast behind him reverberated through the boneyard, but he ignored that too.

He went for Miguel. He was the immediate danger. Still aiming the revolver at the ground, Miguel fired off a shot, stinging the dirt. The snake was already slithering away at speed toward a nearby patch of grass. Spotting Korso coming straight for him, he turned in his direction. But before he could complete the movement, Korso barrelled into him, his left shoulder connecting with Miguel's right hip.

They both went down in a messy heap, landing a few inches from each other.

Miguel recovered fast, still gripping the gun as he got his legs under him, while Korso rolled away to his right, spotting the Remington the other one had dropped lying just a few feet away. He dived toward it, grabbed it by the barrel and leapt to his feet in one continuous, fluid motion. He was about to turn back to Miguel when a gunshot rang out, and a puff of dirt erupted where Korso's hand had just been. Korso jerked his body away, upending the Remington until his hand clasped the grip, his finger resting on the trigger.

Alvaro was still screaming, '*It got me it got me it got me,*' over and over.

Another shot rang out behind Korso. He swivelled round, squeezing the Remington's trigger at the same time, not caring if he hit anything. The blast echoed throughout the area. The unharmed Miguel dived to the ground near his brother, who was rocking back and forth, clearly in agony.

Korso saw Miguel already moving the gun again in his direction, and turned and ran for the plane he'd just vacated, making for the rear stabilisers, waiting for the bullet in the back that would end it all. Another gunshot erupted from behind, but nothing made contact. He reached the tail cone a second later, diving to the ground just as another shot rang out. A large chunk of the left stabiliser disappeared. Korso clambered his way around the tail until the aircraft was between him and Miguel. And anyone else who was still breathing.

He racked the shotgun, the spent shell flying out of the port and a fresh one taking its place. He didn't know how many shells he had left, but he couldn't afford to waste any. He checked behind him and saw the bare remains of the grey chopper lying on its side. Useless. No cover at all. Just past it was the wingless business jet. Not much better. But through the small gap between them, he was able to make out the large turboprop and the Learjet in two sections that he'd been inspecting before Natasha had called him over.

With nothing but flat open ground between here and there.

Korso thought fast, weighing the pros and cons in the blink of an eye. If Jonas had brought his rifle, Korso wouldn't dream of making a run for it. But handguns were far from reliable at a distance. Shotguns even less so. He needed to vacate this immediate area fast, before Jonas and one of the others caught him in a pincer attack. It also occurred to him that he hadn't heard any more gunshots in the last few seconds. Although he could still hear Alvaro screaming. Someone else swore loudly. It sounded like Jonas's voice. He wondered whether Natasha was the cause, whether she was still alive.

Decision made, Korso got to his feet and advanced in a crouch, listening for anything that sounded like breathing, until he reached the gap.

Then he spotted Natasha.

She was already a hundred feet away, her legs pumping hard as she sprinted at those same two wrecks. Nobody was shooting at her.

Korso pushed off, and ran like hell in the same direction.

Fifty

47 minutes and counting...

Korso had only covered thirty feet when he heard the first shot. Nothing hit him, but he instinctively darted to the right, then almost immediately began swerving to the left again. Handgun or not, he wasn't about to make it easy for them. He saw Natasha had already reached the large turboprop plane. She crouched down a few feet away from its nose, under the shadows of the two small crabwood trees.

Korso increased his pace as he veered back, controlling his breathing, taking every yard as it came. He saw Natasha was now aiming something in his direction. Part of him was surprised she still had any ammo left. There was still another hundred feet to go when he heard a third gunshot from behind him. He saw a tiny puff of dirt a few feet to his left as he sprinted by. He swerved in that direction, since it was the less obvious choice, then quickly zagged right again. Straightening up, he saw Natasha had already lowered her gun and was just watching him as he closed the distance.

Eighty feet became fifty. Then twenty.

Seconds later, he collapsed to the ground next to her, breathing heavily.

'I thought you were dead,' she said.

'I was, until you barged into my life.'

He rose to his knees and got his bearings. Directly to his left was the large turboprop, its open nose just a few feet from his position. To his right lay the two halves of the small Learjet. Looking back at the ATP, he saw two men moving around over there. One was Jonas. He was staring into the cargo hold as he held his left arm. The other man was leaning over Alvaro, still on the ground. That had to be Miguel.

'The man lying on the ground,' she said. 'The snake bit him, yes?'

'And more than once. If it was one of those labarias, he won't last much longer. So that's one down.'

'Unfortunately, I only grazed Jonas's arm,' she said. 'He moved too fast for me.'

'And the other one? Hazor?'

'I missed him entirely.'

Moments later, Korso spotted the one called Hazor as he emerged from the cargo hold, holding the machete Korso had dropped. He appeared unharmed.

Korso said, 'So you still have a round left, or did you use them all up?'

'One bullet left. And you?'

'Let's see.' With the Remington's safety on, Korso pumped the forestock and ejected the remaining shells. All three of them. 'Not so good.'

'But better than we started with,' she said. 'As are the odds. When they come for us, we'll have to be ready.'

He looked at her as he reloaded the shotgun. 'Why would they come for us? Jonas isn't stupid. He'll use that little Geiger counter of yours to find your tin, then grab it and fly out of here.'

Natasha reached into her pants pocket and showed him what it contained. 'You mean this little Geiger counter?'

Korso snorted. 'Okay, I didn't expect that. How did you get it back?'

'Jonas dropped it after I shot him. I managed to grab it before I ran.'

'So we're at stalemate. Jonas still needs the Geiger counter in order to identify the right tin. Meaning he can't just leave us out here on our own. On the downside, he's at the plane with the crates and we're not. And with more ammo and guns. He and the other two could wait us out until darkness, which is something we can't afford.'

'Although he doesn't know that.'

'Let's keep it that way. What's the time now?'

She pulled her original phone from her pocket and checked the display. 'Eighteen minutes past five.'

Forty-two minutes left. He looked to the west and saw the sun rapidly making its way toward the horizon. The golden hour. The air was already cooling a little, the shadows growing steadily longer.

'What time does the sun set here?' she asked.

'This close to the equator? Around six, pretty much all year round.'

'So what's your plan?'

'Wait. And see what happens in the next few minutes.'

They waited. Korso kept his eyes on the three men at the ATP. Miguel had dragged his dying brother back so he could rest against the plane's hull. Hazor was currently out of eyesight. Jonas was constantly moving about over there, sometimes disappearing briefly when he entered the plane. No doubt he was thinking through his few remaining options. He'd come to the same conclusions as Korso soon enough, if he hadn't already.

Finally, Natasha said, 'You and I want the same thing.'

'I know,' Korso said, watching the ATP.

'So we are still working together on this?'

'What other choice do we have?'

Korso watched as the three survivors at the ATP conferred heatedly, with plenty of gesticulating on Jonas's part.

'Who is this Jonas, anyway?' he said, as the man in question reached down and picked up Hazor's shotgun from the ground.

'He's an ex-DEA agent turned freelance mercenary, someone unafraid to get his hands dirty. I used him as go-between and bagman on several previous assignments for Mr Nikolic. I knew he had a devious mind, which was essential on this operation since he would have to act as my proxy. Unfortunately, this time he was a little too devious for his own good.'

'Or yours.'

'Mostly mine, as it turns out.'

Korso nodded to himself. All the pieces were starting to fit together. Still one more obstacle left to cross, though. And it was a big one.

'They're coming,' he said.

Natasha turned to look. Jonas, Miguel and Hazor were now leaving the ATP and walking their way. Miguel was reloading his .357, while Jonas was carrying the shotgun in his left hand. That arm seemed to be in good working order again. Hazor carried a machete and the other handgun.

He and Natasha both watched the approaching men in silence. When they'd almost halved the distance, she said, 'I cannot believe they'd approach us directly like this.'

'They won't,' Korso said, remembering the bandolier around Jonas's waist.

The trio halted at the same time, still about a hundred feet away. Jonas raised his right hand to his mouth and pulled something from it with his teeth. Then he swept his arm back and flung the object he'd been holding their way.

'Flashbang,' Korso said, watching the tiny canister fly through the air.

It landed in a patch of grass ten feet in front of the turboprop. He and Natasha immediately turned their faces away, eyes clamped shut, both hands clasped over their ears.

Seconds passed. There was no flash. No bang. Just a faint hissing sound.

Korso turned back and saw dark grey smoke spewing from both ends of the canister, rapidly rising into the still air in huge, thick, billowing plumes. Within seconds a dense smokescreen completely obliterated their view, and then it quickly began moving in their direction. Already, the ATP and the other aircraft were completely lost from sight.

So were the three men.

Fifty-One

Knowing they had seconds to act, Korso turned to Natasha. 'This wreck to our left. You cover the tail, I'll stick here.'

She stood up, the incoming smoke already starting to engulf her. 'Countersign?'

'George, and Romero.'

That half-smile again. 'Watch your back.' Then she vanished into the smoke.

Korso stood and ran toward the nose of the turboprop, or at least where he knew it would be. When his hand touched metal, he leaned his shoulder against the front of the plane while gripping the Remington in both hands, finger resting on the trigger. The fumes were getting much thicker and denser now. Jonas must have lobbed another for good measure.

He wanted to cough, but restrained himself. The last thing he needed was to give himself away. The duration of a smoker was somewhere between sixty and ninety seconds, and Jonas still had an extra on his belt, along with three flashbangs. But he was unlikely to use those without running the risk of blinding Miguel at the same time.

Korso watched, listened. All he saw was smoke. He heard nothing other than the usual bird calls in the

357

distance. Turning his head constantly, he watched for anything solid to emerge from the smog. He glanced right, at the Learjet remains, seeing nothing but more swirling smoke, then peered round the nose at the direction of the ATP. Still nothing.

How long had it been since they'd split up? Twenty seconds? Twenty-five? And still no gunshots.

To his left, the smoke seemed to thin for a brief second. A shape appeared. Indistinct. Possibly human, before melting away again into the fog. Korso raised the shotgun, aiming at the exact spot he'd seen the shape.

'George,' he said, in a clear voice. No response.

Korso squeezed the trigger. The shotgun bucked and there was a scream of pain. Or maybe that's just what he was supposed to think.

Korso racked the pump, then edged his body around the nose of the plane, still keeping low. The smoke wasn't quite so dense down there. He'd progressed a few feet when he thought he saw something on the ground, before it too disappeared.

A gunshot from his right. Korso fell prone to the ground, waiting for the pain to come. None did. He hadn't been hit. He turned in that direction, peering through the smoke, and thought he could make out the trunks of the two crabwood trees separating the planes. Rising to a crouch he ran toward them, one hand out in front of him, keeping as low as possible.

He felt the bark of a tree and stopped, pressing himself against it, looking around in all directions. The gunshot had come from over here. He was sure of it.

Korso noticed sudden movement to his right.

Just as he was turning, something dark hurtled out of the smog and connected with his right ear. He fell back, his head hitting the ground, his ear ringing, his grip on the shotgun gone. He heard it skitter along the ground to his right. Then something heavy landed on his stomach, and a pair of hands immediately appeared in front of his face, and a second later they were clasped around his neck.

Miguel's face emerged out of the smoke. His eyes were wide, his expression crazed, murderous. His hands squeezed even tighter around Korso's neck, cutting off all circulation.

'Kill you for what you did,' he hissed, his face inches away from Korso's. '*Kill you. Kill you.*'

Korso choked, unable to breathe. Miguel had the grip of the possessed. He could already feel his head getting lighter through lack of oxygen. A few more seconds of this and he'd be too weak to do anything.

Reaching up with both hands, he pushed Miguel's elbows upward, instantly disrupting the geometry of the chokehold.

The grip loosened a little, but it was enough. Curling his right hand into a fist, his middle finger knuckles extended, he rammed it upward into the man's throat with every ounce of strength in his body. His extended knuckles connected with Miguel's adam's apple like a piston, and he felt something crumple. The man made a harsh, rasping, choking sound, immediately releasing Korso as he brought his hands up to his own ruined throat.

Korso swivelled his body and got out from under the still choking Miguel, pushing the man off him with his foot while he got his breath back.

The smoke was starting to thin now and he could see Miguel on his knees a few feet away, his body hitching violently as it tried to take in air. Korso felt around the ground until his fingers came into contact with the barrel of the Remington. He picked it up. Still two shells left, but he wouldn't need them. Not for Miguel anyway. His movements were already growing weaker with every passing second.

He heard a gunshot somewhere off to his left, and two more in quick succession. All from a large calibre. Then nothing except the sounds of Miguel's death rasp. Finally, the man collapsed face down on the ground, and stopped moving altogether.

Two down. Two to go. Unless Natasha had finished off her assailant. Or maybe her assailant had gotten the better of her.

Korso got to his feet. He checked Miguel's body, but the man was unarmed. He looked around for a sign of the gun, but the smoke was still too dense for him to see anything. Jonas had probably used all three smoke grenades after all. With his free hand out in front to guide him, Korso began walking in the direction of the two Learjet sections, where he'd heard the earlier gunshot. Miguel could have dropped the gun there. It was probably out of ammo, but he still needed to check. He'd covered a dozen feet or so when his left hip brushed against the steel fuselage of one of the plane sections. His boot made contact with the remains of a rear stabiliser half sunken in the dirt.

He took a few steps back from the plane. The smoke seemed a little thinner here, and he was actually able to see a few feet in front of him. He felt the ground all around him, looking for anything metallic.

Korso jumped at the sudden, piercing shriek of a nearby bellbird, raising the Remington without thinking and looking in all directions. Something had alerted the bird. He heard sounds of movement to his right, saw nothing. But his instincts were yelling at him to stay low.

He dropped prone to the ground.

A second later, there was a shotgun blast from his right. Korso flinched as the lethal buckshot pellets rattled against the jet's hull above him, but he felt no stinging sensations on his body or face. Hoping he'd escaped the blast radius, he rolled and aimed the Remington in the general direction the shot had come from, squeezing the trigger. The gun bucked, the blast satisfyingly loud, but there was no accompanying scream.

Only one shell left.

Korso racked the pump and was just getting to his feet when something hard slammed into his side. He fell to his knees, his free hand against the ground for support. He heard something behind him, a fraction too late.

'Thought it was you,' Jonas said, his shape solidifying as he emerged from the smoke. The Remington was suddenly kicked out from Korso's grip, and a moment later he felt the cold barrel of the other shotgun pressing against his temple.

Korso immediately ducked his head down and swept his arm up, forcing the barrel upward just as it went off. The blast was thunderous. Korso swivelled his body round, at the same time aiming a sweeping roundhouse punch at where Jonas's head should be. His fist connected with flesh and bone, and Jonas yelled out in surprise as something clattered to the ground nearby. The other shotgun. Somewhere to Korso's left.

Korso ducked down to where it landed, and swept a hand across the hard clay earth in a wide radius. His fingers touched metal just as Jonas kicked him hard in the stomach.

'*Bastard*,' Jonas said.

Korso clenched his abdominal muscles to in an effort to compartmentalise the pain, somehow keeping his fingers in contact with the shotgun barrel. Ignoring the agony in his torso, he managed to get a half-decent grip on the barrel just as another kick came his way. Grabbing the firearm, he scrambled his body back along the ground as Jonas's foot swept past his face.

He rotated the gun until his right palm was on the grip, his index finger in the trigger guard. Jonas was already moving in for another kick when he suddenly saw the shotgun aimed at his chest. His eyes widened.

'*Wait*—'

Korso squeezed the trigger. The gun boomed. Jonas fell back against the hull of the plane. His legs crumpled underneath him, and he slid down until he was half resting against the body of the plane. There was a ragged wound in his lower neck, and blood was already staining the pale hull of the jet. Korso also noticed Jonas's shirt was heavily stained with blood just above the left hip. Which explained the scream of pain he'd heard earlier.

Korso was about to get up when he heard sounds of footsteps to his left, from the direction of the turboprop. He swivelled round, shotgun first. The smoke was thin enough now for him to make out an indistinct human figure moving through the haze.

With his finger on the trigger, he called out, 'George.'

'Romero,' came the reply.

He smiled faintly to himself as he took his finger away from the trigger. Natasha appeared out of the smoke a second later, now gripping a semi-automatic in her right hand. Which told its own story. She appeared unharmed.

Using the shotgun for support, Korso lowered his head and was just rising to his feet when something hard slammed into the back of his skull and everything turned black.

Fifty-Two

Korso opened his eyes and saw blue sky above him. Still daylight. He'd only been out for several minutes. He hoped. Not that he had anybody to blame but himself. Natasha had given him fair warning. He should have listened.

Using one hand for support, he slowly got to his feet, still feeling woozy from the blow. Once up, he felt the back of his neck and flinched at the soreness there.

The smoke had completely dissipated. The sun was still making its way into the horizon. Korso figured another fifteen or twenty minutes before it disappeared entirely.

He heard coughing sounds to his right. He turned and saw Jonas in the same position as before, his upper half resting against the hull of the plane, legs splayed out before him.

Jonas was looking at him with half-closed eyes, his breathing faint and laboured. The neck wound was still bleeding profusely, and it was clear he didn't have long left. The ground under him was dark with his blood. Both shotguns were also gone, which came as no surprise.

'You… got… lucky.' Jonas's voice was barely audible.

'We make our own luck.'

'Who…' He stopped as he coughed up blood. He tried again. 'Who… you?'

'Nobody.' The man's eyelids were getting heavier with each passing second. 'You should have played straight, Jonas. Especially with someone like her.'

'Drop… dead… asshole.'

Jonas grinned at him with red teeth. The grin turned into a grimace, and he coughed up about a quart of blood. Then his head fell backward and he exhaled his last breath, staring blankly up at the sky.

Korso crouched by the now lifeless body and patted it down from head to foot. Just to be sure. Nothing. Even the bandolier was missing. Natasha didn't take any chances, but then he already knew that about her. He was about to rise, when he stopped and turned the body over. He patted the man's back pockets, and felt a long thin object in one. He reached in and pulled it out.

–

It took less than a minute to reach the three aircraft carcasses. As he passed the corpse of Alvaro, lying near the ATP, he heard noises coming from the cargo area fifteen feet away. Then Natasha emerged, a caviar tin under her shoulder and the sat phone in her left hand. In her right was Jonas's gun.

Spying him, she raised the gun. 'Do not come any closer.'

'Tell me, was the crack on the head really necessary?'

'Like I said before, I always prepare for the worst.' She placed the caviar tin on the floor of the cargo hold, but held onto the phone. 'You should know that better than anyone.'

'What's the time now?'

She glanced at the phone's display. Showed it to him. 17:49.

'Cutting it close,' he said. 'And that's the special tin you wanted?'

'It is.'

'So what next for me? A bullet to the brain, I suppose?'

'I have not decided yet. Although you don't seem too surprised at the likelihood.'

'I'm not. With Sardoca, there's always a sting in the tail. Now that I've outlived my usefulness, he can't afford to let me live one second longer. And who better to act as my executioner than you?'

'Everybody dies, Korso. It's just a matter of timing.' She paused. 'But I still have one or two unanswered questions. Such as what were those other red flags that gave me away?'

'There was only one more really. But it was a fairly big one.'

'Please enlighten me then.'

'Well, we both know that Nikolic likes to divide up assignments, passing out information on a need-to-know basis, so that there's never any one person who knows the whole plan besides him. But in this case, you and Sardoca had to know most of those details since you were the ones tasked with supervising the transport of this precious cargo of his.'

'Obviously. So?'

'So we agreed that this whole heist had to be an inside job. That it could only have worked with the help of a leak from within Nikolic's organisation. And since only you and Sardoca knew enough about the mission to cause any trouble, it seemed logical that one of you was that leak, possibly even the one who masterminded the whole setup in the first place. Once I discounted Sardoca, that left just you.'

She was silent for a moment. 'Why would you discount Sardoca?'

'Because I know him, and if he *had* been the one behind it there's absolutely no way he would have trusted anyone else to chaperone me on this assignment. Not even you. Also, since he was ostensibly in charge of this operation, it makes no sense that he'd sabotage it for financial motives, knowing that Nikolic would hold him personally responsible if things went wrong. Sardoca's seen Nikolic at his very worst, as have I. And you don't want that kind of rage aimed at you if you can help it.' He arched an eyebrow. 'Do you?'

Natasha looked at him for a few moments without speaking. Then, still holding the gun on him, she raised the sat phone in her other hand and pressed two buttons. They both listened to the ringing tone.

Thirty seconds later there was a click, and a man's voice said, 'Go.'

'Seven two nine nine,' she said. 'I have the item.'

There was a brief pause, then Sardoca said, 'Natasha, you wonderful creature, you've just made my week. Shit, my whole *year*. And by the skin of your teeth too. That serial number on the bottom of the tin. Read it out to me, will you?'

She turned the tin over and carefully recited fourteen numbers.

'That's it all right,' Sardoca said. He sounded happier than Korso had ever heard him. 'Jesus, that's a weight off my shoulders. You don't know how much. Look, I have to get in touch with the boss to let him know, but we'll go over the details once you get back, okay? And good job, Natasha. Damn good job.' There was a pause on the line.

367

'And that final thing I asked you to do, back in Bermuda? Is it done yet?'

She was watching Korso. 'Not yet.'

A sigh. 'Is he nearby?'

'No, he is otherwise engaged at the moment. But it's just the two of us.'

'Good. Then I suggest you carry out the last part of your assignment the moment you get off this line, before he starts getting suspicious.'

'Don't worry,' she said. 'I'll take care of everything.'

Still watching Korso, she ended the call and pocketed the phone. She was still aiming the gun at him.

'One thing about Sardoca,' Korso said, 'he never lets you down.'

Natasha looked at him, and said nothing.

'If he only knew what he's up against. He really doesn't have any idea, does he?'

'About what?'

'About you, Natasha. And about your unique relationship with Nikolic, and how totally outclassed he is in comparison. He may currently enjoy the privilege of being one of the man's few trusted lieutenants, but that's nothing when compared to blood, is it? And blood's always thicker than water.'

'How long have you known?'

'Since that initial plane journey to Tijuana. Watching your profile reminded me a little of Nikolic. More than a little, actually. Especially the nose and cheekbones. Then you kept doing that thing with your earlobe, which only reinforced the effect. Sardoca, of all people, planted the idea in my head back in Bermuda, when he claimed Nikolic treated me like the son he never had. Totally untrue, of course, but it got me thinking along those lines. Also, I remember asking you whether "partner" was the correct term for Sardoca, and you said it was "close enough for now". It was fairly obvious even then that you considered him your junior, even though he believed the reverse.' He paused. 'I take it you were illegitimate?'

'What makes you say that?'

'I worked for Nikolic for two years, and got to know him as well as any man can, so I was aware he never married or had children. Or at least had any that he knew about. Hostages to fortune, he called them. And in his case, he meant it literally. I guess you slipped through the net somehow, although I'm not sure how. No offence to your mother, but I find it hard to picture Nikolic having a relationship with a mere waitress. If that's really what she was.'

'If you must know,' Natasha said with a shrug, 'my birth mother was a call girl. Or hooker, if you prefer. I barely knew the woman, and she barely knew me. Her elder sister was the waitress I mentioned, and it was she who raised me. Can you picture it now?'

He nodded. 'That fits in more with the man I remember. So how did you find out he was your biological father?'

'He told me three years ago, as well as presenting me with the DNA evidence. As you know, he is thorough in all things. Sardoca was the one who initially recruited me into his organisation three years before that, but only because Nikolic subtly pointed him in my direction in the first place. That's his way, as you know. He never goes the direct route.'

Korso knew. Everything fitted together now, like the pieces in a jigsaw. 'And the moment he found out about you, he began secretly grooming you for higher things, right? Such as partnering you up with Sardoca, so you could experience first hand how the business was run at ground level. That's also Nikolic's way. When he finds promising talent, he often throws them in the deep end and watches them sink or swim.'

'Is that how it was with you, Korso?'

'Maybe.'

They looked at each other.

After a long pause, Natasha said, 'I'm still waiting for the question you really want to ask me. Or one of them, at least.'

Korso smiled. 'You mean *why*? It all seems fairly obvious to me. Since you've inherited your father's genes, you've undoubtedly inherited his legendary impatience too. And while you steadily advance your progress up that metaphorical ladder to sit at his side, it's still not happening fast enough for you. So you decided you'd speed things along a little. Hence, your behind-the-scenes plotting of the cargo heist. And with this mysterious asset of Nikolic's as part of the equation, it must have been too good an opportunity to pass up.'

He paused. She motioned with the gun. 'Go on.'

'I'm just trying to figure out how the pilot, Azevedo, initially got wind of the cargo's worth and then got the idea to reconnect with his sister's ex-boyfriend, Kujan, to help organise its removal.' He furrowed his brow for a moment, then smiled as it came to him all of a sudden.

'Something funny?' she asked.

'The apple didn't fall far from the tree, did it?'

'Meaning?'

'Meaning you introduced the idea to Azevedo yourself. That's the only way it could have happened. At some point, you must have mentioned the upcoming shipment to him and hinted at the crates' contents, along with the cargo's true value. All very subtly, of course. You probably also inserted Kujan's name into the conversation somehow, so as to jar Azevedo's memory a little and nudge him along in the direction you wanted him to follow. Then once they were on board, you threw Jonas into the mix to recruit the rest of the crew and keep everyone in line. Jonas called you a manipulative bitch, but he had no idea how calculating you can be, did he? But then, you've learned from a master.'

She smiled at him. 'Sometimes it takes a great teacher to discover where a person's true talents lie. I must admit, Korso, I was impressed not only when you spotted the connection between Azevedo's sister and Kujan so early on, but that you were even aware of Kujan's existence in the first place.'

'I'm just full of surprises. Had I missed that particular lead, though, I'm sure you'd have pointed me in the right direction again.'

'Except with you, I never needed to. You have proved yourself adept at noticing things others miss.'

'Thanks, I guess. What about Papsidera and Adamson? Did you know about them?'

She shook her head. 'Only in the most general terms. Jonas didn't give me their real names. Or rather, the names he did give me turned out to be false. After you and I found Kujan's body in Tijuana, everything else from that moment onward was news to me. But you have still not explained how stealing a shipment from Nikolic could benefit me.'

'That's the easy part. This whole setup was a win– win. Had Jonas kept his end of the deal, you could have miraculously discovered the whereabouts of the missing shipment yourself, eliminating all those involved in the process, and then personally delivered it to Nikolic, thus demonstrating your clear and obvious superiority over Sardoca. After all, that was the main purpose of all this, wasn't it? To make Sardoca look bad in Nikolic's eyes, and so accelerate your own upward trajectory.'

That smile was back. 'But Jonas did *not* keep his end of the deal.'

'Which actually made little difference to you. Whether Jonas double-crossed you or not, Nikolic still held Sardoca responsible for the missing shipment, coming down hard on him and demanding a quick resolution to the problem. So after getting nowhere, Sardoca decided to bring me in as a final solution, bringing you along to watch over me. Probably at your suggestion, am I right?'

She gave a brief nod of her head.

'And so, three days later, here we are. Obviously, recovering the shipment works out better for you, but not finding it would have produced the same result, albeit a less satisfying one. Sardoca's failure would ensure he was no longer part of Nikolic's inner circle, and while no real blame would be left at your feet, you wouldn't have actually progressed any further. But it all worked out to your advantage. You found the shipment *and* the main prize. And I've no doubt you'll make it perfectly clear just who deserves the credit when you report back to Nikolic.'

'He won't take a great deal of persuading,' Natasha said. 'Thanks to my influence, Nikolic already suspects Sardoca is past his best. This episode will merely confirm it. His days are numbered, and I will move ever closer to my end goal.'

'The summit itself,' Korso said. 'But there's only space for one at the very top.'

She shrugged. 'Nikolic is a lot older than you might think, Korso. He just keeps himself in very good shape. However, it's my estimate that he has two, maybe three, years left.'

'Just long enough for you to bleed him dry of everything you need in order to successfully run his organisation all by yourself. It also helps that most people aren't even aware that Nikolic exists in the first place. Other than a few close lieutenants, nobody will actually know he's gone, and you can easily take care of them. His name and his rep are all that matter, and they'll do most of the work for you.'

Natasha's smile gave him all the confirmation he needed.

'My heart bleeds for the guy. It really does.' And for Sardoca too. Clearly, neither man was long for this world, which was fine with Korso. He glanced at the caviar tin at her feet, and said, 'You've known what the Tiger's Tears was from the very start.'

She nodded.

'So are you going to let me in on the secret?'

'Let's just say one of your guesses was not a million miles away from the truth.'

'Really? Which one?'

She shook her head slowly. 'This is Nikolic's property. In a short time it will be mine. And the fewer who know its true contents, the better for me in the long run.'

'So you're not going to carry out the final part of your assignment? Sardoca won't be pleased if he finds out.'

She lowered the gun. 'Since you're unlikely to reveal to either man my involvement in all this, or my future plans, you present little danger to me now. You may live.'

'Thank you,' Korso said, allowing the small switchblade concealed in his shirt sleeve to fall into his hand. He swung his arm forward and hurled the knife, blade first, into the ground, three feet in front of Natasha. 'I guess I won't be needing that anymore.'

Natasha looked down at the knife sticking out of the dirt, then back up at him. She gave a thin smile as she retrieved the switchblade and tucked it into her side pack. 'I thought I'd left you unarmed.'

'You should have checked Jonas's back pockets.'

'I will miss you, Korso.'

'I doubt that.'

'Well, maybe just a little. It's a shame Yannick left us prematurely. He missed out on the second half of his fee.'

'Which you would have paid him, of course.'

'Of course. I pay all my debts, one way or the other. I'm paying one off right now by not killing you. After all, you saved my life in Bilchner.'

'Twice,' he said.

She frowned. 'Twice?'

'First from Jonas in the church steeple, then again from the C4. According to my balance sheet, you still owe me a life.'

Natasha snorted. 'You really are unbelievable.'

'Well, do you honour your debts, or don't you?'

'That depends. What else do you want?'

'Can I assume you can also pilot a chopper, and that you'll be using Jonas's, wherever it is, to head back to the city now?'

'You can assume that, yes.'

'So how about a lift?'

'Anything else apart from that.'

'In that case, how about taking this back with you?' He reached into his pants pocket and brought out the small thumb drive he'd been carrying with him since Bermuda. He lobbed it underhanded to her.

Natasha caught it in her free hand. 'What does it contain?'

'Just a little Trojan malware Dog prepared for me a while back. To any casual observer, it appears to be a simple blank Word document. But send it as an email attachment, and as soon as the recipient opens it up, it grants me immediate and complete access to everything on their operating system. I want you to send it to Sardoca. I need those photos of me permanently deleted, and there's only one way to guarantee it's done properly. And preferably while he's still in the land of the living, for however long that might be.'

'Not very long is my guess,' she said, pocketing the drive. 'But since your goals don't interfere with mine, I'll email this attachment to him tomorrow. The rest is up to you.'

'Good enough.'

She reached down and picked up the caviar tin, then looked over his shoulder. The sun was sinking fast, producing a kaleidoscope of vivid colours that stretched across the sky as stunning purples collided with bright, fiery oranges.

'So this is where we part ways,' Natasha said, circling around him until her back was to the sun. 'You'll have to find your own way back, Korso, but you're a born survivor so I have no doubt you'll make it. And I put that machete back in the hold, so you're not completely defenceless. Oh, and as for your fee, I will honour that too. One of those crates in there is yours, which I realise comes to

375

slightly less than the twenty-five per cent we agreed upon, but that is life. You're welcome to take as much as you can carry. Although you'll have to work fast. In less than twenty-fours, anything left inside that hold will be on its way to Toronto again.'

'You're all heart, Natasha.'

She gave him that half-smile again. 'And I'll also offer you something else for free, if you want it.'

'What's that?'

'A specific location and a time, ten days from now. Would that be of interest to you?'

He blinked at her. 'It might be.'

She gave them to him. Then she said, 'Goodbye, Korso,' and gave a mock salute as she started backing away, toward that narrow strip of open land in the distance that he'd spotted before. When she'd put enough space between them, she turned and broke into a jog.

Korso watched her until she disappeared from sight, then stepped over to the cargo door entrance. He perched on the door sill and stared at the sunset, marvelling at those amazing colours and wondering just how the hell he was going to reach civilisation again. On foot. In the dark. Without food or water. Through uncharted rainforest.

Miles and miles and miles of it.

It was a problem all right.

He was still wondering when he heard what sounded like a diesel engine approaching from the east.

Fifty-Three

Korso got up and moved away from the three wrecks until he was right out in the open, as visible as possible. In the fading light, he could just make out a pick-up about two hundred feet away, both headlights on full beam, coming from the direction of the original dirt track they'd used to get here. It was heading his way, toward the ATP.

When the headlights finally found Korso, he waved an arm back and forth. He had a good idea who was behind the wheel. The vehicle slowed as it came closer, before coming to a complete stop a few feet away. Korso relaxed when he saw the Toyota badge in the grille. The driver pulled the handbrake, but left the engine idling.

It was one of the most beautiful sounds he'd ever heard.

The door opened and Yannick stepped out, grinning widely.

'Hey, Jack,' he said. 'How are things?'

'A lot better now you're here,' Korso said. 'It's good to see you, Yannick.'

Yannick came over to him, and they shook hands. 'Man, when I saw those four guys with guns, I got the hell away from here and just laid low for a while. When I heard all that gunfire, I knew I'd made the right choice. What happened here, man?'

Korso told him. He kept it brief.

Once he'd finished, Yannick whistled softly. 'Holy Mary, Mother of God. So your partner was not one of the good guys, after all.'

'She never was. But at least she kept her word, which puts her a notch above most people I've met.'

'Well, she didn't keep her word to me. She still owes me money.'

Korso was already walking over to the rear of the pick-up. He inspected the flatbed, mentally sizing it up. It looked big enough, especially with the tailgate down.

He turned back to Yannick, and smiled. 'I may have a solution to that.'

–

At 10:47 the next morning, Yannick pulled into one of the short-stay parking bays outside Cheddi Jagan International Airport's main terminal, and killed the engine.

After sleeping in the vehicle overnight, they'd started back at the crack of dawn, rationing out the rest of the food and water as they went. The return journey was no less arduous than the previous day's had been, but each man was a lot more relaxed than when they'd set out. Just for different reasons.

Yannick swivelled round and took another look at the single crate on the flatbed behind them. It had taken a fair amount of effort for two men to lift it, but Korso felt he'd earned it. Part of him wished he could see the look on Natasha's face when she arrived with transport later today, and noticed one crate missing. A small part, though. He wasn't all that anxious to see her again so soon.

'Look, Jack,' Yannick said, 'are you sure about this? That caviar back there is worth a lot of money. You sure you don't want to share the profits?'

'You keep it,' Korso said. 'I already got what I wanted out of all this. Just remember what I told you. Hide the crate somewhere safe, and tell nobody where it is. Not even your wife. Then call the number of that fence I gave you and arrange a meet. And don't get greedy. That stuff may be worth a million dollars US, but you should be happy if he offers you ten cents on the dollar. Or even five.'

'Hey, I'll be more than happy, man. Even fifty thousand is a fortune to me.'

'That's the attitude.'

Korso opened his door, got out of the car. He looked over at the terminal building, watching all the luggage-laden people going inside, all headed for destinations unknown. All just like him. Except he was missing the luggage.

Yannick joined him on the sidewalk. He held out his hand. 'Thanks, man. For everything.'

Korso shook it. 'Good luck.'

'Likewise. So where next for you?'

'I'm kind of curious about that myself.'

Epilogue

'Mr Smith must have had a particularly bad week,' the first host said, *sotto voce*. 'He's in an even worse mood than usual tonight. Practically bit my head off when I dropped a napkin as I was serving him.'

His colleague whispered back, 'Feel sorry for whichever poor hostess he ends up taking upstairs with him later. She'll get the worst of it.'

'You got that right. Christ, why can't they all be like Mr Brown? Nothing ever fazes that man, and he always leaves a mammoth tip.'

'Or Mr Williams. I heard rumours he's some kind of major arms dealer, but you'd never know it. He's always telling me dirty jokes. The hostesses can't get enough of him.'

The two young men, each dressed in identical tuxedos, were carefully arranging some hors d'oeuvres on a marble counter in the sleek, ultra-modern kitchen of the private club's second floor. Set in a large, three-storey town-house at the end of a quiet cul-de-sac in one of the most expensive sections of Mayfair, the club itself had no name, and was so exclusive most people didn't even know it existed. Its membership was extremely limited. One could only join by recommendation, and still there was no guarantee you'd be accepted. Even some billionaires had been unable to gain entry. And definitely no actors. It was said that the annual membership fee was somewhere in the low six figures, but few knew for sure, and they weren't telling. The benefits, though, were something to behold.

The club's Michelin-star chef was currently on a smoke break, and the only other person in the kitchen was another host. Older than the first two, with greying hair and a slight paunch, he was there covering for a host who'd fallen sick two days previously. He had been verified by two other club members, which meant his reputation, and more importantly his discretion, was above reproach. He also wore a tuxedo and the standard white cotton gloves. Bent over another marble counter fifteen feet away from his colleagues, pretending not to listen, he finished positioning the cigars in the oak humidor so they were all perfectly aligned.

Appearance mattered a great deal here. In truth, it was everything.

The host gently closed the lid and polished the oak surface with a cotton cloth, picking up the temperature-controlled humidor in both hands. Without speaking to the other two, he left the kitchen and carefully made his way down the long, plushly carpeted corridor until he finally reached a set of double doors. He used an elbow and shoulder to push through, so the contents of the humidor wouldn't be disturbed, and entered the room.

The bar and lounge area was the very epitome of elegance and good taste, and took up over half of the second floor. Delicate lighting effects gave the room a velvety ambience, while glass panels and intricately placed mirrors made the room seem twice as large. Unobtrusive chillout music seeped out of the state-of-the-art sound system. The fourteen members currently in residence were all seated away from each other, eating and drinking and smoking as they enjoyed the company of the three-dozen hostesses scattered about the room. Each hostess was not only stunningly beautiful, but highly educated. And any one of them was available to a member if he so desired. Or even more than one.

The grey-haired host made his way past the exclusive clientele, never making eye contact with anyone, until he reached the sunken level in the centre of the room where there were four more tables, all occupied. He approached a man sitting at one of them drinking champagne with two gorgeous hostesses: a brunette on one side, a redhead on the other. Their hands were all over him. The man didn't look drunk, but he looked as though he might be soon. There were still a few remnants of white powder on the glass table.

The member took his attention away from the redhead he was canoodling, and aimed his dark gaze at the host as he approached the table. 'What do you want? I'm busy.'

'My sincere apologies for intruding, Mr Smith,' the host said. 'However, my employer and the owner of this establishment asked that I come and offer you a cigar from his own personal supply, as he places you in high regard and wishes to show his respect.'

The member's gaze softened a little. 'He does, huh?'

'Yes, sir.' The host opened the lid and showed him the humidor's contents. 'Rare vintage Arturo Fuente Opus X BBMF cigars, made from the finest Dominican tobacco. They don't come any better. Please, make your choice, sir.'

The redhead whispered something in the man's ear and gave a coquettish giggle. Ignoring her, he sat up and slowly moved his fingers down the row of cigars, before finally picking one. The host gently took it from him, removed a guillotine cigar cutter from his waistcoat pocket, and precisely snipped the cigar just inside the cap. He handed the cigar back, removed a box of matches from the same pocket and lit one. Placing the cigar between his lips, the man leaned forward and drew on the tobacco while the host moved the match around the tip to ensure it evened out perfectly.

'Mr Smith' sat back and let out a plume of smoke, nodding his head in appreciation. 'Nice. Very nice indeed.' He frowned at the host. 'I don't know you, do I?'

'I'm new, sir. Here on temporary assignment, covering for a sick colleague.'

'Make sure you thank your boss for me.'

'I will, sir. Please, enjoy the rest of your evening.'

'That I guarantee.'

The host turned and exited the room as unobtrusively as he'd entered. Still clasping the humidor, he found the fire stairs, descended to the ground floor and soon after, left the building via the side fire exit. He walked down the narrow alleyway and keyed in the code for the gate at the end. Stepping through, he shut the gate behind him, and walked a hundred feet until he reached his rental car. He'd parked on a double yellow line, but there were no traffic wardens about at one in the morning. He unlocked the vehicle and got in.

Korso placed the humidor inside the travel bag on the passenger seat and zipped it closed. Only then did he take off his gloves. After that he removed the expensive hairpiece and the latex and makeup that had helped add twenty years to his appearance, along with the fat pad under his tuxedo.

He waited.

Forty-seven minutes later, a private ambulance entered the quiet street and crawled past him toward the townhouse he'd left. No flashing lights and no siren, which told Korso everything he needed to know. A guard met the two paramedics at the side entrance and they followed him inside. Ten minutes later, they came out pushing a stretcher bearing a covered body, which they pushed into the rear of the ambulance.

It wouldn't have mattered which cigar Sardoca had picked. They were all coated with the same poison Korso had used on Gancharov months before. He'd also exposed the cigars to the air for five hours before Sardoca picked his final smoke, so that the toxin would have completely dissipated shortly after, ensuring no collateral damage to innocent bystanders.

Since members had to book two weeks ahead any time they planned to stay at the club, Natasha had known exactly where Sardoca would be on what day and at what time. Korso had been more than willing to do his part. After Dog hacked into the club's membership list and faked two references, Korso made sure one of the hosts fell sick two days before. The rest, while not easy, had been fairly straightforward.

Five days before, he'd deleted every photo of him in Sardoca's iCloud account, and checked the rest of his operating system to make sure there were no other copies. There weren't. He knew the photos still existed somewhere, since somebody other than Sardoca had taken the shots, but without context, they meant nothing. And other than Sardoca, nobody else had it in for him, or even knew who he was. So with this final task out of the way, he felt he'd finally drawn a line under a part of his past he wanted to forget.

He nodded to himself, satisfied.

A single turn of the ignition key and the engine purred into life. Without looking back, the dead man put the car into gear, and drove off into the night.

Acknowledgements

Thanks goes to my splendid editor, Kit Nevile, for staying on top of things from start to finish, and for being right more often than not. Also, *gracias* to Gregory Vasquez for the Spanish lessons.